SALINE WATER CONVERSION

A collection of papers comprising the Symposium on Saline Water Conversion, presented before the Division of Water and Waste Chemistry at the 137th National Meeting of the American Chemical Society, Cleveland, Ohio, April 1960.

Number 27

ADVANCES IN CHEMISTRY SERIES

American Chemical Society
Washington, D. C.
1960

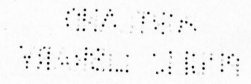

Library of Congress Catalog Card No. 60-53480

PRINTED IN THE UNITED STATES OF AMERICA

ADVANCES IN CHEMISTRY SERIES

Edited and Produced by

American Chemical Society Applied Publications

21 Ag64   EB   5.27   P. G. Brown.

344155

CONTENTS

Introduction

Potable water is the most essential and exotic liquid that exists on this planet. It is a very common but peculiar liquid, and all life is dependent on it. Like air, water is bound up with man's evolution and certainly with his destiny.

It is a common liquid because it is familiar to everyone and is used extensively in our daily lives. Often, however, the importance of water is recognized only when the spigot runs dry. If water is not in the tap, it must be in the reservoir; if not in sight, it must be just over the horizon; or if the fields are parched, the rains are sure to come. This is a common delusion which should be corrected, because the lack of fresh water may be of national importance in the near future.

Water is a peculiar liquid, since it possesses unique properties and those properties depend on the fact that water molecules are chemically active. The chemical and physical properties of water are associated with the type of bonding involved in the water molecule. Chemical changes, such as hydrolysis or rusting of iron, involve the breaking of chemical bonds between the hydrogen and oxygen atoms. Physical changes, such as evaporation in a conversion unit, or the resistance to flow in a pipe, involve breaking of the hydrogen bonds. Because of the hydrogen bonding, water molecules combine not only with molecules of other compounds but even with one another. Thus, water molecules cling to the ions of dissolved salt to form water-encumbered hydrated ions and they cling to one another to form entangling networks through which hydrated ions can be propelled only by tearing the networks apart. That is one reason why considerable energy still needs to be expended in the simplest procedures for converting saline water to fresh water. If water molecules did not have this habit of clinging so tenaciously to other molecules, and to one another, it would be easy to push salt ions past the water molecules and get a separation. But the water would not then dissolve salt, so the problem would not exist.

Potable water is hard to win because of the very properties that make it worth winning. Because of its unique properties, it exists as a liquid instead of a gas and as a liquid it penetrates into and interacts with living tissues to make possible the processes of life. Because it dissolves salts and nutrients, it is essential for the metabolism of all living cells.

The Federal Saline Water Conversion Program is administered by the Department of the Interior through the Office of Saline Water, and the primary objective of that program is to develop low-cost processes for converting saline water to fresh water. This is a most difficult problem—not because of any intricate or new chemistry, physics, or engineering involved, but because of that term, *"low cost."* Solution of this problem will assure this nation, and the world, of an inexhaustible supply of sparkling potable water.

Low-cost saline water conversion is a problem which has not been satisfactorily solved to date. New ideas, new processes, innovations, and improvements on existing processes are needed and can be achieved only through continued research. The development of saline water conversion processes has advanced in a number of broad fields, each of which incorporates a number of different processes. These fields can be conveniently classified as (1) distillation, (2) processes utilizing membranes, (3) separation by freezing, and (4) other physical, chemical, electrical, or biological processes.

The Office of Saline Water, in cooperation with the National Academy of Sciences–National Research Council, conducted a Symposium on Saline Water Conversion in 1957. A very substantial amount of work in this field has been completed since that time and the state of the art has advanced considerably. The material incorporated in this volume is a compilation of the papers presented at the Symposium on Saline Water Conversion sponsored by the American Chemical Society in 1960. Thus the information and data presented update those of the 1957 symposium and represent the current state of knowledge in this field.

W. SHERMAN GILLAM, *Chairman*
Symposium on Saline Water Conversion

Office of Saline Water
U. S. Department of the Interior
Washington 25, D. C.

Objectives and Status of the Federal Saline Water Conversion Program

J. W. O'MEARA

Office of Saline Water, U. S. Department
of the Interior, Washington 25, D. C.

The objective of the saline water conversion program, need for continuing research, status of the research and development, and the demonstration activities are briefly highlighted.

The experience of the Department of the Interior over the past years has clearly revealed one basic fact—water problems, in one form or another, touch all 50 states of the union. These problems vary from area to area, ranging from shortage to excess. Regardless of the cause, as a nation we can no longer regard with indifference the increasing imbalance between the supply and demand for water in the United States.

About 290 billion gallons of water per day are now being used, and this rate of demand is causing increasingly severe water problems in many sections of the country. In 1957, a study conducted by the U. S. Geological Survey revealed that in over 1000 cities and communities, representing one seventh of the nation's entire population, water shortages of varying degrees required their citizens to endure restricted use of water.

If the present rate of demand can cause a problem of this magnitude in a year of moderate drought, what will be the scope of the problems one may have to face in just 20 years when, according to the U. S. Geological Survey the demand for water will more than double, reaching the immense total of 497 billion gallons per day? The year 1980 does not mark the peak of demand; the consumption curve is expected to continue to rise as the population continues to grow.

The population gain has already created an increasing imbalance between the supply and demand for water in the United States. Although there is a growing public awareness of the problems that must be faced to maintain adequate supplies of water, the availability of water for every need has long been taken for granted. Only in recent years has the public realized that water suitable for man's use may be a limited commodity.

Water is cheap. In most United States cities one can purchase a ton of clear, pure, fresh water, delivered to the home or factory, for about 5 cents—or 20 cents per 1000 gallons—but water is used in such tremendous quantities that it requires vast sums of money to provide the facilities to collect it and put it to beneficial use wherever it is needed. Naturally, water supplies nearest the point of demand were the first to be developed. As these sources become inadequate to meet growing demands, cities are forced to reach considerable distances to tap additional sources of supply, at sites more expensive to develop.

Long ago, Southern California outgrew its local supplies and had to reach 240 miles across deserts and mountains to the Colorado River for its water supplies. This project, once criticized as a wasteful overdevelopment, will soon be inadequate. In the 1960 general election the citizens of California will vote on the most expensive proposition ever placed on a ballot. They are being asked to approve a $1.75 billion bond issue to harvest the fresh water of the Feather River in Northern California, transport it over 400 miles, lift it about 4000 feet over the Tahachapi Mountains, and deliver it to the Metropolitan Los Angeles area.

The increasingly complex problem of providing adequate supplies of water is not limited to a few hot and arid areas of the South and Southwest, but also embraces regions in the humid East.

Sources of Water

The task of providing ample supplies of fresh water for the America of tomorrow may indeed be our No. 1 domestic problem. At least one implication of the ever-increasing use of water is unmistakable: We must find new sources of fresh water, and two of the most likely sources are the great oceans and the vast reserves of brackish inland waters.

Man has been trying for a long time to brew a drink of fresh water from the sea, probably a lot longer than most people realize. For centuries people generally have known how to turn the trick: Just distill it. The basic concept of the science is probably as old as the teakettle. But what the world is still searching for is the answer to the question: How does one do this on a large scale at a cost cheap enough to substitute for or augment water from conventional sources?

The first practical conversion units came with the advent of the steamship and its requirement of fresh water for boilers. Today, most of the large ocean-going vessels have their battery of evaporators. The Forrestal class carriers of the United States Navy, for example, carry four 50,000-gallon-per-day evaporators to supply the water needs of those huge ships and their large crews.

While shipboard supplies of water are vital to navies and the maritime industry, the saline water conversion program of the Department of the Interior is interested in a different phase of the over-all problem. Aboard ship the primary interest is a reliable supply of water; the cost of the water is of secondary consideration. The interest of the Office of Saline Water is centered on land-based plants that can produce fresh water from the sea at low cost, the latter being the important factor.

Land-Based Plants. The United States Government's work in this field goes back to 1952, when Congress passed the Saline Water Act to provide for research and development of practical methods of producing fresh water from saline sources. The 1952 Act authorized $2,000,000 for a 5-year program. In 1955, the Act was amended by increasing the authorization to $10,000,000 and extending the life of the program through fiscal year 1963.

A plant on the Island of Aruba, in the Caribbean, is now producing 2,700,000 gallons of fresh water per day at a cost of about $2 per 1000 gallons. Of the land-based plants scattered around the globe, with a combined capacity of about 20,000,000 gallons of fresh water per day, the plant at Aruba is the most efficient. Based on present cost standards, these plants are expensive producers, but they are in existence because the cost of water from alternative sources is even higher. Over the past several years the department has barged over 100,000,000 gallons of fresh water from Puerto Rico to supply the minimum requirements of the people of St. Thomas, Virgin Islands, at a cost of about $6 per 1000 gallons.

Public Law 85-883, approved by President Eisenhower on September 2, 1958, added a new responsibility to the office. It authorizes $10,000,000 for the design, construction, and operation of five saline water conversion plants to demonstrate the reliability, engineering, operating, and economic potentials of sea or brackish water conversion processes.

The law provides that three of these plants shall be for the conversion of sea water to fresh water—one each to be located on the East Coast, the West Coast, and the Gulf Coast. At least two of these plants shall have a capacity of 1,000,000 gallons of fresh water per day. Two of the plants will be designed to convert brackish water to fresh water—one to be located in the Northern Great Plains and the other in the arid areas of the Southwest. One of these plants must have a capacity of at least 250,000 gallons per day. Each plant must utilize a different process.

An accurate barometer of the nationwide interest in the saline water conversion program is provided by the number of requests received from civic bodies, public officials, industrial organizations, and private citizens asking consideration for their area as a site for one of the authorized plants. Nearly 200 applications have been received from cities and communities in every state on the coastal perimeter, from 12 inland states, and from Alaska and Hawaii.

Secretary Seaton has selected five processes and four sites for the demonstration plant program. Several of those processes are described in considerable detail in the papers that follow.

The first demonstration plant will be located at Freeport, Tex. Utilizing the long-tube vertical multiple-effect distillation process, it will be designed to produce fresh water from the sea at the rate of 1,000,000 gallons per day. W. L. Badger Associates, Inc., Ann Arbor, Mich., performed the architectural and engineering services. Invitations for construction bids were issued on March 14 and the Office of Saline Water sold over 125 sets of plans and specifications for this plant, which provides a second indication of the sharp interest in the saline water conversion program. Bids were opened on May 24. On June 8, a contract for $1,246,250 was awarded to the successful low bidder, the Chicago Bridge & Iron Co.

The second demonstration plant will consist of a multistage flash process for a 1,000,000-gallon-per-day plant to be located on the West Coast. A site on Point Loma at San Diego has been selected for this plant. The Fluor Corp., Whittier, Calif., has been awarded the architectural and engineering contract for the distillation plant, and it is planned to let a construction contract in November.

A process that was no more than a laboratory phenomenon when the Office of Saline Water was authorized in 1952 has been rapidly developed to the point where it is now one of the most economical processes for the conversion of brackish water to fresh. This process, electrodialysis, was selected for the third demonstration plant. It will be located at Webster, S. D. The Bureau of Reclamation Laboratories in Denver, Colo., prepared the specifications for this plant which will be designed to produce 250,000 gallons of fresh water per day. Operating on water containing between 1500 and 1800 parts of salt per million parts of water, this plant will remove more than 1 ton of salt daily to produce product water with less than 500 parts of salt per million parts of water which is required to meet U. S. Public Health Standards for good drinking water. Construction specifications for this plant were available August 1, and sealed bids will be opened on October 4, 1960.

The fourth process—forced-circulation vapor-compression—will be designed to produce at least 250,000 gallons of fresh water per day in a plant to be located at Roswell, N. M. Aside from providing badly needed supplemental water to the city, the plant offers a second exciting possibility.

Continued heavy pumping necessary to meet the growing demand is gradually lowering the water table in Roswell's present fresh water aquifer. It has reached a point where saline water is beginning to encroach and endanger the source of fresh water. By pumping saline waters from the brackish water aquifer, this encroachment may be retarded and at the same time, by providing fresh water from the conversion plant, the city can reduce its pumping from the fresh water aquifer, which may permit a gradual recharge of the aquifer.

For the fifth plant, a freezing process will be utilized. This plant will be located at a yet to be selected site on the East Coast. It will be designed to produce fresh water in the range of 150,000 to 350,000 gallons per day. The site will be selected this fall, but construction is not contemplated before the fiscal year 1962.

The conversion of saline water to fresh water by freezing is relatively new, but it is believed to have great potential. Theoretically, freezing has several inherent advantages over conventional distillation processes—for example, the lesser tendency toward scaling and corrosion because of the low operating temperatures involved, and the lower energy requirement to freeze sea water as compared to the energy required for the evaporation of sea water.

Freezing is so new that the world's first freezing process pilot plant began operating in October 1959 at the Carrier Corp. plant in Syracuse, N. Y. Preliminary tests have been completed and the equipment is being dismantled for shipment to a seashore location for further operational testing. The Blaw-Knox Co. of Pittsburgh has been awarded a contract to build a 35,000-gallon-per-day pilot plant to test another freezing process developed at Cornell University. This process is based on the flash evaporation of a volatile and immiscible hydrocarbon, such as butane, in direct contact with sea water to cause part of the water to freeze.

Other pilot plant activity includes testing of solar stills at an experimental station near Daytona Beach, Fla. At the Bureau of Reclamation Laboratories in Denver, the Office of Saline Water has two electrodialysis units, one built by Ionics, Inc., Cambridge, Mass., and the other by the Central Technical Institute, T.N.O., of the Netherlands. A Japanese electrodialysis unit is on order and will be tested at the Denver Laboratories. Various types of membranes are also being tested at Denver. Distillation experiments are continuing in research facilities located at Wrightsville Beach, N. C.

Research and development contracts with universities, research organizations, and industrial firms are probing into the fields of heat transfer, scale prevention, corrosion, membranes, gas hydrates, solvent extraction, and many others, all designed to help attain the goal of low-cost converted water.

The plants about to be built will demonstrate the progress that has been achieved through 8 years of research that has been supported by an average annual appropriation of less than $725,000. When the Office of Saline Water was authorized in 1952, the cost of conversion ranged upward from $5 per 1000 gallons. The two 1,000,000-gallon-per-day demonstration plants are expected to produce fresh water from the sea for about $1 per 1000 gallons. Engineering extrapolations indicate that when these processes are incorporated in multimillion-gallon-per-day plants savings will be obtained which will reduce the total cost of conversion to about 50 cents per 1000 gallons, and prices even lower than that may be expected for the conversion of certain brackish waters.

These estimates of cost are based on the standardized procedure for estimating saline water conversion costs published by the Office of Saline Water. That procedure includes all costs at today's prices—land, capital investment, interest, operating costs, maintenance, taxes, insurance, and a rather severe 20-year amortization schedule.

The demonstration plant program has captured the interest and imagination of the nation and the world, but plant construction is not the key to low-cost conversion. While these plants are being constructed, the research and development program will be continued—for research is the key to progress. One must turn to scientific and technological research to develop a new source of supply that can provide an ever-growing percentage of tomorrow's water.

RECEIVED for review July 7, 1960. Accepted August 2, 1960.

Thermodynamics of Some Desalting Processes

BARNETT F. DODGE

Chemical Engineering Department, Yale University, New Haven, Conn.

ALLEN M. ESHAYA

Brookhaven National Laboratory, Upton, Long Island, N. Y.

A thermodynamic analysis of the energy requirements of desalting processes is presented, to clarify
the conditions under which such calculations are
valid. The effects of departure from isothermal
operation, finite product recovery, differential as
opposed to single-stage operation, and salt concentration in the feed are examined. A comparison
shows that there is essentially no difference between
the energy requirements for a distillation and a
freezing process. The minimum heat consumption
and maximum number of effects for a multiple-effect
evaporation plant are calculated. The above analysis leads to the conclusion that efficiencies in the
range 10 to 20% will be very difficult to achieve.

Much has already been written on this subject and one may well ask if another paper
is justified. The authors' purpose is not to treat the subject exhaustively nor even to
present very much that is strictly new, but rather to clarify and amplify certain aspects
of the subject which either have not been adequately treated or have not been entirely
clear in their meaning. It is frequently stated that the minimum work for the separation of fresh water from sea water is 2.9 kw.-hr. per 1000 gallons of water produced.
Murphy *et al.* (8) give the figure of 2.89 kw.-hr. for 25° C., but there is a numerical
error in the calculation because, using the figures in this report, the authors obtain 3.19
kw.-hr. The citation of a single figure like this can be misleading because it depends on
certain factors, notably temperature and more particularly degree of recovery or yield
of fresh water. Furthermore, the type of process can influence the figure for "minimum
work" of separation, but in this case it is not the thermodynamic reversible work that is
meant, because that is independent of process of mechanism and dependent only on
initial and final states.

Other points to be considered are:

The figure usually given for reversible work of separation is for an isothermal process. Because some of the actual processes under consideration are by no means isothermal, one is left in some doubt as to whether the comparison between the actual work
requirement and the isothermal reversible work is a legitimate one. Therefore in

giving a figure for minimum work it is desirable to remove the restriction to isothermal conditions. This can be done in principle, but practical considerations make it desirable to assume isothermal processes in most instances.

It is commonly stated that because the heat of freezing of water is only one seventh of the heat of vaporization, the work requirement for a freezing process can potentially be much less than for a distillation process. This is based on false reasoning.

When the minimum work requirement for demineralization is compared with the actual requirement of operating processes, it is found that the latter have an energy efficiency of the order of only 2 to 5%. This has led some to conclude that great improvement is easily possible and that as a consequence costs can be greatly reduced. The authors will show that whereas some improvement can certainly be expected, it will be very difficult to achieve efficiencies in the range 10 to 20% and that it is not at present feasible to get efficiencies above 25% or even that high. The low efficiencies are, of course, attributable to the driving forces which are necessary in any practical process, as contrasted with the reversible process that assumes zero driving forces. These driving forces are the finite temperature differences, pressure differences, concentration differences, e.m.f. differences, etc., which are necessary for equipment of practical size. Any reduction in a driving force always entails an increase in size and hence cost of equipment and because the total costs of a desalting process are about equally divided between costs of energy and fixed costs on equipment, one reaches a cost minimum at an efficiency which is generally less than 20%.

The maximum number of effects in a multiple-effect evaporation system and a comparison of energy economy of multiple-effect evaporation with that of vapor-compression distillation are discussed.

Minimum Work of Separation

This can have a variety of meanings. The reversible, isothermal work for any process regardless of mechanism is given by the equation

$$-W = \Delta H - T\Delta S = \Delta F \tag{1}$$

which is based solely on the two laws of thermodynamics.

ΔH = enthalpy in final state − that in initial state
ΔS = entropy in final state − that in initial state

Both of these are for an isothermal change.

T is the constant absolute temperature at which the process takes place. Negative work refers to work done upon the system to cause the process to take place. The following equation applies to any reversible process, whether isothermal or not,

$$-W = \Delta H - T_0\Delta S = \Delta B \tag{2}$$

The temperatures may change throughout the process and the temperatures of the final states do not need to be the same as the initial temperature. T_0 is the temperature of the environment or the lowest temperature at which heat can be freely discharged.

If the isothermal process is conducted at a temperature near the ambient, there is, of course, little difference between Equations 1 and 2, but the difference is considerable for isothermal processes carried out at elevated or very low temperatures.

Equation 2 would be easy to use if one had convenient tables of the properties H and S for the states desired. One has to assume an arbitrary value for T_0—a common one is 530° R. Such data are not available in convenient form and one generally is forced to use Equation 1, which is satisfactory in this instance, because we are concerned with processes that are approximately isothermal and operated at temperatures around the ambient temperature.

First consider the removal of pure water from an initial or feed solution of concentration x_1 expressed as mole fraction of salt. Because the removal of water will change the concentration of the solution and since, to fulfill the condition of reversibility, the water vapor removed must at all times be in equilibrium with salt solution, a differential treatment is indicated. Write Equation 1 in the form

$$-dW = \Delta F dn \tag{3}$$

where dn is the small increment of water removed at any instant. One can also write

$$\Delta F = RT \ln a_B \tag{4}$$

where a_B is the activity of water in the salt solution. Taking the standard state as that of pure water and assuming water vapor at low pressure to be an ideal gas, Equation 3 can be put in the form

$$-W = \int_{n_1}^{n_2} RT \ln \frac{p}{p^0} \, dn \tag{5}$$

One can take a constant amount of water produced—namely, 1000 gallons or 462 pound-moles—and let n_1 and n_2 be the initial and final number of moles of salt solution. If $y = $ fractional yield,

$$y = 1 - \frac{x_1(1 - x_2)}{x_2(1 - x_1)} \tag{6}$$

$$n_1 = 462 \frac{x_2}{x_2 - x_1} \tag{7}$$

$$n_2 = 462 \frac{x_1}{x_2 - x_1} \tag{8}$$

Assuming an initial solution of 100 pound-moles of a 3.50% NaCl solution or 35,000 p.p.m. ($x_1 = 0.01105$) which is generally assumed to represent normal sea water, the following table may be constructed for 25° C.

Table I. Data for Use in Calculation of Work of Separation for Various Yields

100 y	x_2	n_2	m_2	$a_A{}^a$	$a_B{}^a$
0	0.01105	100	0.620	0.1733	0.9796
10	0.01227	90.2	0.689	0.210	0.9773
20	0.01379	80.2	0.775	0.264	0.9744
30	0.01573	70.3	0.888	0.343	0.9706
40	0.01833	60.3	1.034	0.461	0.9657
50	0.0219	50.5	1.186	0.601	0.9606
60	0.0272	40.6	1.550	1.036	0.9479
70	0.0359	30.8	2.065	1.920	0.9292
80	0.0530	20.9	3.13	5.56	0.8879
90	0.0995	11.05	6.16	38.4	0.7522
(Sat. solution) 100	1.00	1.105	...	...	0.7522

^{a} (9).

To obtain work directly in kilowatt-hours per 1000 gallons we write Equation 5 in the form

$$-W = \frac{0.620T}{100 - n_2} \int_{100}^{n_2} \log_{10} \frac{p}{p^0} \, dn \tag{9}$$

for T in °R.

The integral is evaluated by plotting $\log_{10} \frac{p}{p^0}$ vs. n and taking the area under the curve between given limits of n.

For the special case of $y = 0$ (zero yield) Equation 9 is indeterminate, but one can go back to Equation 1 and write

$$-W \text{ (kw.-hr. per 1000 gallons)} = 0.620T \log_{10} a_B$$

For $T = 536°$ F. (25° C.), $a_B = 0.9796$ and $W = 2.98$

This figure (or a similar one depending on temperature and data chosen) is the one usually quoted as the minimum theoretical work. Actually it is a very unrealistic figure, not only because it assumes complete reversibility of all operations, but also because it would involve the pumping of an infinite amount of sea water as feed and the pumping work would be infinite. As recovery is increased the theoretical separation work increases but the pumping work decreases and the sum of the two, the total work, would pass through a minimum at some particular value of per cent recovery. The theoretical pumping work will depend on an assumed head. The following calculated figures for 50% recovery will show the order of magnitude to be expected:

25-foot head, 100% pump efficiency $W = 0.159$ kw.-hr. per 1000 gallons
50-foot head, 100% pump efficiency $W = 0.318$ kw.-hr. per 1000 gallons
50-foot head, 70% pump efficiency $W = 0.455$ kw.-hr. per 1000 gallons

At recoveries approaching 50%, the energy for feed pumping becomes a relatively minor quantity compared to the separation work.

For 50% recovery the area under the curve (value of the integral in Equation 9) is -0.614 and $W = -4.12$ kw.-hr. per 1000 gallons. For 90% recovery, which corresponds to saturation at 25° C., the value of the integral is 2.245 and the work is 8.40 kw.-hr. per 1000 gallons. From these and similar calculations one could plot curves of separation work, pumping work, and total work vs. per cent recovery. Gilliland (5) has presented such curves, and whereas the general trends agree with present calculations, the absolute values differ appreciably. Since he gave no details on the basis for his curves, the authors do not know how the difference arises.

Another Method for Reversible Work

It may be of interest to show how the reversible work for any percentage yield can be calculated by another equation which does not involve a graphical integration. Designating the feed, concentrated brine, and fresh water streams as 1, 2, and 3, respectively, we can write for an isothermal, reversible process

$$-W = n_2F_2 + n_3F_3 - n_1F_1 \tag{10}$$

Utilizing the well-known thermodynamic relations

$$F = \Sigma x_i\mu_i \tag{11}$$

$$\mu_i = RT \ln a_i + \mu_i^0 \tag{12}$$

We can transform Equation 10 to

$$-W = RT\{n_3[x_3 \ln a_{A3} + (1 - x_3) \ln a_{B3}] + n_2[x_2 \ln a_{A2} + (1 - x_2) \ln a_{B2}] - n_1[x_1 \ln a_{A1} + (1 - x_1) \ln a_{B1}]\} \tag{13}$$

The standard-state constants, μ_i^0, have dropped out and so we can use activities based on any standard state. For the special case of pure water as product, $x_3 = 0$ and $a_{B3} = 1.0$ (for pure water as standard state) and the n_3 term in Equation 13 $= 0$ provided a_{A3} is not zero. Values of a_A are included in Table I. For a sea water feed of 35,000 p.p.m. NaCl, and pure product, Equation 13 becomes

$$-W = 4.57T\{n_2[x_2 \log a_{A2} + (1 - x_2) \log a_{B2}] + 0.01725n_1\} \tag{14}$$

The values of a_A given in Table I were calculated from values of activity coefficients tabulated by Robinson and Stokes (9). The relation for this is

$$a \text{ (based on molality)} = (\nu_1^{\nu_1}\nu_2^{\nu_2})m^\nu\gamma_1^{\nu_1}\gamma_2^{\nu_2} \tag{15}$$

which for the case of sodium chloride reduces to

$$a \text{ (of solute)} = a_A = (m_\pm\gamma_\pm)^2 \tag{16}$$

or since $m = m_\pm$ for NaCl, one can write

$$a_A = (m\gamma_\pm)^2 \tag{17}$$

The following values were calculated:

Recovery, %	50	90
W, kw.-hr. per 1000 gallons	4.15	8.20

(For zero % recovery the equation is indeterminate.)

Considering the fact that these calculations were made on a slide rule and that relatively small differences of large numbers are involved, the agreement with the previous method is very good.

Differential vs. Single-Stage Process

The general separation process that has been discussed is often referred to as a "differential process" because it proceeds in a series of infinitesimal steps with complete equilibrium being maintained at all times. Another type of process referred to as "single-stage separation" will also be considered because it is somewhat more representative of conditions that might be approached in certain actual processes. Whereas the differential separation process is best visualized as a batch process, the single-stage process is best thought of as a continuous process. A feed stream enters the separation system and there emerges a stream as pure water and another as a concentrated brine. No details of the mechanism inside the system need be considered. The only restriction is that the two emerging streams be in equilibrium. This introduces an irreversible effect (except for the limiting case of 0 % recovery) because the water produced is in equilibrium with only the final brine concentration instead of the whole range of concentrations from the feed to the discharged brine. The work for such a process is generally referred to as "theoretical separation work" because it represents the minimum work for a process with these terminal conditions, but it should not be confused with the "minimum reversible work" which assumes complete thermodynamic reversibility. The work for the single-stage process per pound-mole of water produced is given very simply by

$$-W = RT \ln a = RT \ln \frac{p}{p^0} \qquad (18)$$

where a is the activity of water in the concentrated brine stream leaving the separator. With the aid of the data in Table I the following results were calculated for 25° C.

Recovery, % $\longrightarrow$	0	50	90	100
W, kw.-hr. per 1000 gallons $\longrightarrow$	2.98	5.80	41.0	41.0

Since the residual solution is saturated at 90% recovery, an additional yield does not affect the work. In the paper previously referred to (5), the work for single-stage separation is plotted vs. per cent recovery but the values are considerably lower, especially at the higher yields, than the ones reported here. As no details on the method were given in the previous paper, the authors are unable to explain the discrepancy. The value for 0% is obviously the same for both the differential and single-stage processes.

The work requirement, of course, is less if the separated water is not 100% pure, but it is believed that for all cases of practical interest, the difference between the work to produce pure water and that to produce a water containing as much as 500 p.p.m. of NaCl would be negligible.

Effect of Salt Concentration in Feed

The concentration of salt in the feed will have a considerable effect on the theoretical work, as can readily be shown with the aid of either Equation 5 or Equation 13. If the case of a brackish water containing 5000 p.p.m. of NaCl is considered at 25° C., because it is the temperature for which activity data are most readily available, Equation 13 appears to be more suitable than Equation 5 for this calculation and it will be used. For such a dilute solution the value of a_A cannot be obtained from the table previously used and use will be made of the Debye-Hückel limiting law or rather a modification of it in the following form (9):

$$\log j_{\pm} = -\frac{0.509 \sqrt{m}}{1 + \sqrt{m}} + 0.150m \tag{19}$$

This is a special form applicable to an electrolyte such as sodium chloride. $j_{\pm}$ is the mean ionic activity coefficient on the mole-fraction scale which is equal to $\gamma_{\pm}$ at this dilution. The activity of water is linear with m in this region and hence accurate values are obtained merely by interpolation (9). For 50% recovery from a feed of 5000 p.p.m., the following values were calculated:

x	m	γ_A	a_A	a_B	
0.00155	0.0861	0.790	0.00462	0.9971	(Feed)
0.00310	0.1722	0.754	0.0224	0.9943	(50% recovery)
0.01539	0.868	0.660	0.3280	0.9713	(90% recovery)

By Equation 13 for the case of $x_3 = 0$, one calculates:

For 50% recovery, W = 0.71 kw.-hr. per 1000 gallons
For 90% recovery, W = 1.05 kw.-hr. per 1000 gallons

With brackish waters, the energy requirement is much less than for sea water for the same yield, or for the same energy expenditure much higher yields are obtainable. This may be of considerable practical significance. For one thing, it would reduce the pumping cost for the feed to a negligible amount.

Energy Requirements for Distillation and Freezing Processes

The continually repeated statement that freezing processes in general have a much lower energy requirement than vaporization processes because the heat of melting is only one seventh of the heat of vaporization, is based on a false premise. All vaporization processes as well as freezing processes are essentially heat-pumping processes and the work requirement for heat pumping depends not only on the quantity of heat to be pumped but also on the temperature difference over which the heat is to be pumped. The net result of these two factors is that the work requirements for these two processes are about comparable. This can be demonstrated by some calculations.

It may not be immediately apparent that any vaporization process is essentially a heat-pumping process. When heat is used to vaporize water from a salt solution, the vapor evolved has all this heat still available as enthalpy and the only net result is that it is slightly degraded in temperature because of the boiling-point elevation (BPE) of a salt solution. The heat can all be reutilized merely by restoring it to its former temperature—i.e., by pumping it to a higher level. The same general result can be accomplished by using the degraded heat to evaporate water from a solution boiling at lower pressure—multiple-effect principle—but eventually the heat has to be pumped back to the original temperature level and the principle remains the same. Without this kind of a recovery operation, a vaporization process is so inefficient that it could not be considered for practical use. In other words, any vaporization process of practical value is, in the last analysis, based on heat pumping.

The basic equation for reversible heat pumping is, of course

$$W = Q \frac{T_1 - T_2}{T_2} \tag{20}$$

where T_1 and T_2 are the two temperature levels and Q is the heat taken in at T_2.

Before proceeding to use this equation some consideration must be given to the boiling point elevation of sodium chloride solutions. This varies with concentration and with temperature level. Because somewhat conflicting values have appeared in some of the recent literature on saline-water conversion, it seems desirable to digress for a moment to give the basis for the present values. The International

Critical Tables (7) give values of vapor pressure of 5.0 and 7.5% NaCl solutions over the range of 0° to 110° C. From these data the BPE for a 7.0% solution (50% recovery) at 1 atm. is readily calculated to be 2.34° F. From the ideal solution law (which should apply well to water in dilute solutions) and the Clausius-Clapeyron equation we get

$$\Delta T \text{ (BPE)} = \frac{RT_B^2}{L_v} x \tag{21}$$

T_B is the boiling point of pure solvents and L_v its latent heat of vaporization. Since $x = 0.0454$ assuming 100% dissociation into ions, ΔT is calculated to be 2.32° F., in excellent agreement with the previous figure. The method of calculation based on Equation 21 is particularly useful because with it the BPE is readily obtained for any concentration and pressure. Values are also given in the International Critical Tables (6) of N (formality) $vs. \frac{\Delta t_B}{x}$, where $\Delta t_B =$ BPE at 1 atm. in ° C. and $x =$ mole fraction. From a graph of these values the BPE for a 7% NaCl solution at 1 atm. is calculated to be 2.27° F.

A vapor-compression process can be considered at a temperature level of 160° F. where BPE = 1.9° F. per 1000 gallons of product, $Q = 2410$ kw.-hr., and W (Equation 20) = 7.40 kw.-hr. The value of BPE read from Figure 7 of a report to the Office of Saline Water (1) is 1.65° F. Using this value, W by Equation 20 = 6.40 kw.-hr.

The freezing point of a 7% NaCl brine is 24° F. and the heat of freezing must be pumped from this level to 32° F., where it can be discharged to melt the ice. An energy balance readily shows that the work of pumping (discharged as heat) cannot be discharged to the ice but must be pumped up to the ambient temperature level. Furthermore, any heat leak into the low-temperature system and any inefficiencies in low-temperature heat exchangers will also have to be discharged at ambient temperature. For the present it will be assumed that the heat of freezing is all picked up by the refrigeration system at the 24° F. level (t_2) and that the ambient temperature is t_0, which will be taken as 70° F. Then, from the two fundamental laws of thermodynamics,

$$W = Q \left(\frac{T_1 - T_2}{T_2} \right) \left(\frac{T_0}{T_1} \right) \tag{22}$$

Substituting numerical values, $W = 6.28$ kw.-hr. per 1000 gallons. The difference between this figure and the corresponding one for the vapor-compression process is not very significant. In fact, when one considers actual, as compared to these idealized, processes the work for the refrigeration processes can be calculated as greater than, or less than, that for the vaporization process depending on the particular assumptions made with respect to driving forces.

The theoretical work for the freezing process could be reduced by picking up the heat of freezing at a series of levels between 32° and 24° F. instead of all at the lowest level. However, even a two-stage refrigeration system would complicate the equipment to such an extent that the gain in lowered energy requirement would probably be more than compensated by an increase in fixed charges.

Actual Processes Considered from a Thermodynamic Standpoint

The actual, or practical, process differs from the ideal, reversible one by irreversible effects, the most important of which are:

Pressure drop in lines and equipment due to fluid friction
Throttling processes
Finite temperature difference between fluids exchanging heat
Heat conduction along solids
Heat leak into the system from the surroundings
Fluid mixing when there is a difference in temperature or concentration
Mass transfer with finite concentration gradient
Joule heating in electric current flow

Polarization effects at electrodes

Mechanical friction, as in pumps and compressors

These effects can never be completely eliminated and frequently must remain of considerable magnitude, if the size of the equipment is to be kept within reasonable bounds.

Every irreversible effect entails a "loss" in the second-law sense—i.e., a loss in availability—and the over-all result is an increase in the energy output in the form of either work or heat. An analysis of the losses is sometimes useful to indicate where the greatest effort for improvement should be made. Such an analysis can be made in a rigorous manner by application of the equation

$$W_s \text{ (total shaft work)} = W_r \text{ (reversible work)} + T_0 \Sigma M \Delta S \qquad (23)$$

T_0 is the temperature at which large amounts of heat can be discharged (heat sink). The derivation of Equation 23 is given in several books dealing with engineering applications of thermodynamics. $\Sigma M \Delta S$ is sometimes called "lost work." In this form, the assumption is implicit that the only heat reservoir is the surroundings at T_0. When heat is taken from reservoirs above the ambient, the following relation (3) holds:

$$W_s = \Delta H - T_0 \Delta S + T_0 \Delta S_t - \Sigma(Q_i + T_0 \Delta S_i) \qquad (24)$$

where

ΔS_t = total entropy change of system and surroundings
Q_i = heats from heat reservoirs except the surroundings at T_0
ΔS_i = entropy change of these reservoirs

Since $(Q_i + T_0 \Delta S_i)$ is the minimum work to restore the heat reservoirs, taking heat in at T_0, and since $\Delta H - T_0 \Delta S$ is ΔB which $= W_r$, it is recognized that Equation 24 is the same as 23, if the work to restore heat reservoirs is included in the W_s. The term $\Sigma M \Delta S$ which is to be applied around each significant piece of equipment—pumps, compressors, heat exchangers, expansion valves, etc.—needs a little explanation. Consider a heat exchanger transferring heat between fluids A and B with the temperatures at the hotter end designated by 1 and at the colder end by 2. Then we can write

$$\Sigma M \Delta S = M_A(S_{A1} - S_{A2}) - M_B(S_{B1} - S_{B2}) \qquad (25)$$

Equation 23 is simple to use if entropy values are readily available, but this is seldom the case, especially when solutions are involved. One can often calculate the values he needs from available fundamental data coupled with reasonable assumptions, but this is time-consuming. For present purposes a less rigorous and more practical method of showing the effect of irreversibilities can be used.

To illustrate the method and further amplify the comparison between vaporization and freezing processes, one can return to the latter comparison.

The following assumptions will be made:

	Vaporization	Freezing
Δt in auxiliary heat exchangers—i.e., those exchanging heat between feed solution and the two outgoing product streams	0	0
Recovery of fresh water from sea water of 3.50% NaCl	50%	45%[a]
Temperature level of main operation	160° F. (B.P.)	24° F. (F.P.)
Mean temperature difference in the main heat exchangers, melter and condenser	5° F.	10° F.[b]
Heat leak into system, B.t.u. per 1000 gallons	0	1000[c]
Efficiency of heat pumping—generally decreases with temperature level	0.70	0.65
Temperature of surroundings	70° F.	70° F.
Work requirements, kw.-hr. per 1000 gallons, calculated from previously established relations	38.5	38.0

[a] 10% of the fresh water is assumed to be needed to wash the mother liquor from the ice crystals.

[b] The Δt for freezing is the minimum in the freezer. This difference in Δt's is based on the fact that the heat-transfer coefficients in the evaporator will be much higher than in the

freezer. On the other hand, the use of direct contact between refrigerating agent and salt solution, thus eliminating some of the resistance to heat transfer, may permit a lower Δt and appreciably reduce the energy requirement for the freezing process.

    c Assumed to be about 0.1% of the total heat to be pumped and from a level of 32° F.

Two significant observations emerge from this comparison:

Using the most reasonable assumptions one could make, the work requirements are almost identical.

Small but reasonable allowances for necessary driving forces—irreversible effects— have multiplied the ideal work by a factor of nearly 6. The energy efficiency of these processes is about 11 or 15%, depending on whether the differential or the single-stage process is taken as the standard of comparison. These figures are based on the minimum work of separation for 50% recovery. If one takes the absolute minimum of 2.98 kw.-hr. per 1000 gallons (0% recovery) the corresponding figure is 7.8%.

This kind of a calculation shows why present efficiencies of saline-water conversion processes are so low and why efficiencies of the order of 20% are about the maximum that could be expected in the foreseeable future. The relative importance of the various factors contributing to the energy requirement is easily estimated by assuming various values. Suppose that it were possible to reduce the temperature difference for heat transfer in the freezing process from 10° F. to 1° F., all other assumptions remaining the same. The calculated work is now 13.3 kw.-hr. per 1000 gallons or about $1/_3$ of the previous figure. This emphasizes the great importance of temperature differences to the work requirement.

Instead of assuming an efficiency figure for heat pumping, one can set up an actual flow sheet of a proposed process, make reasonable assumptions about the various irreversible effects, and calculate an energy requirement. This approach is more time-consuming and the results are still dependent on the particular assumptions made. Many calculations of this type have been made for a vapor-compression process shown in Figure 1 and for a freezing process shown in Figure 2. The process shown in Figure 1 is a combination of vapor compression and flash evaporation.

Fresh feed from stream 1 combines with recirculated brine from stream 13 and the combined stream, 14, enters the main heat exchanger, where sensible heat is added, but no vaporization occurs because the pressure is maintained slightly above the vapor pressure. All vaporization occurs in the flash tank and the vapor is compressed and desuperheated and becomes the heating medium for the main exchanger. As only a small fraction of the brine evaporates (around 0.005) the majority is recirculated as stream 13, the remainder being discarded in 8.

A diagram of a freezing process is shown in Figure 2. This is a conventional process involving the use of a refrigerating agent which does not come in direct contact with the salt solution. There are two refrigeration circuits, one of which discharges heat to the melting ice and the other to sea water. Typical sets of conditions for the two processes are given in the following tables.

Table II. Conditions, Assumptions, and Calculated Energy Requirement for the Process of Figure I

Brine velocity in main exchanger, feet per sec.	8
Fraction of brine flashed on one pass	0.005
Mean Δt in exchanger, ° F.	2.83
Temperature of brine leaving exchanger, ° F.	212
Compressor pressure ratio	1.15
Compressor efficiency, %	80
Compression work, kw.-hr. per 1000 gallons	38.5
Pumping work, kw.-hr. per 1000 gallons	8.0^a
Total work, kw.-hr. per 1000 gallons	46.5

    a This figure depends on various assumptions in regard to the piping arrangement, pump efficiency, entrance and exit losses, etc. It is a rough figure, but based on many detailed calculations and is believed to be a reasonable one.

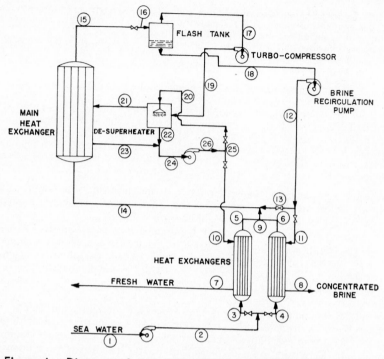

Figure 1. Diagram of a vapor-compression process developed by authors

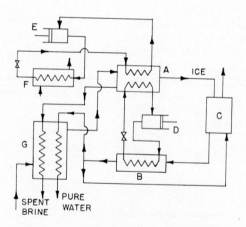

Figure 2. Diagram of refrigeration process

A. Freezer   D. Compressor 1
B. Melter   E. Compressor 2
C. Ice-crystal washer   F. Sea-water cooled condenser
              G. Auxiliary heat exchanger

Table III. Conditions, Assumptions and Calculated Energy Requirement for the Process of Figure 2

Sea water temperature, ° F.	65
Minimum Δt in all heat exchangers, freezer and melter, ° F.	10
Refrigerant	Ammonia
Compressor adiabatic efficiencies, %	75
Per cent of pure water needed to wash salt	10
Heat leak from surroundings	Negligible
Latent heat of freezing from a dilute sodium chloride solution assumed to be same as for pure water	
Maximum concn. of mother liquor	7.0% NaCl
Freezing point of 7.0% NaCl, ° F.	24
Power requirements other than for refrigerant compression were neglected	
Work, kw.-hr. per 1000 gallons	48

As predicted, the calculated energy requirements turned out to be about the same for the two processes, but either of these figures can be modified significantly by changing the basic assumptions.

The work requirement for any vapor-compression process is a linear function of the temperature difference across the evaporating surface, at least up to a Δt of 20° F. This straight lines does not pass through the origin because of the effect of BPE.

Minimum Heat Consumption

So far only the energy requirement for a process in the form of work has been considered. Freezing, vapor compression, and reverse osmosis processes are examples of processes that require a work input. There are, however, other important processes, such as multiple-effect evaporation and flash evaporation, for which the energy input is in the form of heat. How does one relate the energy requirement of these processes to the minimum work of separation? One method is to convert the heat requirement to a work equivalent by means of the Carnot cycle. If T is the absolute temperature of the heat source and T_0 the heat-sink temperature, then one can use the familiar relation

$$W = Q \frac{T - T_0}{T} \tag{26}$$

If a multiple-effect evaporator system produces 10 pounds of fresh water per pound of saturated steam at 35 p.s.i.a. ($t = 259°$ F.) and $t_0 = 70°$ F., the work equivalent per 1000 gallons of fresh water is 60 kw.-hr. and the energy efficiency using the differential process with 50% recovery as the standard, is 6.9%. This calculation assumes that the available heat is simply the latent heat of condensation at the constant temperature of 259° F.

If the heat source is changing in temperature one should use the availability function previously defined by Equation 2. Thus, if the heat source is superheated steam at 815° F. and 850 p.s.i.g., the availability with reference to a dead state of liquid water at 70° F. is $(1404.3 - 38.0) - 530 (1.5936 - 0.0745)$ B.t.u. per pound $= 561$. Steam at this condition is used in the new six-effect evaporator system on Aruba (2), after first being used to generate power by expansion in turbines. Assuming 5 pounds of water evaporated per pound of steam and 111 kw.-hr. generated per 1000 gallons of water (based on the published figure of 12500 kw. for a plant capacity of 2.7×10^6 gallons per day) the work equivalent of the steam per 1000 gallons =

$$\frac{561 \times 8330}{5 \times 3413} = 274 \text{ kw.-hr.}$$

The net work equivalent $= 274 - 111 = 163$ kw.-hr. The water recovery is about 40% and the theoretical minimum work requirement is about 3.8 kw.-hr. per 1000 gallons. On the basis of these figures the energy efficiency of this process is 2.3%.

Maximum Number of Effects in a Multiple-Effect Evaporator

From a purely theoretical standpoint, without regard to economics, the Δt across an evaporator can approach zero, but there is a definite upper limit to the number of effects because of the BPE of the solution. This arises from the fact that steam generated from a boiling salt solution is slightly superheated with respect to the pressure, but it can only be effectively used as saturated steam. Consequently a Δt equivalent to the superheat, or the BPE, is lost in each effect or there is a minimum Δt per effect which is equal to the BPE. The BPE varies with concentration and somewhat with temperature and a rigorous calculation would require a stepwise calculation from one effect to the next. This would be a very tedious calculation and not worth the effort. With some reasonable assumptions one can make an approximation that is good enough. Thus, if one assumes 50% recovery from an initial 35,000 p.p.m. of NaCl and an over-all temperature range of 25° to 100° C. and assumes a forward feed, so that the concentrated solution is at the lowest temperature, the average BPE is estimated to be 1.27° F. and the maximum number of effects $= \dfrac{75 \times 1.8}{1.27} = 107$. For the same temperature range, but a constant concentration of 35,000 p.p.m. (0% recovery), average BPE $= 0.93°$ F. and $n = 145$. For this same condition Murphy (8) calculates 149. The figure given in the report is 166, but there is a numerical error. Such figures may have some scientific interest, but they have very little practical value because a limit to the number of effects is fixed by economics far below these values. It is probable that, for the temperature range considered here, the economical maximum number lies somewhere between 10 and 20 (5).

A question that arises in connection with distillation processes is: How does a vapor-compression process compare with a multiple-effect evaporation process on the basis solely of energy cost? This is readily answered as follows. The work of compression as kilowatt-hours per 1000 gallons is given by a specific form of Equation VIII. 134 (4):

$$W = \frac{0.1345 T_1(r^2 - 1)}{\epsilon r} \tag{27}$$

where

T_1 = compressor intake temperature

Let

WC_E = cost of electrical energy for compression, in cents per 1000 gallons of distillate

If

w_1 = pounds of water evaporated per pound of steam in a single-effect evaporator and if one assumes that the same value holds for each effect of a multiple-effect evaporator, it follows that

Σw = total pounds evaporated per pound of steam in n effects $= \dfrac{w_1(1 - w_1^n)}{1 - w_1}$

Cost of steam per 1000 gallons $= \dfrac{8.33 C_s}{\Sigma w}$

Equating the two costs, one gets the relation

$$n \text{ (equivalent No. of effects)} = \frac{\log\left[1 - \dfrac{61.8(1 - w_1)r\epsilon C_s}{w_1 T_1(r^2 - 1)C_E}\right]}{\log w_1} \tag{28}$$

With this one can quickly estimate the equivalent number of effects for any given set of circumstances. If $w_1 = 0.90$, $\epsilon = 0.75$, $C_s = 55$, and $C_E = 0.70$, and if we take the case of 1-atm. intake pressure to the compressor and a 2° F. BPE, the following values are obtained:

Δt across heating surface of vapor-compression evaporator, ° F.	3	5	10	15	20
Vapor pressure of boiling solution, p.s.i.	16.22	16.86	18.56	20.40	22.38
Pressure ratio	1.103	1.146	1.262	1.389	1.52
Equivalent No. of effects	∞	∞	∞	21.4	11.3

It is evident that for any Δt less than about 12° F. in the vapor-compression evaporator, the energy cost will be less than that of the multiple-effect evaporator even if the latter had an infinite number of effects. With a 15° F. Δt in vapor compression it would require a 20-effect evaporator for equivalent energy cost.

Important processes such as reverse osmosis, the various ionic membrane processes, and flash evaporation have not been discussed here. For a more comprehensive treatment of the subject of minimum energy requirements, reference is made to the report by Murphy (8).

Nomenclature

a	=	activity
B	=	availability (thermodynamic function)
BPE	=	boiling point elevation
F	=	free energy
H	=	enthalpy
$j_{\pm}$	=	mean ionic activity coefficient on the mole fraction scale
L_v	=	latent heat of vaporization
M	=	mass
m	=	molality
$m_{\pm}$	=	mean ionic molality
N	=	formality
n	=	number of moles
p	=	pressure
p_0	=	vapor pressure of pure solvent
Q	=	quantity of heat
R	=	universal gas constant
r	=	pressure ratio in a compressor
S	=	entropy
T	=	absolute temperature
T_B	=	boiling point of solvent
T_0	=	absolute temperature of a heat sink
W	=	work
W_r	=	reversible work
W_s	=	shaft work
w	=	pounds of water evaporated per pound of steam
x	=	mole fraction
y	=	fractional yield of pure water

Greek letters

γ	=	activity coefficient
$\gamma_{\pm}$	=	mean ionic activity coefficient, molal scale
Δ	=	finite difference
ϵ	=	adiabatic efficiency of a compressor
μ	=	chemical potential
μ_0	=	chemical potential in standard state
ν_1, ν_2	=	number of cations and ions, respectively, from one molecule of salt. For NaCl, both are equal to 1
ν	=	$\nu_1 + \nu_2$
Σ	=	summation of terms

Subscripts

A, B refer to components; A for salt, B for water
1, 2   refer to initial and final states or to two temperature levels
1, 2, 3 refer to feed, concentrated brine and fresh water, respectively
i refers to any component

Literature Cited

(1) Badger, W. L., Associates, Inc., "Critical Review of Literature on Formation and Prevention of Scale," Office of Saline Water Research and Development Program, Rept. 25 (July 1959).
(2) *Chem. Eng.* **63**, 128 (October 1956).
(3) Denbigh, K., *Chem. Eng. Sci.* **6**, 1–9 (1956).
(4) Dodge, B. F., "Chemical Engineering Thermodynamics," p. 355, McGraw-Hill, New York, 1944.
(5) Gilliland, E. R., *Ind. Eng. Chem.* **47**, 2410–22 (1955).
(6) International Critical Tables, Vol. III, p. 326, McGraw-Hill, New York, 1928.
(7) *Ibid.*, p. 370.
(8) Murphy, G. W., *et al.*, "Minimum Energy Requirements for Sea Water Conversion Processes," Office of Saline Water Research and Development Program, Rept. **9** (April 1956).
(9) Robinson, R. A., Stokes, R. H., "Electrolyte Solutions," p. 461, Butterworths Scientific Publications, London, 1955.

RECEIVED for review July 28, 1960. Accepted August 2?, 1960.

Heat of Concentration and Boiling Point Elevation of Sea Water

R. L. CLARK, K. J. NABAVIAN, and L. A. BROMLEY

Department of Chemical Engineering,
University of California, Berkeley, Calif.

Values of the heat of concentration and heat capacity of sea water near room temperature have been measured experimentally. The heat of concentration values compare favorably with those calculated from the vapor pressure data given by Arons and Kientzler by use of the Clapeyron equation. The heat capacity agrees with the values reported by Cox and Smith. Calculated values for the heat of concentration and boiling point elevation from 77° to 302° F. at salinities up to 9% are presented in both tabular and graphical form.

A knowledge of the thermodynamic and physical properties of sea water is needed in the analysis of any process for converting sea water to fresh water. Chambers (*3*) has summarized [mainly from Sverdrup *et al.* (*6*)] many of the physical properties of sea water.

No data were available on the heat of concentration of sea water. A simple calorimeter was built for the measurement of this heat effect near room temperature, and later was used to measure heat capacities of sea salt solutions.

The heat effect measured was for the reverse of concentration—i.e., mixing:

$1/2$ pound H_2O + $1/2$ pound concentrated sea water $\rightarrow$ 1 pound normal sea water

$$(3.5\% \text{ salinity}) \quad (1)$$

$\Delta H_{84.9° \text{ F.}} = 0.0416 \pm 0.004$ B.t.u./pound normal sea water—i.e., solution cools on mixing

The sea water was obtained from La Jolla and was concentrated to half its original weight before dilution. Just enough sulfuric acid was added to prevent the precipitation of solids during the concentration. This procedure may alter the salt composition somewhat, but it is representative of most evaporation processes.

The measured heat capacities at 23° C. (73.4° F.) were:

Normal sea water (3.5% salinity). $C_p = 0.964 \pm 0.01$ B.t.u./lb./° F.

Concentrated sea water (7.0% salinity). $C_p = 0.995 \pm 0.01$ B.t.u./lb./° F.

These values differ considerably from early measurements (*2, 3*). Recent data of Cox and Smith gave $C_p = 0.954$ B.t.u./lb./° F. for normal sea water at 23° C. (*4*).

From our values and those for water, the rate of change of ΔH with temperature (for Reaction 1) is calculated to be:

$$\left(\frac{\partial \Delta H}{\partial T}\right) 73.4° \text{ F.} = \Delta C_p = -0.033 \pm 0.01 \text{ B.t.u./lb. sea water/° F.}$$

The same quantity determined from vapor pressure data calculations is:

$$\Delta C_p = -0.023$$

In view of the experimental difficulties that arise in measuring heats of mixing above room temperature, no further experimental work was attempted.

High temperature heats of mixing were calculated from the vapor pressure data of Arons and Kientzler (1) as follows:

Neglecting liquid volume and assuming ideal gas behavior for the vapor, the Clapeyron equation for pure water and for sea salt solutions becomes

$$\frac{dP_1}{dT} = \frac{P_1 \lambda_1}{RT^2} \tag{2}$$

$$\frac{dP_2}{dT} = \frac{P_2 \lambda_2}{RT^2} \tag{3}$$

Subtracting Equation 3 from Equation 2 (at the same temperature)

$$\frac{d(P_1 - P_2)}{dT} = \frac{1}{RT^2}(P_1 \lambda_1 - P_2 \lambda_2) \tag{4}$$

defining

$$\Delta P = P_1 - P_2 \tag{5}$$

$$\Delta \lambda = \lambda_2 - \lambda_1 \tag{6}$$

$$\frac{d(\Delta P)}{dT} = \frac{\lambda_1}{RT^2}\left[\Delta P - \frac{P_2 \Delta \lambda}{\lambda_1}\right] \tag{7}$$

Dividing by ΔP and rearranging

$$\frac{d \ln \Delta P}{d \frac{1}{RT}} = -\lambda_1 \left[1 - \frac{P_2 \Delta \lambda}{\lambda_1 \Delta P}\right] \tag{8}$$

A plot of $\ln \Delta P$ vs. $\frac{1}{RT}$ will have a slope of $-\lambda_1\left[1 - \frac{P_2 \Delta \lambda}{\lambda_1 \Delta P}\right]$ from which $\Delta \lambda$ may be determined.

The values of $\Delta \lambda$ which were obtained are:

	Temp., ° F.					
	77	122	167	212	257	302
Chlorinity, ‰	Water Evaporated at Constant Composition, B.t.u./Lb.					
10	−0.09	0.52	0.65	0.63	0.42	0.18
20	−0.18	1.10	1.46	1.36	0.92	0.41
30	−0.27	1.80	2.37	2.20	1.50	0.66
40	−0.39	2.60	3.38	3.24	2.19	0.96
50	−0.51	3.50	4.52	4.40	2.98	1.31

To calculate the heats of mixing it is necessary to know the relative partial molal enthalpies of the salt and the water in the sea salt solutions. This quantity for the water, $\bar{L}_1$, is arrived at as follows:

For pure water boiling at saturation temperature, T_s and pressure P_1, the heat of vaporization is the difference between the enthalpy of the vapor per pound, H_{V1}, and the enthalpy of the liquid water per pound, H_{L1}, or

$$\lambda_1 = H_{V1} - H_{L1} \tag{9}$$

The heat of vaporization for a sea salt solution boiling at the same temperature and at its own saturation vapor pressure, P_2, is the difference between the enthalpy of the vapor per pound, H_{V2}, and the enthalpy per pound of the water in the salt solution, $\overline{H}_{L2}$.

$$\lambda_2 = H_{V2} - \overline{H}_{L2} \tag{10}$$

Combining Equations 6, 9, and 10 and from the definition of $\overline{L}_1$, one obtains

$$\overline{L}_1 = (\overline{H}_{L2} - H_{L1}) = (H_{V2} - H_{V1}) - \Delta\lambda \tag{11}$$

The quantity $(H_{V2} - H_{V1})$ is the negative of the enthalpy change on compressing (isothermally) the vapor above the sea salt solution from pressure P_2 to pressure P_1:

$$H_{V2} - H_{V1} = \int_{P_1}^{P_2} \left(\frac{\partial H_V}{\partial P}\right)_T dP \tag{12}$$

But

$$\left(\frac{\partial H_V}{\partial P}\right)_T = V - T \left(\frac{\partial V}{\partial T}\right)_P \tag{13}$$

Using a virial equation of state for the vapor

$$V = \frac{RT}{P} + B \tag{14}$$

$$\left(\frac{\partial V}{\partial T}\right)_P = \frac{R}{P} + \left(\frac{\partial B}{\partial T}\right)_P \tag{15}$$

The simple equation of Callendar (5) for the second virial coefficient was used.

$$B = 0.01602 \left[1 - 26.3 \left(\frac{373.1}{T}\right)^{10/3}\right] \text{cu. ft./lb.} \tag{16}$$

Substituting Equations 13 to 16 into Equation 12 to calculate $(H_{V2} - H_{V1})$ and then substituting into Equation 11, the values of $\overline{L}_1$ obtained are:

	Temp., ° F.					
	77	122	167	212	257	302
Chlorinity, ‰	Water in Solution, B.t.u./Lb.					
10	+0.09	−0.52	−0.64	−0.61	−0.39	−0.14
20	+0.18	−1.09	−1.44	−1.32	−0.86	−0.31
30	+0.27	−1.79	−2.34	−2.14	−1.40	−0.51
40	+0.40	−2.57	−3.33	−3.15	−2.05	−0.74
50	+0.52	−3.47	−4.46	−4.29	−2.79	−1.01

To calculate the relative partial enthalpy of the salts in sea water it was necessary to integrate the Gibbs-Duhem equation graphically.

$$\int d\overline{L}_2 = -\int \frac{N_1}{N_2} d\overline{L}_1$$

where $\frac{N_1}{N_2}$ is the weight ratio of water to salt.

The composition conversions used are:

Chlorinity, ‰	Salinity, %	N_1/N_2, Lb./Lb.
10	1.81	54.3
20	3.61	26.7
30	5.42	17.5
40	7.22	12.8
50	9.03	10.1

As it was impossible to integrate the Gibbs equation to the zero of $\bar{L}_1$ (no data were available at extremely low salt contents), all values of $\bar{L}_2$ are referred to the lowest data available—i.e., $10\%_o$ chlorinity. With this new reference state only differences of $\bar{L}_2$ have any meaning. In the following calculations only differences were used.

The heat effect on mixing for the reaction

$$\text{Pure water} + (\text{sea water})_R \rightarrow (\text{sea water})_p \tag{17}$$

$$N_0 \text{ lb. water} + \begin{Bmatrix} N_{1R} \text{ lb. water} \\ N_{2R} \text{ lb. salt} \end{Bmatrix} = \begin{Bmatrix} N_{1p} \text{ lb. water} \\ N_{2p} \text{ lb. salt} \end{Bmatrix} 1 \text{ lb. normal sea water}$$

is given by

$$\Delta H = \Delta L = N_{2p}\bar{L}_{2p} + N_{1p}\bar{L}_{1p} - N_{2R}\bar{L}_{2R} - N_{1R}\bar{L}_{1R} - 0 \tag{18}$$

$$N_{2p} = N_{2R} = \text{pounds of salt} \tag{19}$$

Rearranging,

$$\Delta H = N_{2p}(\bar{L}_{2p} - \bar{L}_{2R}) + N_{1p}\bar{L}_{1p} - N_{1R}\bar{L}_{1R} \tag{20}$$

The heat of concentration—i.e., negative of the heat of mixing for Reaction 1, calculated from Equation 20—is shown in Figure 1.

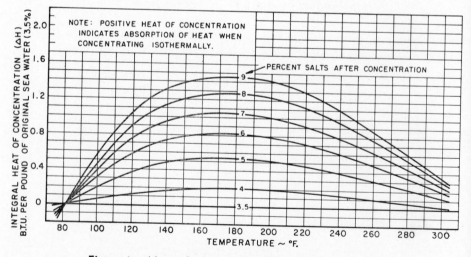

Figure 1.   Heat of concentration for normal sea water

$\triangle H$ for reaction : 1 lb. normal sea water = liquid water + concentrated sea water (3.5% salinity)

Boiling Point Elevation

The boiling point elevations were obtained by extrapolation with the Clapeyron equation:

$$BPE = \Delta P \left(\frac{RT^2}{P_2 \lambda_2} \right)$$

The values obtained are:

	Temp., ° F.					
	77	122	167	212	257	302
Chlorinity, ‰	Boiling Point Elevation, ° F.					
10	0.26	0.29	0.30	0.32	0.34	0.37
20	0.56	0.62	0.67	0.70	0.74	0.82
30	0.89	1.01	1.09	1.13	1.20	1.32
40	1.22	1.46	1.54	1.66	1.75	1.91
50	1.67	1.96	2.06	2.25	2.38	2.61

These boiling point elevations are plotted in Figure 2. They differ markedly from the values reported previously (2, 3). Their accuracy is to approximately ±0.1° F. below 150° F. and better above 150° F.

The accuracy of the calculated heats of mixing is to approximately ±0.2 B.t.u. per pound of sea water. The lower temperature values depend on small differences of vapor pressures and hence will be greatly affected by experimental errors. The reasonable agreement of the measured and calculated values of ΔC_p for Reaction 1 is encouraging.

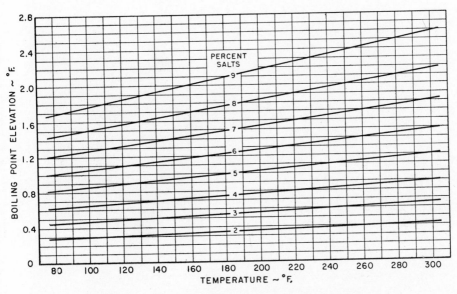

Figure 2. Boiling point elevation for sea salt solutions

Literature Cited

(1) Arons, A. B., Kientzler, C. F., *Trans. Am. Geophys. Union* 35, No. 5 (October 1954).
(2) Badger Manufacturing Co., Hickman, K. C. D., "Research on and Development of Badger-Hickman Centrifugal Distillation Techniques and Equipment," U. S. Dept. Interior, Saline Water Conversion Program, Progress Rept. 12 (November 1956).
(3) Chambers, J. T., University of California Institute of Engineering Research, "Properties of Sea Water," private communication.
(4) Cox, R. A., Smith, N. D., *Proc. Roy. Soc. London* A252, 51–62 (1959).
(5) Dorsey, N. E., "Properties of Ordinary Water Substance," p. 78, Reinhold, New York, 1940.
(6) Sverdrup, H. U., *et al.*, "The Oceans," Prentice-Hall, New York, 1940.

RECEIVED for review July 7, 1960. Accepted July 21, 1960.

Corrosion of Metals in Sea Water

FREDERICK W. FINK

Battelle Memorial Institute, 505 King Ave., Columbus 1, Ohio

The Office of Saline Water is directing a large number of investigations into the feasibility of new processes for producing fresh water starting with sea or brackish water as a source. It is desired that these plants last for 20 years or more. This paper points up ways in which the economic waste resulting from corrosion in saline water plants can be avoided. The article is based on a review of the corrosion literature and on consultations with marine experts in the field. Of the many materials for distillation plants, steel is the most important. It can be used to handle sea water below 250° F., if proper steps are taken such as the removal of all air (oxygen) from solution. For severe service and better performance metals like titanium, Hastelloy C, Monel, cupro-nickels, aluminum, aluminum brass, or Admiralty brass are used.

The ocean, which covers more than 70% of the earth's surface, is considered by many to be a challenging frontier. Such government agencies as the Navy, the Department of the Interior, the Bureau of Mines, the Maritime Commission, the Department of Agriculture, etc., have recognized the importance of the sea from their own special viewpoints for many years. Government activities, such as the demonstration plants of the Office of Saline Water to convert sea water to fresh water, the 7 mile deep-sea-diving "Bathyscaphe" under Navy sponsorship, and plans for studying hydrofoil ships, provide examples of newer activities connected with the sea. The latest nuclear-powered submarines can visit most parts of the oceans, even those under the ice.

Private interests are engaged in intensive studies related to the ocean. One can mention the oil- and sulfur-mining industries with their Texas towers, some of which are far out to sea. New types of telephone and power cables and pipelines are being placed on the sea bottom. Shore-based operations by chemical companies are making use of sea water to obtain magnesium, bromine, and sea salt. Pharmaceuticals are being extracted from sea-growing vegetation and from marine animals. Many shore-based installations use sea water for cooling and, in some special cases, for sanitation or for fire-protection services.

This increased activity on the sea, in the sea, and under the sea focuses attention on the need for knowledge of the behavior of metals in these environments. It has been known for years that sea water will attack most of the common metals. In some service conditions, certain living organisms in the sea cause marine fouling on the exposed metal surfaces leading to corrosion or interference with functioning of the equipment.

Corrosivity of Sea Water

Aqueous corrosion is electrochemical in nature and involves the passage of electric currents. The current enters the solution at local anodes and leaves the solution at cathodic areas on the metal. In the case of steel, ferrous ions enter the solution at the anode and hydrogen is deposited at the cathode.

Very pure water, because of its high resistivity, makes difficult the passage of corrosion currents through the solution from anodic to cathodic areas. For ambient temperatures, highly purified water, free from dissolved oxygen, is not corrosive to metals such as steel.

The addition of sodium chloride to water forms a solution which tends to be corrosive to steel and other common metals. However, if the solution is completely air-free, its corrosivity may not be much greater than that of pure water.

Sea water contains, in addition: sulfate, bicarbonate, bromide, and fluoride ions. Laboratory experience indicates that, at the same pH, sulfate solutions tend to be less corrosive than similar chloride solutions. The presence of bicarbonate ions in water, from dissolved CO_2, promotes some corrosion attack on many metals. It also should be mentioned that the pH of sea water normally ranges form 7.50 to 8.25, indicating that some free hydroxyl ions are always present.

Bromides and fluorides are very corrosive; but, being present only in small amounts, their effects in sea water probably are masked by the very high chloride content. In experimental work, a continuous supply of fresh, clean sea water is essential if the effects of such minor constituents on the corrosion of a metal are to be evaluated.

One might expect sea water to be corrosive because the solution is a good electrolyte, it contains ions known from experience to promote the attack on common metals, it contains dissolved oxygen which promotes the attack—e.g., by reacting with nascent hydrogen formed at the cathode—and it contains a multitude of forms of organic life, some of which affect metal corrosion.

Natural processes, operating both at the surface and at great depths, result in most of the ocean being stirred continuously. It is found that the relative proportions of dissolved salts are virtually the same everywhere, although the total salt content (salinity) may show appreciable variations with geography.

The more important ions found in a sample of North Pacific Ocean surface water, as reported by Lyman and Abel (5), are tabulated below.

Cations	Per Cent	Anions	Per Cent
Na^+	1.056	Cl^-	1.898
Mg^{+2}	0.127	SO_4^{-2}	0.265
Ca^{+2}	0.040	HCO_3^-	0.014
K^+	0.038	Br^-	0.0065
Sr^{+2}	0.001	F^-	0.0001
Sum	1.262	Sum	2.184
H_3BO_3, undissociated			0.003

Total 3.449

Natural vs. **Synthetic Sea Water.** It is not always realized that natural sea water is a completely different medium from synthetic sea water from the corrosion standpoint. A primary factor is the presence of biological effects in natural sea water that are not present in the synthetic mixture.

One effect is that bio-fouling of the metal surface often promotes localized attack. When a barnacle or mussel attaches itself to a plate of stainless steel in sea water, a differential aeration corrosion cell is formed. Intense local pitting results which may lead to complete perforation in a relatively short time. In one case a 0.75-inch thick stainless steel plate was perforated beneath a barnacle base after 9 months of immersion in sea water.

A variety of animals and plants, as well as colonies of microorganisms, may deposit from natural sea water onto the metal surface. The life processes and decomposition products may contribute directly to attack on the metal. Fouling may obstruct flow in heat exchangers and pipes, leading to such corrosive effects as are caused by overheating or impingement at local high-water velocities.

Some organisms enter a marine piping system in their larval stages, then anchor themselves to sites such as interior tube walls. If these larvae are allowed to grow, the local turbulence may result in severe corrosion. The organisms may be killed by chlorination, by flooding temporarily with fresh water, by hot sea water, or by toxic materials such as sodium pentachlorophenol. Even when the organisms are killed, their decomposing bodies may still clog the sea-water system and cause corrosion.

Two facts concerning the corrosion behavior of metals in sea water stand out:

Although there is variation in temperature, salinity, and content of living organisms, the rates of attack—especially for steel—are of the same order of magnitude at many different locations throughout the world.

The relative order of resistance of metals as determined by their corrosion rates in natural sea water is not readily simulated with synthetic sea-water preparations in the laboratory.

Factors in Salt Water Corrosion. Because of expediency, and in spite of the situation discussed above, much work has been done in the laboratory with saline solutions made up to simulate sea water. Hache (*3*) has carried out some very interesting experiments concerning the corrosion of steel in sodium chloride solutions. In Figure 1, Hache shows the effect of temperature on the corrosion of iron by air-saturated and deaerated solutions containing 30 grams per liter of pure NaCl in doubly distilled water. The effect of oxygen in increasing corrosion up to about 50° C. (122° F.) is seen. Above this temperature, the solubility of oxygen is very limited. It is for this reason that the curves become the same. In the range from 10° to 50° C. (50° to 122° F.), the corrosion increases at the rate of about 5% per ° C. Such a temperature dependence had been reported earlier by Palmaer (*7*).

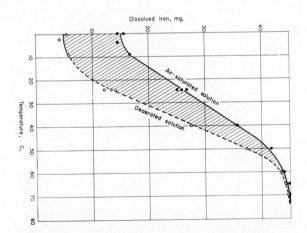

Figure 1. Effect of temperature and aeration on the corrosion of iron in 3% sodium chloride solution

Figure 2 illustrates corrosion behavior and oxygen solubility as a function of the salinity of the solution at a fixed temperature. It is to be noted that a small variation in salinity in the neighborhood of the normal 3.5% content of sea water has no effect on oxygen solubility and little effect on corrosion rate.

Factors in Sea-Water Corrosion. The effects of temperature and salinity in sea water are believed to be similar to those found in salt water, discussed above. Good quantitative information is not yet readily available.

Hache (*3*) concluded that light has an inhibiting effect on corrosion by sea water and that the results of corrosion tests conducted in total darkness were less prone to scatter.

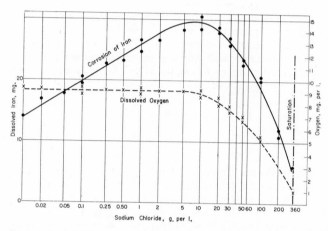

Figure 2.   Variation of corrosion as a function of salinity at 24° C.

Many other parameters tend to influence the corrosion of metals immersed in sea water. When two metals of different potentials are galvanically coupled, the acceleration of the attack on the less noble metal of the two is observed frequently. A small area of an anodic metal coupled to a large area of a second metal that is cathodic can be particularly dangerous. A useful guide to help predict unfavorable combinations is the galvanic series of metals in sea water (*9*). The reverse situation—namely, a small cathode coupled to an anode that is large in area—often proves satisfactory in service.

Some metals depend on formation of a protective film for corrosion resistance in sea water. A fresh supply of oxygen brought to the surface of the metal tends to promote the corrosion reaction in some cases, and in others it helps form desired protective films. If a critical velocity of flowing sea water is exceeded, the film may be eroded away. The velocity for useful corrosion resistance is low for copper, higher for aluminum, cupro-nickels, and aluminum bronzes, and highest for stainless steels, Hastelloy C, and titanium.

Protective films on metals also can be destroyed and corrosion accelerated by the impingement of a high-velocity stream of sea water onto the metallic surface. The inlet ends of condenser tubes, are frequently attacked (Figure 3,*a*). Jet tests have been devised for ranking the susceptibility of metals to such impingement attack. A corrosion cell is formed between the bare surface directly under the jet (anode) and the adjacent filmed surface (cathode). These jet tests give more dependable information, if natural sea water is continuously supplied to the equipment.

Usually, the corrosion-fatigue limit of a metal in sea water is lower than in fresh water. Repeated flexing allows the corrosion to proceed at the breaks in the protective film where active metal is exposed.

Cavitation corrosion is caused by repeated pounding resulting from rapid collapse of vapor bubbles. On a metal surface where there is a violent flow of water, such as that of a ship's propeller, the pressure at some area may be reduced to where localized boiling forms bubbles of vapor. At another site, these bubbles suddenly collapse.

The resultant hammering may, in time, cause the surface layer to fail and pieces of metal to flake off. The active metal sites, thus exposed, may in turn be rapidly attacked by sea water. It has been found difficult to develop a laboratory test that will accurately simulate cavitation attack as it occurs in actual marine service.

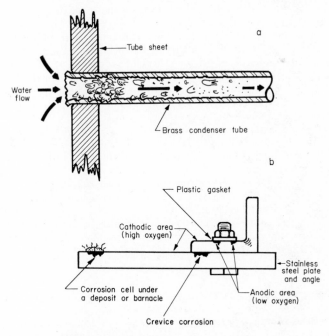

Figure 3.　Corrosion in sea water

a. Inlet impingement attack due to excessive turbulence
b. Concentration cells

The importance of bio-fouling to corrosion has already been mentioned. Marine fouling is likely to occur in all the oceans from the Arctic to the Tropics, especially during the breeding period. In northern waters, fouling occurs only during the summer, whereas in the Tropics it is practically continuous. Copper and some of its alloys, high in copper, normally are not susceptible. However, any treatment that prevents the toxic copper ions from forming may result in a tendency for copper to foul. Corrosive attack on some metals actually may be stifled by fouling. For many metals, localized attack can be more serious under fouled areas (Figure 3,b). At velocities of 2 to 3 feet per second or more, metals usually are not apt to foul. Once the organisms become attached, as during a shut-down or off-period of a plant, extremely high velocities may be needed to dislodge them at the start-up.

Differential aeration can play an important role in producing accelerated attack on metals in sea water—for example, at crevices. These crevices may be formed by loosely attached marine organisms, by debris, or by close-fitting surfaces to which sea water has restricted access (Figure 3,b).

The corrosion behavior tends to follow much the same pattern in clean sea water the world over. If there is pollution, it may cause an unbalance of the pH, change the marine organism concentration, decrease the dissolved oxygen, or alter the ionic balance of sea water. Pollution normally results in saline waters' becoming considerably more aggressive to one or more metals. Specific tests must be made to determine the applicability of a metal in each type of polluted water. Sulfides, which are often found in such waters, tend to promote corrosion of both ferrous and nonferrous metals.

Scale Formation by Sea Water. As sea water is heated (1), its scale-forming constituents tend to become supersaturated. Scale crystals will be deposited at the point of highest temperature, which may be the metal surface through which heat is being introduced. The bicarbonate ion is partly transformed to carbonate ion and to carbon dioxide. The carbonate ion reacts with calcium, which precipitates as calcium carbonate. As the sea water is heated still further, the remaining carbonate ion in the water decomposes to free carbon dioxide and hydroxyl ions. The latter combine with magnesium which precipitates as magnesium hydroxide. Both of these scale-forming reactions can be inhibited by slightly acidifying the incoming sea water.

As the sea water is heated still higher, a point is reached at which calcium sulfate will precipitate. This reaction is much less readily prevented than the first two, and it is reported to occur only above 325° F. in sea water heated under pressure.

Thus, there are three major scale components in sea water: calcium carbonate, magnesium hydroxide, and calcium sulfate.

From the standpoint of corrosion protection, a slight amount of mineral scale formation—if the thickness can be controlled—is desirable. This helps to explain why, in some cases, sea water is found to be less corrosive than a brine of sodium chloride with the same salinity. However, in applications where heat is being transferred across the metal wall, the presence of scale markedly affects the efficiency. In distillation units, a method of corrosion control based on intentional mineral-scale formation would thus lead to greater fuel consumption.

These scales also can be produced electrolytically by applying cathodic current to the metal surface immersed in sea water. As a result of the hydroxyl ions formed at the cathode, the film of sea water at the metal surface becomes highly alkaline and scale is precipitated.

Metals Used in Sea Water

Ferrous-Base Metals. STEEL. Steel finds wide use in sea water, especially as a structural material such as for ships, off-shore drilling towers, piling for piers and docks, and sea walls. It is also used as piping to handle sea water. Compared to other metals, steel is one of the least expensive materials of construction.

Steel is the basic material of construction for many sea-water plants. Even though it may corrode in some sections of a plant, such as a distillation unit, its low initial cost may result in lower over-all costs if good design and good corrosion-control practices are followed.

The rate of attack for immersed conditions is fairly uniform in unpolluted sea water and averages about 5 mils per year. General attack, when it occurs, has been observed to be a linear function of time—that is, it continues at a fairly uniform rate, despite an accumulation of corrosion products or marine growth.

Often, however, steel is subject to pitting attack by sea water. The deepest attack on steel is reported to be about 10 to 15 mils per year. The presence of mill scale on the steel—especially when it covers a large portion of the exposed area—significantly increases the rate of pitting, and penetrations of about 20 mils per year can be expected. This is a result of the mill scale serving as large cathodes to the small, bare anodic areas. Pitting attack often tapers off with continued exposure.

A recent paper by Forgeson, Southwell, and Alexander (2) gives the results of an 8-year exposure of structural steels to tropical sea water. It was found that small additions of copper did not alter the corrosion of mild steel. Steels containing 2 and 5% of nickel were definitely inferior to mild steel on the basis of both general and local attack. Steels containing 3 and 5% of chromium were more resistant than mild steel for the first 3 years, but then corroded significantly more than mild steel during the remaining 5 years. The amount of pitting also was greater for chrome steels during the latter period. For complete immersion, mild steel is preferred. In other experiments conducted in San Diego Harbor, California, the rate of pitting for mild steel was found to be as high as 60 mils per year (8).

WROUGHT IRON. Wrought iron has found considerable application in marine-based structures and in piping. While wrought iron, according to some sources, appears to be more resistant than mild steel to general and localized corrosion by sea water, there is no general acceptance of this material by operators of marine plants. Advantage is sometimes taken of its directional physical properties where corrosion resistance also is needed. It should be mentioned that for the same initial cost a much thicker wall can be purchased in a cast iron or a steel pipe than for one of wrought iron. Until directly comparable engineering data are developed in the economic use of wrought iron vs. steel or cast iron in sea-water plants, many experienced marine operators hesitate to specify it in place of other less expensive ferrous materials.

An older form of wrought iron, as produced in England, contained slag layers. These layers, when suitably oriented, were found in some corrosion environments to prevent pitting attack from progressing deeply into the metal. While this behavior accounts for the longer lifetime of the ancient form of the material, it does not follow (according to marine specialists) that the modern fibrous form of wrought iron will greatly outlast steel in identical sea-water service.

CAST IRON. The iron phase in cast iron is readily attacked by sea water, as is the case for mild steel. If the layer of graphite left with the corrosion product is dense and compact, further corrosion tends to be stifled. If the layer is porous, corrosion may be accelerated by the galvanic action between the graphite and the iron beneath. The attack then approaches a rate similar to that found for the pitting of mild steel.

Aluminum and Aluminum Alloys. Aluminum can be employed in sea water as a resistant material of construction. Experiments at Fort Belvoir, Virginia, and elsewhere, indicate that by proper corrosion-control practices, aluminum can be used for an entire plant which processes sea water. The sea water entering the plant should be free of all metallic ions, especially copper or nickel. It is essential, in such a plant, that no copper-base alloys be used at all and that galvanic couples to most other metals be avoided.

To obtain longer lifetime in sea-water service, aluminum-clad tubing is recommended. Properly chosen, the cladding acts as a sacrificial metal and the attack will not penetrate into the base metal until most of the cladding has been consumed by corrosion. The aluminum usually chosen for cladding is both more corrosion resistant and slightly anodic to the base alloy. The fact that a metal is more anodic than an adjacent one in the galvanic series for sea water does not necessarily imply it will corrode at a higher rate when exposed uncoupled.

Aluminum alloys have been used to fabricate heating coils for tankers in which crude oil and sea-water ballast are alternate cargoes. Savings in weight and in losses due to corrosion are reported to be very favorable compared with mild steel.

Stainless Steels. In special circumstances, under carefully controlled conditions, some grades of stainless steel have given good service in sea water. Most authorities strongly recommend caution in the use of stainless steel for service in sea water.

In heat exchanger service, stainless steels can be used at much higher velocities than most common metals. There is, nevertheless, the ever-present possibility that stress-corrosion cracking may take place. This becomes much more likely as the metal temperature is raised. Any points at which high stress and high chloride concentrations occur are particularly prone to this type of failure.

Stainless steel also is susceptible to crevice corrosion and deposit attack. Differential aeration cells, formed between stagnant and well-aerated areas on the metal surface, may promote rapid attack.

It is found that Type 316, containing molybdenum, is more resistant to the initiation of pits. However, once a pit is started, the rate of penetration may be of the same order as for a molybdenum-free alloy.

Since the process side in a heat exchanger may demand stainless steel, as in the case of a marine-based chemical plant that has been forced to use sea water for cooling purposes, it is necessary to consider measures for obtaining optimum service. The cooling water should be free from solids which could deposit on the tubes. The velocity should not be allowed to drop much below 5 feet per second. Crevice areas and stagnant areas should be minimized or eliminated by design. Residual and service stresses should be held to the lowest possible levels. Under such carefully controlled conditions, stainless steel could give good service.

Stainless steel pump impellers are giving excellent service in sea water. The same may be said for stainless steel ship propellers now in use on coastal vessels. In both cases, it is essential that the stainless steel not be left for long periods between runs in stagnant sea water.

Stainless steel generally withstands polluted sea water and polluted brackish water better than copper-base alloys. Substituting an austenitic stainless screen for silicon-bronze trash racks has resulted in greatly improved service at a west coast power plant. Normally stainless steel screens, because of the crevices involved (where the wires cross), are not recommended for use in sea water. This alteration of the usual corrosion mechanism, presumably related to the hydrogen sulfide content of polluted sea water, needs to be studied.

Monel. Extensive use for handling sea water is provided by Monel. It has given excellent service in heat exchangers, piping, sheathing to protect steel at the half-tide zone, valves, pump impellers, and fittings in general. Monel has been used in fabricating distillation units. In one type, a Monel heat exchanger "basket" can be made to flex in order that the sea-water scale will drop off, thus restoring its thermal efficiency. This service is considered much too severe for most metals. Monel shafts, such as the harder K Monel, are resistant to corrosion fatigue in sea-water service. Marine experience, in general, considers Monel one of the best all-around metals for handling sea water.

Copper-Base Alloys. There is a wide range of copper-base alloys that have given good service in sea water. Admiralty brass, 70 Cu–29 Zn–1 Sn, plus an inhibitor such as arsenic, has found wide use as condenser tubes in marine-based plants using sea water for cooling. While it is not so resistant as the cupro-nickels, it often seems to be preferred because of the lower initial cost.

Another widely used alloy in cooling-water service is aluminum brass, 76 Cu–22 Zn–2 Al. The aluminum content improves the resistance to velocity and impingement. This alloy seems to be more susceptible to pitting than some of the other copper alloys in stagnant sea water. Arsenic is added as an inhibitor of dezincification.

The high-tin bronzes—e.g., 90 Cu–10 Sn—are known to have excellent lifetime in sea water as condenser tubes. Undoubtedly, their cost has restricted the wider use of these resistant alloys.

Ordinary copper is not recommended for sea-water plants if the water velocities are much greater than 2 feet per second. It remains to be demonstrated whether copper can be employed in contact with completely deaerated sea water at much higher velocities.

CUPRO-NICKELS. At the present time, most marine operators agree that the cupro-nickels are the most useful material of construction for sea-water plants. Since World War II, the 90 Cu–10 Ni alloy modified with about 1.5% of iron has become well established. The lower nickel content results in a cost advantage over the 70 Cu–30 Ni alloy. Alloys containing 70 Cu–30 Ni or 80 Cu–20 Ni, each with added iron, are preferred by some designers to withstand more severe conditions.

The cupro-nickels have been widely accepted as the best available alloy for condenser tubes. For handling hot sea water, there has been some favorable experience with cupro-nickel for pumps and heat exchangers.

Titanium. Unlike other metals, titanium normally does not pit, is not susceptible to stress corrosion, is free from local corrosion under fouling organisms, is free from impingement and cavitation attack at velocities which attack copper-base alloys, and is not susceptible to sulfide attack in contaminated sea water. Experiments with water velocities at 20 to 50 feet per second show no attack on titanium.

Titanium and its alloys are said to be less susceptible to mineral scaling in sea water than most other metals. (The corrosion products on a metal, such as steel, probably help to anchor sea-scale deposits.) Although thermal conductivity is low, the over-all efficiency, taking full advantage of the very high velocities permitted, can be greater than with material used at present in sea-water applications involving high rates of heat transfer.

Methods of Protection

Protective Coatings. A variety of protective coatings is available for steel in sea-water service. For such applications as ships' hulls, normal practice is to apply compatible antifouling paint over the corrosion-resistant primer coating system. Figure 4 shows panels which have resisted fouling for a year or more as compared with adjacent panels where the experimental coating is not protective.

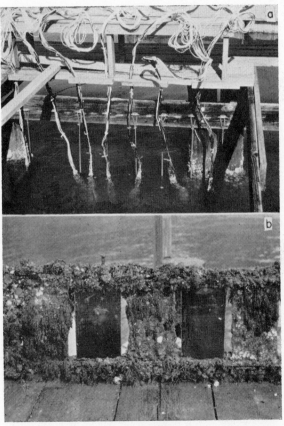

Figure 4. Experiments at Battelle's Daytona Beach
Marine Station

a. Effect of cathodic protection on paint systems
b. Antifouling paint studies

Cathodic Protection. Steel can be protected by cathodic current, supplied either from sacrificial anodes or an external direct current source. The method is effective for completely immersed steel—i.e., for surfaces on structures below the low-tide level. Current consumption can be greatly reduced by applying a suitable paint system to the steel before it is immersed in sea water. Such a paint system should be alkali resistant.

Aluminum can be cathodically protected, but caution must be employed. If there is too much alkali developed as a result of too high a cathodic current, the aluminum will be attacked. Figure 4 shows a cathodic-protection experiment being conducted at Battelle's marine station.

Water Treatment. Many years have been spent in developing corrosion inhibitors for ordinary waters. Only a very few such treatments have been studied for use in sea water. For a once-through plant, corrosion prevention by the use of inhibitors usually is found to be too costly.

If sea water is first deaerated, only a small amount of corrosion inhibitor, if any, probably would be needed to prevent attack on steel, or copper-base alloys. For aluminum, oxygen is needed to promote a protective film.

Most of the interest, so far, has been in developing water treatments for scale prevention, not corrosion prevention.

Design Consideration in Heat Exchangers

In choosing materials for sea-water, heat exchanger, or evaporator service, many factors—such as cost, availability, efficiency, as well as corrosion—must be considered. Materials available in wrought forms, such as tubing and sheet, have been highlighted in this review. All of these metals can be fabricated by well-established methods including welding. While the thermal conductivity for the alloys varies considerably, the property of interest to the designer is the over-all rate of heat transfer in service. For efficiency, thin protective films on the surface are to be preferred to heavy deposits of scale and corrosion products. Where space and weight are important, such as on board ship, an expensive material (such as titanium) might cost less in the long run because of its freedom from maintenance expense.

Heat Exchangers Using Cooling Water. Tubular-type heat exchangers used in marine service are among the most critical in a distillation plant. One troublesome area in a tube and shell-type heat exchanger is at the inlet ends of the tubes. Impingement corrosion, which is caused by high-velocity turbulent flow, is encountered most frequently over the first 6 inches of the inlet ends of the tubes (Figure 3,a). Beyond this point, the flow usually tends to be laminar unless there is some obstruction in the tube.

Impingement attack at the inlet ends can be minimized by providing a suitable amount of cathodic current. While this current does not enter the tube ends to any great depth, it protects the first few inches. The current may be provided by sacrificial anodes made from iron, zinc, aluminum, or magnesium.

If sacrificial anodes are used in condenser water boxes, it is desirable to select a type that will last for several years. Pure zinc or specially formulated zinc anodes have regained favor in recent years with some operators. High-purity zinc is said to be self-regulating and does not require a resistance to control the current. In some cases, the tube sheet and tube ends also are coated to reduce the current drain on the anodes.

Another method of providing protective current is to use the heads or water boxes as sacrificial anodes. These water boxes, when made of heavy steel or of cast iron, provide galvanic protection to the tube ends and tube sheet as they corrode.

Incidentally, the small amount of iron introduced into sea water by such corrosion, or by intentional chemical addition, is considered beneficial by some authorities for promoting protective films on copper-base alloys. Reduced attack can also be accomplished by flaring the tube ends to facilitate streamline flow. It is essential that the cross-over area in the head or channel be larger than the cross-sectional area of the tubes to reduce turbulence. Munro (6) recommends 125% for the cross-over area in water boxes for sea-water service. Also from the standpoint of turbulence, side entry is preferred to axial entry at the front end of the condenser.

If the ferrous heads or water boxes in a condenser are lined with a protective coating, or with a metal such as Monel, the inlet tube ends will no longer receive cathodic protection from the iron to copper alloy couple. Impingement attack at the tube ends may be expected to be more severe. Sacrificial anodes, as already described, probably will be needed. For painted water boxes, the anode design and placement must be carefully designed. Too much current may result in blisters on the paint coating and undesirable mineral scale on the tube inlet section. There are reports that pieces of dislodged paint coating have caused sudden plugging of condenser tubes with serious loss of cooling capacity.

In certain chemical plants, the process solution being cooled is under pressure or is very corrosive. It is found expedient in some cases to put the low-pressure sea water on the shell side of the heat exchanger. Under these conditions, the steel shell will suffer more rapid attack because of galvanic coupling to the copper-base alloy tubing. However, only the outer tubes are "seen" by the shell in this couple. Nevertheless, this represents a large cathode.

For each condenser-tube alloy, there is a recommended maximum as well as minimum velocity in sea-water service. Silt or other fine solids in the cooling water is a complicating factor. It may be helpful to raise the minimum velocity to the point where the silt is always maintained in suspension.

In brackish waters, the same general corrosion principles may apply as for sea water. Experience has also shown that there may be considerable variation from plant to plant in the performance of metals, even where the cooling water comes out of the same general source such as a deep bay or estuary. There are coastal sites where the salinity may show very marked seasonal fluctuation. Protective film formation is essential for long lifetime in condenser tubing. Tubes installed at the season of the year when conditions are most favorable to form protective films tend to give longer service.

The use of sacrificial anodes for protection of the heads of the heat exchanger may not be so effective in brackish water. The water may be very corrosive because of pollution or contamination, even when the salinity is relatively low. More anodes, with closer spacing, normally are needed to give sufficient protection in brackish water than in sea water.

Evaporators and Heat Exchangers for Handling Hot Sea Water. Relatively little information is available on materials of construction for elevated-temperature service with sea water. Usually, one also must consider the attack by flue gas, steam, or other medium on the other side of the metal barrier.

Cupro-nickels are recommended for consideration in evaporator service, especially if sea water is to be handled at 200° F. or higher. Monel should give good service. There is some interest in using either Type 316 stainless steel or Alloy 20. Because of the danger of stress corrosion, precautions must be taken with these latter two materials. Hastelloy C is said to be very resistant to hot sea water.

From a corrosion viewpoint, the metal with the most outstanding promise for seawater heat exchangers is titanium. Laboratory experiments starting with sea water, and heating under pressure to above the critical temperature, have indicated titanium to be greatly superior to Hastelloy C and Monel, under these conditions (4). All indications suggest that titanium is the most resistant of the commercially available metals to sea water at temperatures up to 750° F.

At the present time, it is recommended that the heat-transfer surfaces of evaporators and the heat exchangers for handling hot sea water be made of 70% copper, 30% nickel alloy with 0.7% iron. This alloy has given excellent service in heat exchangers aboard ships under a wide variety of service conditions.

Pumps. Materials of construction for pumps vary with the type of service. At lower velocities, sea water has been handled successfully in pumps using casings made from cast iron. Cast iron containing a few per cent of nickel is reported to be finer grained and to have smaller graphite flakes. This may explain its superior performance for sea-water service compared with ordinary cast iron.

After a year or two in sea water, a residual layer of graphite forms on the cast-iron surface. If a cast-iron pump casing becomes graphitized, the potential relationship is reversed and the casing may become cathodic to the bronze impeller. The latter can now be expected to corrode at a higher rate. Many operators prefer a more resistant material for the casing, such as Monel, a bronze, or a cupro-nickel. This avoids the above problem with cast iron.

Although impellers are commonly made of one of the bronzes, many operators prefer Monel and S Monel because of the longer service obtained.

Several instances of corrosion cracking of austenitic stainless steel pump shafts have been reported. It is found that pump shafts of K Monel give excellent service in sea water.

The lifetime of the pump, particularly the impeller, is greatly extended if it is operated below its rated capacity for fresh water when it is used for sea water.

For handling hot sea water, Carpenter 20 impeller and casings have been used with success. Cupro-nickel also has been used for pumps handling hot sea water.

Impingement or Erosion-Corrosion. A considerable number of failures in sea-water service tend to occur on the downstream side of valves, fittings, branch connections, etc. Excessively high sea-water velocities and turbulence were involved. It is not considered good practice to control rates of flow by throttling at the valve, since this introduces turbulence just beyond the valve. Valves should be used for isolation service. Good hydraulic design is essential for long lifetime in a plant for handling sea water. Velocities in pipes, etc., should be in the range recommended for the material in sea water.

Intake to Plant. Clean sea water (or brackish water) free from suspended matter is essential from an operational standpoint. Shell fish, trash, etc., if allowed into the water system in the plant, may become lodged at critical points, such as heat exchanger tubing.

Conclusions

For economy in construction and operation of plants for handling saline water, particular attention must be paid to corrosion factors. Steel can be used in many applications, if it is protected by the use of coatings or is given cathodic protection. Allowance also can be made in the design for the corrosion of steel. If it does not conflict with other design factors, incoming sea water should be deaerated to control steel corrosion. Corrosion inhibitors and chemical treatment may be employed to reduce the attack, but frequently this method is too costly.

A large number of copper-base and nickel-base alloys (such as cupro-nickels, Monel, and aluminum brass) have been used in sea-water service with success. Special materials such as Hastelloy C, Illium, and titanium are available for extremely corrosive situations. The evidence, so far, indicates titanium to be outstanding and to rank above other commercially available metals in corrosion resistance under conditions involving high temperature, velocity, and other adverse environmental conditions.

Chlorination to a residual of 0.5 p.p.m. is widely used. It is required to prevent fouling of the Monel or bronze intake screens, the ducts, pipes, etc., throughout the system. Experience has shown that chlorination, unless carefully controlled to low residuals, tends to increase the corrosivity of saline waters.

Sacrificial anodes frequently are used to protect the rotating steel frame which supports the Monel screens at the plant intake.

Recently, aluminum has been demonstrated to be a very useful material of construction for sea-water plants. Special care must be taken with aluminum to avoid contact with most other metals. Heavy metal ions in the incoming sea water, such as copper, must be removed before the water enters an aluminum installation to prevent local attack such as pitting.

With greatly increasing interest in the ocean for many purposes, the corrosion experts will be increasingly active in helping to design corrosion-resistant apparatus and plants for sea-water service.

Acknowledgment

The author is indebted to a large number of specialists who generously contributed time, experience, and ideas to this paper. The author very much appreciates the support of the Office of Saline Water on a project closely related to the subject of this paper.

Literature Cited

(1) Badger, W. L., and Associates, Inc., Ann Arbor, Mich., "Critical Review of Literature on Formation and Prevention of Scale," Research and Development Progr. Rept. No. 25, Office of Saline Water, July 1959.
(2) Forgeson, B. W., Southwell, C. R., Alexander, A. L., *Corrosion* 16, No. 3 (1960).
(3) Hache, A., *Rev. mét.* 53, No. 1 (1956).
(4) Laserson, G. L., *et al.*, "Extraction of Fresh Water from Sea Water in the Supercritical State," to the Office of Saline Water, by Nuclear Development Associates, Inc., White Plains, N. Y., NDA 32-2, p. 36, July 31, 1954.
(5) Lyman, John, Abel, R. B., *J. Chem. Educ.* 35, 113–5 (1958).
(6) Munro, J. D., *Proc. Am. Petrol. Inst.* 34, 19 (1954).
(7) Palmaer, W., *J. lutte contre corrosion*, 18–24 (1938).
(8) Peterson, M. H., Waldron, L. J., "An Investigation of the Corrosion Rate of Mild Steel in San Diego Harbor," Natl. Assoc. Corrosion Engrs., 16th Ann. Conf., Dallas, Tex., March 14–18, 1960.
(9) Uhlig, H. H., ed., "Corrosion Handbook," p. 416T, Electrochemical Society, 1948.

RECEIVED for review July 15, 1960. Accepted July 28, 1960.

The Place of Solvent Extraction in Saline Water Conversion

DONALD W. HOOD and RICHARD R. DAVISON

Texas A & M College, College Station, Tex.

No method of desalination is likely to be best in all circumstances and the conditions most favorable for solvent extraction are investigated. In this process, saline water is contacted with an organic solvent to produce a more concentrated raffinate and an extract containing the low salinity water which separates upon heating. The solvent is recycled and the product and raffinate are stripped of the residual solvent content. Data on both the extracting and stripping steps indicate their practicality. Of the many types of compounds investigated as solvents, secondary and tertiary amines are the best in every respect, except that the resulting high pH precipitates magnesium. Low temperatures in the process minimize scale and corrosion and make possible the use of low-level heat, and by varying the solvent mixture, the operating temperature may be varied to suit ambient conditions. As for any stagewise process, the costs are less for low salinity feed. From a competitive standpoint, water of low magnesium and 5000 to 10,000 p.p.m. solids are favored.

The complexity of the problem and the diversity of operating conditions in saline water conversion make it unlikely that any process based on one principle or phenomenon will provide the most efficient conversion in all operating situations encountered. The art of saline water conversion has now reached a level at which one can begin to take stock with respect to the particular advantages of the many different processes in any given situation. The final selection of a process will only be possible after careful consideration of process operation data as applied to the conversion problem at hand. Since such data are available on but very few processes at the present time, it is only possible to project on the basis of theory and experience those points which set apart one process from another. The purpose of this paper is to present information now available which may help to locate the solvent extraction process in its rightful position in the saline water conversion field.

Solvent extraction was proposed as a method for saline water conversion by Hood and Harwell in 1953 (1), and has been under investigation since that time through support of the Office of Saline Water at Texas A & M College. A number of review articles have been published concerning this process (2–5).

Process

The process operates on the principle that certain solvents which contain strong electronegative atoms within the molecule have the property of forming hydrogen bonds with water molecules and yet because of their hydrophobic side chain draw the water-solvent couple into the solvent phase. Substitution of alkyl groups on or near the nitrogen, as in branched secondary or tertiary amines, results in extreme sensitivity of solubility to temperature, making it possible to separate solvent and water by a small change in temperature. With these configurations of the solvent molecule, water is extracted from the brine solutions with the exclusion of salt. A schematic of the extraction process is shown in Figure 1. If reflux is necessary, slight modifications will

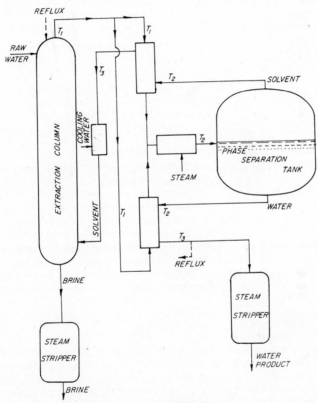

Figure 1. Schematic of solvent extraction process for saline water conversion

be required. Feed water enters at the top of the extractor (or intermediately, if reflux is required) and the solvent is contacted in countercurrent flow by the solvent entering the extractor at the bottom. The extract, which contains appreciable water and a little salt, leaves the extractor and flows through the heat exchange system. The extract is divided into two streams: One exchanges heat with the stripped solvent, and the other with the separated water. Hot extract from the exchanger enters the extract heater from which it emerges at a separation temperature T-2 before entering the separator. The stripped solvent flows back to the exchangers and through a cooler from which it is recycled to the extractor. The water from the separator flows through the exchangers and through the product solvent recovery unit. If reflux is used, part of the product water stream is removed prior to solvent removal and returned to the extraction column. Many modifications of this basic process have been considered, with particular reference to type of extractors, sources of heat, and thus modification of heat exchangers and solvent recovery processes. In essence, however, all consist of the three basic parts: extraction, separation, and solvent recovery.

In Figure 2, the solubility curve of a typically good solvent is shown. In this curve the weight per cent of water in the solvent is plotted *vs.* temperature. If one chooses an extraction temperature of 38° C., the solvent will dissolve approximately 30% water. If a lower temperature is used and thus a higher water content, the

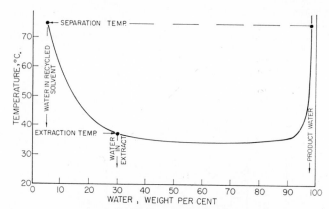

Figure 2. Typical solubility diagram of typical solvent useful in saline process

solvent dissolves water which contains increasing amounts of salt. Experience has shown that a water content of the extract in excess of 35 to 40% usually causes excess solution of salt in the solvent phase for optimum operation. Figure 3 shows the effect of solvent water content on the selectivity of water over salt for some secondary and tertiary amines. If the solvents represented were then heated to 75° C., all except 8% of the water would phase out. After phase separation of water and solvent, the solvent can be recycled through the extraction phase to make the process continuous.

Solvent Chemistry

During this investigation about 400 solvents have been studied for suitability in the solvent extraction process. Included in this group have been esters, fatty acids, aldehydes, ketones, alcohols, glycerol ethers, ethylene glycol, propylene glycol, thioethers, ethanolamines, amino ethers, phosphate and phosphite esters, morpholine derivatives, a large variety of substituted aromatic and cyclic compounds, and primary, secondary, and tertiary amines. Of this vast array of compounds, it appears that only those compounds containing strong electronegative groups such as oxygen, nitrogen, and possibly phosphorus, have properties useful in this process. Of these, the nitrogen-containing compounds and particularly the amines are found to have by far the best solvent properties. The solubility curves for some of the amines are shown in Figure 4. This figure points out rather dramatically the effect of one carbon atom in a compound and the effect of substitution in the aliphatic chain with respect to the nitrogen atom. Methylpentylamine and methylbutylamine are not particularly useful because, in the case of the former, the solubility curve is too perpendicular and, in the latter, insufficient water is lost by heating within normal temperatures. Although the methylpentylamine is somewhat better than methylbutylamine, the solubility does not change sufficiently with temperature for a good solvent; however, ethylisopropyl and ethyl *sec*-butylamine which contain a methyl group alpha to the nitrogen show great improvement in solubility properties. In the case of ethylisopropylamine, an almost ideal solvent situation results except that the operating temperature is much higher than is desirable. Conversely, the ethyl *sec*-butylamine requires an extraction temperature that is too low for an effective solvent. There are a number of amines which have solvent properties similar to those shown. The final decision with respect to selection is based on the comparative cost of synthesis, the selectivity of water over salt, density, viscosity, ease of phase separation, molecular weight, and other physical and chemical properties desirable in the process.

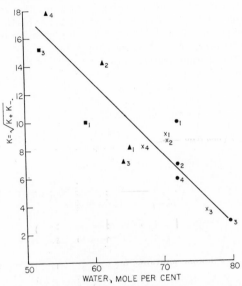

Figure 3. Effect of solvent content on the selectivity of water over salt for some amines

1. *n*-Methyl-1, 3-dimethylbutyl-
   amine
2. *n*-Ethyl sec-butylamine
3. *n*-Ethyl *tert*-butylamine
4. *n*, *n*-Dimethyl *tert*-butyl-
   amine

● 0.1% NaCl

× 1.0% NaCl
▲ 5.0% NaCl
■ 10.0% NaCl

$$k = \frac{\left(\dfrac{salt}{salt + water}\right) water}{\left(\dfrac{salt}{salt + water}\right) solvent}$$

$$K^+ = Na^+$$

$$K^- = Cl^-$$

In our extensive investigation, practically all structural configurations of the amines which contain five and six carbon atoms were obtained commercially or synthesized. The properties of many of the amines have been found suitable, but the authors have been unable to find a solvent which happened to fall in the right operating temperature range. Further study indicated that mixtures of solvents both of which had near ideal properties but were difficult to use in the process because of operating temperature, would give solubility curves of almost ideal characteristics when mixed in the right proportions. Data obtained for two of these are shown in Figure 5. These data show that an extraction temperature from 18° to 55° C. is possible by use of mixtures of these two amines. In the desert southwest the feed water will have a temperature between 25° and 35° C., and in order to allow for heat of solution of the water in solvents, an extraction temperature between 35° and 45° C. would result. For this condition, a combination of one part triethylamine and two parts methyldiethylamine provides a near-ideal solvent. Triethylamine is the best solvent of the two and therefore, operation at colder temperatures would be somewhat advantageous. A feed water temperature of 12° to 15° C. would allow use of triethylamine as a single solvent.

A second important point of consideration is the short temperature range required for this system of solvents. The 1 to 2 mixture of methyldiethylamine-triethylamine dissolves 35% by weight of water at 40° C. and at a separation temperature of 55° C. it dissolves only 10% water. A feed water temperature of 30° C. would be desirable and to heat to the separation temperature by means of heat exchangers, a source of heat at 65° C. would be adequate.

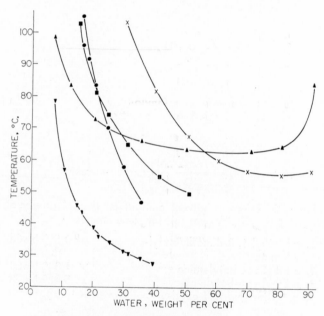

Figure 4. Effect of structure on water solubility

X—X n-Methylbutylamine
●—● n-Methylamylamine
■—■ n-Ethylpropylamine
▲—▲ n-Ethylisopropylamine
▼—▼ n-Ethyl sec-butylamine

In order to test the laboratory data obtained, a small extractor system was used with those solvents having suitable properties, which were obtainable in sufficient quantities for testing, using natural waters or sodium chloride solutions. The extraction system consists of a 2-inch packed column approximately 4 feet high to which water and solvent were fed countercurrently. An analysis of the resulting extract feed and brine was made to determine the material balance for the system. The data obtained from this column using diisopropylamine as solvent are shown in Table I. The feed concentration was 2000 p.p.m. of sodium chloride. The product contained 490 p.p.m., of which part was the amine hydrochloride. In practice, this would be replaced in the solvent recovery system by an equivalent amount of sodium to give the total salt content indicated. Sufficient data have been obtained to indicate that the calculations

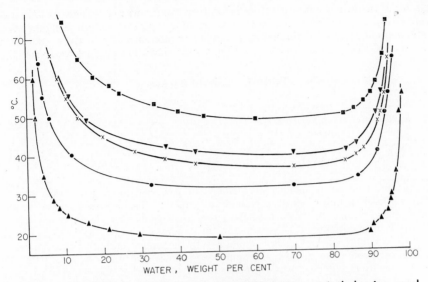

Figure 5. Solubility diagram of methyldiethylamine, triethylamine, and mixtures of the two

▲—▲ Triethylamine
■—■ Methydiethylamine
X—X 1-2 mixture
▼—▼ 1-3 mixture
●—● 1-1 mixture

based on laboratory data are compatible with those obtained in practical extraction studies. Similar runs with this column using actual brackish water obtained from brine wells gave comparable results. In this experiment, no reflux was used and the column gave about three theoretical stages. It is expected that the mixed solvent system previously indicated would give better results than diisopropylamine, but sufficient quantities of solvent have not been available for such testing.

Table I. Production of Fresh Water from Salt Water with Diisopropylamine

	Sodium		Chloride
Meq.	P.p.m.	Meq.	P.p.m.
	Feed—Salt, 2000 p.p.m.		
33.3	800	33.3	1200
	Product—Salt, 491 p.p.m.		
6.0	144	8.4	325
2.4 (amine as sodium)			
	Raffinate—Salt, 7150 p.p.m.		
128	3090	115	4060

Solvent Recovery

From the time of inception of this process, much concern has been indicated concerning the problem of solvent recovery from the product water and raffinate. This concern stems from two important considerations: first, the cost of solvent losses; and second, the possible toxicity of the remaining solvent. To investigate solvent recovery on a scale useful in plant scale-up, a laboratory system was constructed which uses a steam stripper consisting of a 6-inch packed column approximately 6 feet tall. Water containing amine was fed through the stripper countercurrently to the steam and the data shown in Table II were obtained. These data show that product water containing

Table II. Solvent Recovery

| Rate, Lb./Hr. | | Water Feed | Amine Concn., P.P.M. | |
Water feed	Steam overhead	Temp., ° C.	Feed	Product
394	21.1	83	3200	3.3
394	26.4	85	3200	1.6

3200 p.p.m. of diisopropylamine was stripped to a concentration of approximately 2.5 p.p.m. with 0.06 pound of steam per pound of product. This represents very favorable solvent recovery and the steam used from this process will provide approximately one half the heat requirements necessary for the separation stage. It is expected that stripping in a more efficient column would reduce the amine concentration even further. From an economic point of view, this amount of solvent constitutes a loss of 0.02 pound of amine per 1000 gallons of water produced. At an estimated cost of $0.50 per pound for the amine, the solvent losses would amount to $0.01 per 1000 gallons of product. From the toxicity point of view, it is not possible to estimate what additional amine removal will be necessary since few data on chronic toxicity of amines to humans are available. Some data on toxicity of aliphatic amines to poultry have been presented in the literature. Clark and Dubose (2) found that chickens fed 25 mg. of n-octylamine per kilogram of body weight for 10-week periods gave no statistical evidence of damage. Acute toxicity was reached only when the diet contained 1100 mg. per kilogram of body weight. While these data are not directly applicable in establishing the chronic toxicity level of aliphatic amines to humans, yet assuming similar effects, a human would need to drink approximately 750 liters of product water per day containing 2.5 p.p.m. of amine, in order to reach the lower limit set for chickens. Should it be necessary to reduce the amine content below that provided by stripping with steam, laboratory tests have shown that amine solutions of this concentration quickly lose their amine content when allowed to stand in a laboratory for a period of 1 to 2 days, indicating rapid bacterial decomposition. These data would imply that storage of the water for brief periods or use of trickle filters would be advantageous in removing the last traces of amine in the water product.

Limitations of the Process

Certain limitations exist for this method of saline water conversion. First, due to the fundamental properties of solutions of water in solvents, the process is most applicable to low saline waters or those commonly classified as brackish, in a range of 2000 to 10,000 p.p.m. of total salt. There are several reasons for this. This is a stagewise process so that the number of stages and reflux required are a function of the ratio of feed to water product concentration. Also, increasing salt concentration reduces the solubility of water in the solvent. Because it is necessary to circulate at least two to two and a half times as much solvent as water product with larger amounts for higher salt concentration, the problem of heat exchange and extraction with these large quantities of solvent becomes important. The economics of heat exchange necessitate that some thermal energy be discarded to the environment rather than attempt to make a closed heat system. However, since the process can utilize extremely low cost steam or even hot water for a good portion of its heating cycle, part of this limitation is removed. Secondly, since the solvents found to have the best solvent properties produce solutions sufficiently alkaline to precipitate magnesium hydroxide, it is necessary to remove magnesium from water prior to extraction, or to feed a very low magnesium containing water. A third limitation, while apparently not important except from a psychological point of view, is the small quantity of amine that may remain in the product water. It is likely, there will be some resistance to use of this water by the general public, but such a limitation should be much less than that imposed by initiation of the chlorination of water for sanitary purposes some years ago.

Advantages of the Process

The process has several distinct advantages that set it somewhat apart from many of the other processes. First, and possibly most important, is the versatility of the process with respect to energy sources, since essentially free heat may be obtained from such sources as exhaust steam, or gases of industrial engines, cooling water from condensers, solar heaters, or from any other source with a relatively low temperature heat. Under present concepts of development of the process, approximately one half the energy required will need to be low pressure steam. This steam may be produced by flashing a large quantity of water at temperatures available from cooling towers. Secondly, the process lends itself well to adaptation to existent environmental conditions. Feed water ranging in temperatures from 18° to 55° C. can be handled by alternating the nature of the solvent composition to give the most economic advantage. Some advantage is realized, based on present solvents, in the lower temperature feed water. Thirdly, the process is especially applicable to brackish waters which are more likely to be located

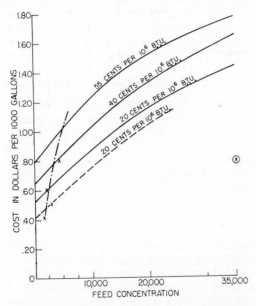

Figure 6. The effect of feed concentration on the cost of product water at various heat costs as compared to membrane and freezing processes for feed water at 25° C., in 10,000,000-gallon-per-day plant

——— Ethyl sec-butylamine
- - - - - 1-2 mixture of triethylamine and methyldiethylamine
x-.x-. Ionic membranes
⊗ Freezing process

at points of need than sea water. In this regard, the process competes favorably with the ionic membrane processes currently in operation. It has the advantage that the cost of water produced increases much less rapidly with salt content of the feed than it does in the membrane process. The solvent extraction process is therefore adaptable to a range of feed water concentration between 5000 and 10,000 p.p.m. in which few, if any other processes, are especially adaptable. In Figure 6, cost data are presented for the solvent extraction process in which the concentration of salt *vs.* estimated cost is plotted. It is believed that lower cost energy than $0.20 per 10^6 B.t.u. will be practical under certain circumstances. Energy cost reduction would affect the curve in an approximate proportional manner as is indicated for the data given for *n-ethyl-sec-*butyl-amine. The data on ionic membranes are taken from pilot plant data of Ionics, Inc. (*7*). From these data it is indicated that very low saline waters are converted at a somewhat lower cost by the membrane system, but in the range from 5000 to 10,000 p.p.m. the solvent extraction process appears to have decided advantage. The data for the freezing process as applied to sea water are taken from the Carrier Corp. Report (*8*). While cost data are not available for brackish water using the Carrier process it is not expected that much advantage will be realized from lower feed water-salt concentrations.

Finally, in those processes requiring high temperature, the problems of scaling and corrosion present formidable barriers to economic production of fresh water. In solvent extraction, the problem of scaling is eliminated by the low temperature of the operation, and the solvents eliminate the growth of sliming and incrusting organisms. Corrosion in this system is expected to be minimal because of the inhibitory action of amines toward corrosion of iron. In Table III, data are presented on the corrosion of mild steel in the amine-water solutions. These data show that even a 5% sodium chloride solution which contains 2% of diisopropylamine gives a corrosion rate of less than 1 mil per year or less than 20% of that reported for sea water. In the lower salt content waters, the rate of corrosion is negligible.

Table III.   Corrosion of Mild Steel in Amine Water Solutions

	A	B	C
Wt. loss/specimen, gram	0.0585	0.0015	0.0054
Wt. loss/sq. cm., gram	3.6×10^{-3}	9×10^{-5}	3.3×10^{-4}
Thickness loss, mil	0.11	0.003	0.012
Thickness/yr., mil	0.62	0.017	0.064

Test period 64 days: temp. 30° C., specimen area 16.3 sq. cm.

A.   5% sodium chloride plus 2% diisopropylamine in water
B.   2% diisopropylamine in water
C.   30% water in diisopropylamine

Conclusions

Extraction of potable water from saline waters by means of immiscible solvents has been shown to be theoretically possible, experimentally feasible, and economically attractive. Data presented show the process to be especially adaptable to the conversion of feed water in the range of 5000 to 10,000 p.p.m. It is adaptable to use of low-quality heat such as hot water from cooling towers or low pressure waste steam. By use of mixed solvent systems, the process can be optimized to take advantage of seasonal changes in temperature and sources of cold feed water and low-level heat sources. The process, in general, is somewhat more economical when a cold source of feed water is available.

The problems of corrosion and scaling inherent to most of the other processes are virtually eliminated in this process; however, magnesium must be removed from high magnesium waters because of precipitation at the high pH values of amine-water systems.

Economic recovery of solvent from the water products can be readily accomplished by steam stripping. Small remnant concentrations (1 to 2 p.p.m.) may be removed by bacterial decomposition, either on storage or by use of trickle filters.

The solvent extraction process has not yet undergone pilot plant investigation, and all the above estimates are based on small laboratory or bench scale experiments. If further testing under practical conditions substantiates the laboratory observations, it appears that the solvent extraction process definitely has an area of specialization in the over-all saline water conversion program.

Literature Cited

(1) Bosworth, C. M., Carfagno, S. S., Barduhm, A. J., Sandell, D. J., "Further Development of a Direct-Freezing Continuous Wash-Separation Process for Saline Water Conversion," Carrier Corp., Office of Saline Water, Research and Development Progr. Rept., No. 32, p. 31, Washington, D. C., 1959.
(2) Clark, S. P., Dubose, R. T., *J. Agr. Food Chem.* 8, 47 (1960).
(3) Dankese, J. P., Kirkhum, T. A., Maheras, G., Mintz, M. S., Powell, J. H., Rosenberg, N. W., "Design, Construction and Field Testing Cost Analyses on the Experimental Electrodialysis Demineralizer for Brackish Waters," Ionics, Inc., Office of Saline Water, Research and Development Progress Report, No. 11, Washington, D. C., 1956.
(4) Davison, R. R., Hood, D. W., Office of Saline Water, U. S. Dept. of Interior, Publ. 568, 408–16 (1957).
(5) Davison, R. R., Isbell, A. F., Smith, W. H., Jr., Hood, D. W., "Development of the Solvent Demineralization of Saline Water," Annual Rept., 1958.
(6) Davison, R. R., Jeffrey, L. M., Whitehouse, U. G., Hood, D. W., "Research on Liquid-Liquid Extraction for Saline Water Conversion," Office of Saline Water Research and Development Progr. Rept., No. 22, December 1958.
(7) Davison, R. R., Smith, W. H., Jr., Hood, D. W., *J. Chem. Eng. Data* 5, 420 (1960).
(8) Harwell, K. E., Futrell, M. D., Hood, D. W., "Desalination by Liquid-Liquid Extraction," 1st Ann. Rept., A. & M. Research Foundation, Ref. 54-54T, 1954.

RECEIVED for review July 20, 1960. Accepted August 1, 1960. Contribution from Department of Oceanography and Meteorology, Agricultural and Mechanical College of Texas, Oceanography and Meteorology Series No. 168. Work sponsored by Office of Saline Water, U. S. Department of Interior, Contract No. 14-01001-174.

Exploratory Research on Demineralization

ARTHUR ROSE, R. F. SWEENY, T. B. HOOVER, and V. N. SCHRODT

Applied Science Laboratories, Inc., State College, Pa.

Six ideas have been investigated for possible use in desalinization. The first two, involving use of ion retardation resins, are advanced; the next step is to obtain enough data to make economic calculations. The third idea, use of algae in a regenerative multistage process, has been briefly studied, but seems worthy of further work. Precipitation of salt is only a general idea, but a challenging one. The last two ideas, recompressive freezing and electrolysis, apparently have no chance of success.

Sea water demineralization research has largely been of a developmental nature. Processes already known to be workable, if not economical, have been chosen, then "debugged" or in some cases radically modified in order to adapt them to the peculiarities of the desalinization problem. In contrast to this approach, the work reported here has been an endeavor to explore unknown areas, and to investigate the mere scientific possibility of various methods.

The objective was to lay the foundation for a process which will produce water at less cost than any process now known. In view of recent advances in desalinization, and considering present costs for municipal water, one might wonder if such an objective is worthwhile. A reasonable cost for municipal water at the distribution point (assuming new facilities must be purchased) is 38 cents per 1000 gallons. This is within the range (30 to 50 cents) expected for water from desalinization processes now in the advanced stages of development (evaporation, freezing). However, there is no obvious reason for being satisfied with making desalinization competitive—it should be possible to reduce costs of desalinization below those for pumping fresh water into large communities. Another incentive is the possibility of capturing the agricultural market, which requires water at less than 12 cents per 1000 gallons.

The problem in this exploration was to try to find new ideas on how to make water for 10 to 20 cents per 1000 gallons.

In order to obtain potable water from sea water, one must either remove good water from the solution or remove salt from the solution, leaving the good water behind. Most well known desalinization processes work on the principle of removing good water from solution; the ion membrane process is the notable exception. It seems obvious that, since sea water is 96.5% water and only 3.5% salt, it would be preferable to remove the salt. Such processes received special attention in the work reported here.

The ideas investigated included complete demineralization and divalent ion removal using amphoteric or ion retardation resins, salt removal using algae, recompressive freezing, the precipitation of salt by radiation, and electrolysis of sea water with recombination of hydrogen and oxygen in a fuel cell. No attempt was made to obtain extensive, precise, or conclusive data. Although the economics of a process must inevitably enter the final decision, such consideration was not allowed to inhibit the initial thoughts and investigations. It is all too easy to find reasons why any process will be too costly.

Ion Retardation Resins

One approach which almost certainly deserves further attention is based on the use of amphoteric or ion retardation resins, which have the capacity to remove both positive and negative ions simultaneously from a solution (Figure 1). The resin holds both ions in close proximity, and the positive and negative charges tend to neutralize one another because they occupy adjacent positions on the resin. There is no need to supply energy actually to neutralize the ions.

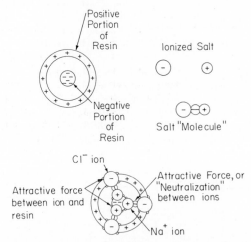

Figure 1. Ion retardation resin working scheme

There is no doubt that these resins remove salt. But the resin must obviously be used over again, thus requiring a step in which the salt is removed from the resin. The proposed process depends on mixing fresh or regenerated resin with salt water at a relatively low temperature, possibly room temperature, and, after it has removed the salt from saline water, washing the resin with part of the product water at a high temperature. Even a modest difference at the two temperatures in the distribution of salt between liquid and resin will enable such a process to work, if a multistage method of contacting is used. Suppose line A in Figure 2 represents equilibrium conditions for a resin in contact with salt water of various concentrations at room temperature and line B represents equilibria at a higher temperature. This resin could be used in a multistage contacting process such as that shown in Figure 3, where there are two contactors. In the desalinization contactor, sea water is sent in at one end, regenerated resin at the other end. Thus, the regenerated resin works on the "pure water" end of the contactor, and the partially loaded resin works on fresh sea water. The loaded resin is sent to the regeneration contactor, and washed, at an elevated temperature, with part of the purified water. The principle of countercurrent contacting is again used to obtain a maximum driving force for regeneration.

The constructions in Figure 2 represent a graphical calculation much like the McCabe-Thiele calculation in distillation. Here, the operating line of the upper con-

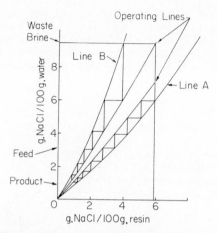

Figure 2. Typical equilibria for resin and salt water at two different conditions

struction is the regeneration line, the slope is the amount of resin divided by the amount of wash water, and the steps are the number of washing stages. The lower construction is for desalinization. Since the amount of resin must be the same in both contactors, the degree of spread between the two operating lines is indicative of the inverse of the reflux ratio. Although present preliminary laboratory data on just one resin indicate that such a process is feasible, there are not yet enough data available to support cost predictions. The possibility of devising more suitable resins also exists.

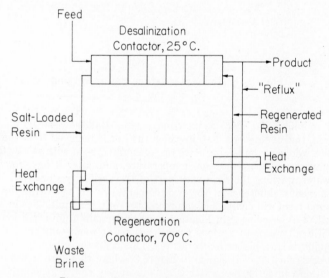

Figure 3. Ion retardation resin process

A variation of this process may prove to be valuable in preparing feed for evaporators. A major difficulty in all distillation and evaporation methods is the deposit caused by magnesium ions. The amphoteric resin preferentially removes these ions. However, a very concentrated solution of sodium ions will displace magnesium ions. It would seem possible to contact the resin with sea water to remove magnesium, evaporate the resulting magnesium-free salt water, then displace the magnesium ions from the loaded resin by contacting with the concentrated brine containing sodium ions from the evaporator. This process is shown schematically in Figure 4.

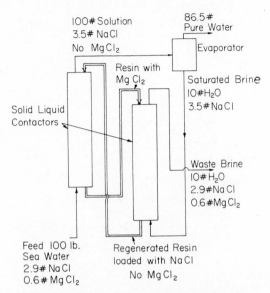

100# Solution
3.5# NaCl
No MgCl₂

86.5#
Pure Water

Evaporator

Resin with
Mg Cl₂

Saturated Brine
10#H₂O
3.5#NaCl

Solid Liquid
Contactors

Waste Brine
10# H₂O
2.9#NaCl
0.6#MgCl₂

Feed 100 lb.
Sea Water
2.9# NaCl
0.6# Mg Cl₂

Regenerated Resin
loaded with NaCl
No MgCl₂

Figure 4. Process for removing divalent ions

Again, preliminary data indicate this process is feasible, although there are not sufficient data to support economic calculations.

Algae

Another method which may be worthy of further investigation is the removal of salt with algae. It was found in the authors' laboratories that many types of algae show remarkable adaptability to saline solutions. In a saline solution, salt tends to concentrate in the algae. Thus, one possibility is simply to grow algae in saline solution, thus removing the salt from the water (probably in several stages) and discarding the salt-rich algae. Such a process could be accelerated with a cheap source of carbon dioxide. The necessary nutrients would come from natural sources in the sea. Previous proposals and investigations along this line have been greeted by more or less elaborate proofs that the suggested processes will not be economic, or will not work at all. The authors' alternative is to use a stagewise and countercurrent regenerative process, whereby the algae will remove salt in the presence of heat, sunlight, or other energy and give salt up to sea water when energy is at a lower level. Such a process might resemble the ion retardation resin process, the algae taking the place of the resin.

Salt Precipitation

Because water is such a common substance, its properties are often accepted as "normal." Actually, water is extremely abnormal. If saline solutions were ideal, one would expect a solubility of sodium chloride in water at 0° C. of only 500 p.p.m. All that is needed then for demineralization is to influence the solution in some way so as to make it relatively ideal. The salt would then simply precipitate, leaving good water. Some thought has gone into the type of influence needed. The association of water molecules around salt ions (Figure 5) is what holds the salt in solution. The hydrogen atoms of the water molecules, which are somewhat positively charged, turn away from the

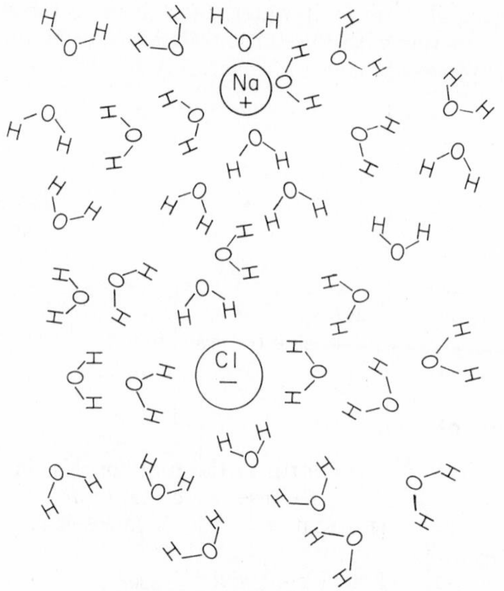

Figure 5. Hydration of ions

positively charged sodium ions, and are attracted to the negatively charged chloride ions. These molecules form a sheath of "hydration" around the ions, preventing them from attracting one another and consequently precipitating. If this little bit of order in the water can be sufficiently disturbed, the salt should precipitate. This might be done by a properly selected form of radiant energy. If the attractive force between water and ions has a characteristic energy, or a reasonably narrow range of energy, it would seem possible to submit the solution to selected radiation (of wave length corresponding to the associative energy) and achieve precipitation of the salt. Such radiant energy would undoubtedly be expensive, but it is conceivable that the amount needed would be in the vicinity of the minimum energy requirement for separating salt and water.

The elegant approach to the problem is to investigate spectra of water and salt solutions. The appearance of a concentration-dependent absorption band would indicate a likely region for radiation in order to cause precipitation. A partial investigation of the infrared absorption of saline water was not conclusive as to the existence of concentration-dependent bands. It is also possible that such bands may exist at radio frequencies, and these should be studied.

The preceding ideas are considered worthy of further study. The following schemes were also considered, but do not appear worth further effort.

Recompressive Freezing

Recompressive freezing is analogous to recompressive distillation. Pure ice will melt below 0° C., if it is compressed. Thus, one could theoretically start a process by freezing ice from sea water, at about −4° C., separate ice from brine, then freeze another batch of ice by compressing the first one to such a pressure that it will melt below −4° C., and simultaneously absorb the heat of fusion from the ice being frozen. Such a process could be continued, with the only energy requirement that of compressing the ice. It is essentially one way of pumping heat to a higher temperature.

On first consideration it seems a good idea. But there are several serious difficulties.

Even in an imaginary idealized form, the process would involve heat transfer through one wall and two films, while a process using expansion of a light hydrocarbon in direct contact with saline liquor for the freezing step, and also direct contact of the hydrocarbon and ice for the melting step, would involve only two films. Detailed calculations for the direct expansion-type process suggest that its energy efficiency is already sufficiently high to raise a question as to whether any competitive scheme can have a major energy advantage.

Calculations of the energy requirement for the process, if it is carried out in a continuous manner, indicate that the efficiency would only be about one tenth that of the familiar ammonia refrigeration cycle, unless the energy released when the melted ice is decompressed could be efficiently recovered. Achievement of the latter in actual practice requires invention of some practical mechanical arrangements.

Entrainment difficulties would be at least as serious as with other freezing processes.

It is conceivable that a batch version of the process might be devised, and that this would be free of the energy penalties of the continuous flow process, and that heat transfer resistances would be comparable or less than with a direct contact refrigerant, but even in these events a major over-all advantage does not seem likely.

Electrolysis with Use of Fuel Cell

Several schemes have been put forth in the past for desalinization by use of electrolysis. They had been discarded because of the large amounts of energy required. The idea was resurrected in anticipation of much more efficient recovery of energy through the use of fuel cells.

One new way in which electrolysis could be used is by simply electrolyzing sea water to hydrogen and oxygen and then converting these to water in a fuel cell, which would supply the energy to decompose more water. Such enormous amounts of energy are used in this process that to be competitive, the over-all efficiency of the electrolysis fuel cell combination would have to be over 99.5%. It is doubtful that this could ever be attained. Other schemes of electrolysis in which sodium and chlorine are removed are subject to the same disadvantage.

RECEIVED for review August 8, 1960. Accepted August 23, 1960.

Energy Computations for Saline Water Conversion by Idealized Freezing Processes

HENRY M. CURRAN

St. Edward's University, Austin 4, Tex.

Theoretical energy equations are developed for saline water conversion by means of idealized freezing processes utilizing reversible refrigeration machines. These equations may be used to compute the minimum energy required for saline water conversion by a freezing process at specified values of extraction ratio, ambient saline water temperature, and heat exchange temperature differentials. Minimum energy values so computed provide criteria for feasibility analyses and for comparison of actual freezing processes.

Among the more important economic factors involved in large-scale conversion of saline water are the amount and cost of the energy necessary for operation of the conversion processes. The purpose of this paper is to establish the theoretical energy required by certain idealized conversion processes utilizing freezing.

The theoretical amount of energy required for the reversible partition of a multicomponent system having a particular component ratio is equal to the change in free energy corresponding to this partition. In the case of saline water conversion, the theoretical amount of energy required is equal to the change in free energy corresponding to the reversible partition of saline water into potable water and concentrated brine. This theoretical energy is a function of the extraction ratio—i.e., the potable water output divided by the potable water fraction of the saline water input—and approaches its absolute minimum value as the extraction ratio approaches zero. Because any actual conversion process must necessarily be thermodynamically irreversible, the actual energy requirement for a specified extraction ratio must always exceed the theoretical energy requirement for a reversible process at the same extraction ratio.

In this paper idealized conversion processes utilizing reversible refrigeration machines are analyzed with respect to energy requirements. First, energy equations are established for a completely reversible process. Several irreversible modifications of this process are then analyzed.

The Freezing of Saline Water

The use of freezing for saline water conversion is based on the physical principle that ice crystals obtained by freezing an aqueous salt solution are pure water in the solid phase. Because of the commensurate densities of the ice crystals and the residual brine, there is no automatic separation of the pure water phase from the brine corresponding to the separation of vapor in distillation processes. Thus saline water conversion by freezing involves the two basic operations of formation of ice crystals and separation of these crystals from the residual brine. In general, these are distinct operations, but it is physically possible to effect them simultaneously. Perfect separation of ice and brine is assumed in each of the processes discussed in this paper.

Depending on the freezing process, the freezing of saline water produces one or the other of two basic ice formations:

1. Ice-brine slush, essentially a slurry of ice crystals in brine, the over-all salinity ranging from that of the feed water down to about one half of this value.

2. Ice-brine solids consisting of connected crystal lattices containing brine in inter-crystalline spaces, the over-all salinity ranging from that of the feed water down to potable values.

Two basic freezing methods may be distinguished:

1. Indirect freezing in which the heat of crystallization is removed from the saline solutions through a solid barrier.

2. Direct freezing in which the heat of crystallization is removed by partial evaporation of the solvent, or by contacting the solution with an immiscible refrigerant.

Depression of Freezing Temperature. One of the colligative properties of solutions of nonvolatile solutes is that the freezing temperature is lower than that of the pure solvent. The depression of the freezing temperature is approximately proportional to the mass ratio of solute to solvent—that is,

$$\Delta T = -KZ \tag{1}$$

in which K is a constant of proportionality and Z is the mass ratio of solute to solvent.

For sea water, which is the principal saline water being considered for conversion, the depression of the freezing temperature is closely approximated by taking $K = 52.41$ for the Kelvin scale (1) or $K = 94.34$ for the Rankine scale.

Taking s as the mass fraction of salt in the saline water, we may write

$$Z = \frac{s}{1 - s} \tag{2}$$

and

$$T = T_o - \frac{Ks}{1 - s} \tag{3}$$

where T is the equilibrium temperature for ice in contact with saline water having a salt mass fraction s, and T_o is the freezing temperature of pure water.

Ice Fraction. The mass fraction, I, of ice produced by cooling a unit mass of saline water having an initial salt mass fraction s_i from its freezing temperature, T_i, to a lower temperature, T, is

$$I = \frac{s - s_i}{s} \tag{4}$$

where s is the solute mass fraction in the residual solution at temperature T.

By combination of Equations 3 and 4, I is obtained as a function of T:

$$I = 1 - s_i \left[1 + \frac{K}{T_o - T} \right], \quad T \le T_i \tag{5}$$

Extraction Ratio. In the idealized processes discussed the saline water is assumed cooled to a final temperature, T_f, and the resulting ice is assumed to be perfectly separated from the residual brine. When melted, this ice becomes the fresh water product.

Thus the extraction ratio, r, defined as the mass ratio of fresh water product to the water content of the saline water input, is directly proportional to the final ice fraction, I_f:

$$r = \frac{I_f}{1 - s_i} = \frac{T_i - T_f}{T_o - T_f} \qquad (6)$$

Reversible Refrigeration Machines

All of the idealized conversion processes discussed are assumed to incorporate reversible refrigeration machines.

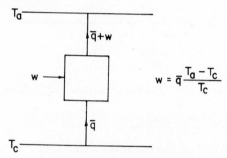

$$w = \bar{q}\frac{T_a - T_c}{T_c}$$

Figure I. Type I reversible refrigeration machine

Type I. Figure 1 illustrates reversible refrigeration machines of Type I. This machine receives an amount of heat $\bar{q}$ reversibly at temperature T_c and discharges it reversibly at a higher temperature, T_a. By the first principle of thermodynamics the necessary energy input, w, must also be discharged reversibly at T_a. The coefficient of performance of this machine is the same as that of a Carnot refrigeration machine. Thus we have

$$c.p. = \frac{\bar{q}}{w} = \frac{T_c}{T_a - T_c} \qquad (7)$$

which yields

$$w = \bar{q}\,\frac{T_a - T_c}{T_c} \qquad (8)$$

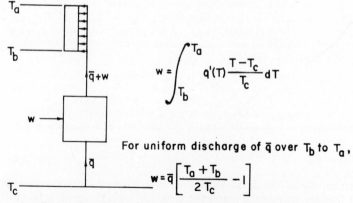

$$w = \int_{T_b}^{T_a} q'(T)\frac{T - T_c}{T_c}\,dT$$

For uniform discharge of $\bar{q}$ over T_b to T_a,

$$w = \bar{q}\left[\frac{T_a + T_b}{2\,T_c} - 1\right]$$

Figure 2. Type II reversible refrigeration machine

Type II. Figure 2 illustrates reversible refrigeration machines of Type II. This machine receives an amount of heat $\bar{q}$ reversibly at temperature T_c and discharges it reversibly over a higher temperature range from T_b to T_a. Taking T as any temperature between T_b and T_a and assuming a Type I machine operating between T_c and T which receives a differential amount of heat dq at T_c, we have the differential equation,

$$dw = dq \, \frac{T - T_c}{T_c} \tag{9}$$

Making the further assumption that the discharge of $\bar{q}$ over the range T_b to T_a is expressible as a function $q(T)$, the energy input is

$$w = \int_{T_b}^{T_a} q'(T) \, \frac{T - T_c}{T_c} \, dT \tag{10}$$

If q is a linear function of T—that is, $\bar{q}$ is discharged uniformly over the range T_b to T_a—the energy is

$$w = \frac{\bar{q}}{T_a - T_b} \int_{T_b}^{T_a} \frac{T - T_c}{T_c} \, dT = \bar{q} \left[\frac{1/2(T_a + T_b)}{T_c} - 1 \right] \tag{11}$$

Equation II differs from Equation 8 for a Type I machine only in having the average of T_a and T_b in the place of T_a.

Type III. Figure 3 illustrates reversible refrigeration machines of Type III. This

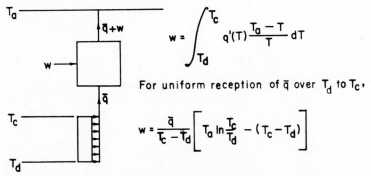

Figure 3. Type III reversible refrigeration machine

machine receives an amount of heat $\bar{q}$ reversibly over a temperature range from T_d to T_c and discharges it reversibly at temperature T_a. Taking T as a temperature in the range T_d to T_c, and assuming a Type I machine operating between T and T_a which receives a differential amount of heat dq at T, the differential equation for energy input is

$$dw = dq \, \frac{T_a - T}{T} \tag{12}$$

Assuming that the reception of $\bar{q}$ over the range T_d to T_c is expressible as a function $q(T)$, the energy input is

$$w = \int_{T_d}^{T_c} q'(T) \, \frac{T_a - T}{T} \, dT \tag{13}$$

If q is a linear function of T—that is, $\bar{q}$ is received uniformly over the range T_d to T_c—the energy required is

$$w = \frac{\bar{q}}{T_c - T_d} \int_{T_d}^{T_c} \frac{T_a - T}{T} \, dT = \frac{\bar{q}}{T_c - T_d} \left[T_a \ln \frac{T_c}{T_d} - (T_c - T_d) \right] \tag{14}$$

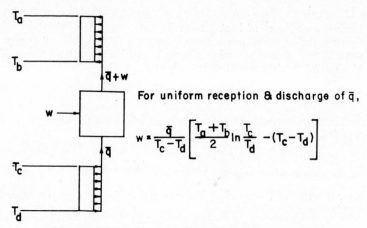

For uniform reception & discharge of $\bar{q}$,

$$w = \frac{\bar{q}}{T_c - T_d}\left[\frac{T_a + T_b}{2}\ln\frac{T_c}{T_d} - (T_c - T_d)\right]$$

Figure 4. Type IV reversible refrigeration machine

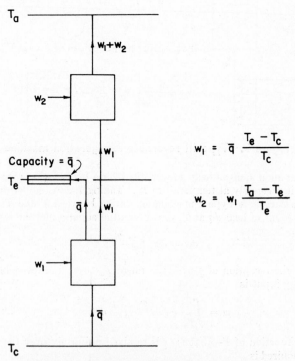

$$w_1 = \bar{q}\,\frac{T_e - T_c}{T_c}$$

$$w_2 = w_1\,\frac{T_a - T_e}{T_e}$$

Figure 5. Combination of two Type I reversible refrigeration machines in series to utilize a limited isothermal reservoir

Type IV. Figure 4 illustrates reversible refrigeration machines of Type IV. This type of machine receives an amount of heat $\bar{q}$ reversibly over a temperature range T_d to T_c and discharges it reversibly over a higher range, T_b to T_a. This may be considered as a combination of a Type II machine with a Type III machine. Limiting the present discussion to the special case of uniform discharge of over the range T_b to T_a, it may also be considered as a Type III machine with discharge at $1/2(T_a + T_b)$ in place of T_a. The energy is then given by the corresponding modification of Equation 13 as

$$w = \int_{T_d}^{T_c} q'(T)\ \frac{1/2(T_a + T_b) - T}{T}\ dT \tag{15}$$

For the case of $\bar{q}$ received uniformly over the range T_d to T_c, modification of Equation 14 gives

$$w = \frac{\bar{q}}{T_c - T_d} \left[1/2(T_a + T_b) \ln \frac{T_c}{T_d} - (T_c - T_d) \right] \tag{16}$$

Combinations of Reversible Refrigeration Machines. Reversible refrigeration machines may also be used in combination in order to effect the utilization of heat reservoirs of limited capacity. Figure 5 illustrates two machines of Type I in series to utilize an isothermal reservoir at T_e having a capacity just equal to $\bar{q}$. The first machine receives $\bar{q}$ at T_c and discharges $\bar{q}$ at T_e, the energy input being w_1. Because the heat rejection corresponding to w_1 cannot be accomplished at T_e, a second machine receives w_1 at T_e and discharges it at T_a. From Equation 8 we have

$$w_1 = \bar{q}\ \frac{T_e - T_c}{T_c} \tag{17}$$

and

$$w_2 = w_1\ \frac{T_a - T_e}{T_e} \tag{18}$$

Equation 18 also applies when the first machine is of Type III, w_1 then being obtained from Equation 13 or 14.

[Another way of obtaining the same result would be by the use of Type I machines in parallel, one receiving $\bar{q}(T_c/T_e)$ at T_c and discharging at T_e, the other receiving $(1 - T_c/T_e)$ at T_c and discharging at T_a.]

First Idealized Process

The first idealized process, illustrated in Figure 6, deviates from complete reversibility only in minor simplifying assumptions. Saline water enters the process at temperature T_u. (This is assumed to be the lowest temperature to which the saline water can be cooled by heat exchange with the coldest medium in the environment. The condition $T_u > T_o$ is also assumed.) The incoming saline water is then cooled by perfect countercurrent heat exchange with the fresh water product and the waste brine down to the melting temperature of ice, T_o, the mean specific heat-temperature function of the effluent streams being assumed equal to the specific heat-temperature function of the incoming saline water. (This assumption introduces an error of negligible magnitude in the energy equations to follow.) Further cooling to the initial freezing temperature, T_i, is accomplished by perfect countercurrent heat exchange with ice and waste brine, supplemented by a refrigeration machine, R_3, this auxiliary refrigeration being necessary because the specific heat of ice is only about one half that of water.

Below temperature T_i changes of enthalpy may be conveniently assumed to be composed of two components, one corresponding to the sensible cooling of the saline water, and the other corresponding to the removal of latent heat of crystallization to form ice crystals. Thus, the sensible cooling below T_i is accomplished by further perfect countercurrent heat exchange supplemented by refrigeration machine R_3, and heat of crystallization is received by another refrigeration machine, R_1.

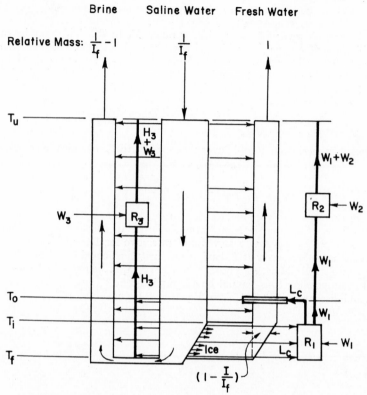

Figure 6.   Schematic diagram of first idealized process

As crystals of ice are formed, they are perfectly separated from the residual brine and passed to a melting tank, being raised to the melting temperature, T_o, en route by the previously mentioned countercurrent heat exchange with the incoming saline water.

Freezing and removal of ice are continued to a final temperature T_f, at which point the brine attains its highest concentration and is disposed of as waste, after being raised back to temperature T_u by absorbing heat from the incoming saline water.

Refrigeration machine R_1 transfers the heat of crystallization from the freezing temperature range to T_o, where it is absorbed by the ice acting as an isothermal heat sink.   The water obtained by melting the ice is then raised to temperature T_u by absorbing heat from the incoming saline water before being discharged as the fresh water product.

For steady-state operation, the capacity of the ice in the melting unit to absorb heat isothermally is just equal to the heat of crystallization removed in freezing the ice.   Thus another refrigeration machine, R_2, is employed to transfer the additional heat rejected by R_1 to the saline water mass, which, in this idealization, may be considered as having infinite heat-absorbing capacity at its ambient temperature, T_u.

Refrigeration machine R_1 is of Type III, receiving heat of crystallization over the range T_f to T_i and discharging it isothermally at T_o.   In order to utilize Equation 13 for the energy input, the rate of heat reception with respect to temperature must be known.

For a unit mass of ice formed over the temperature range from T_f to T_i the amount of heat of crystallization received by R_1 between some intermediate temperature T and T_i is

$$L = L_c \frac{I}{I_f} \tag{19}$$

in which L_c is the heat of crystallization per unit mass of ice. Since I is a function of T, with a negative first derivative, within the range T_f to T_i the differential equation for the rate of reception of heat of crystallization is

$$dL = -\frac{L_c}{I_f} I'(T)\, dT \tag{20}$$

Equation 13 may now be modified to give

$$W_1 = -\frac{L_c}{I_f} \int_{T_f}^{T_i} I'(T)\, \frac{T_o - T}{T}\, dT \tag{21}$$

W_1 being the energy input to R_1 per unit mass of ice formed over the range T_f to T_i. Equation 5 gives $I(T)$. Substitution of the derivative into Equation 21 yields

$$W_1 = K\, \frac{L_c\, s_i}{I_f} \int_{T_f}^{T_i} \frac{dT}{T(T_o - T)}$$

$$= K\, \frac{L_c\, s_i}{I_f T_o} \ln \frac{T_i(T_o - T_f)}{T_f(T_o - T_i)} \tag{22}$$

At the condition of the extraction ratio approaching zero, corresponding to the production of a unit mass of fresh water from an infinite mass of saline water, the value of I_f also approaches zero, so that Equations 21 and 22 may not be used. In this case, however, R_1 becomes a Type I machine and the energy input is given by modification of Equation 8,

$$W_1 = L_c\, \frac{T_o - T_i}{T_i},\, r \to 0,\, I_f \to 0 \tag{23}$$

Refrigeration machine R_2 is of Type I, so that the energy input is

$$W_2 = W_1\, \frac{T_u - T_o}{T_o} \tag{24}$$

As previously noted, refrigeration machine R_3 is needed to augment the sensible cooling obtained by heat exchange. Taking as a basis the production of a unit mass of ice, the fraction of a mass unit of saline water which cannot be cooled by countercurrent heat exchange is $(1 - C_j/C_s)$ in the range T_i to T_o and $(1 - C_j/C_s)(1 - I/I_f)$ in the range T_f to T_i, C_j and C_s being the specific heats of ice and saline water, respectively. These specific heats may be assumed constant with negligible error. The factor $(1 - I/I_f)$ accounts for the decrease in the brine mass as ice is formed.

The differential equation for sensible heat received by R_3 is

$$dH_3 = (1 - C_j/C_s)(1 - I/I_f)\, C_s\, dT$$

$$= (C_s - C_j)(1 - I/I_f)\, dT,\, I = 0 \text{ when } T \geq T_i \tag{25}$$

and the energy input is

$$W_3 = (C_s - C_j)\left[\int_{T_f}^{T_o} \frac{T_u - T}{T}\, dT - \frac{1}{I_f} \int_{T_f}^{T_i} I(T)\, \frac{T_u - T}{T}\, dT\right]$$

$$= (C_s - C_j)\left[T_u \ln \frac{T_o}{T_f} - (T_o - T_f) - \frac{1}{I_f} \int_{T_f}^{T_i} I(T)\, \frac{T_u - T}{T}\, dT\right] \tag{26}$$

The integral on the right of Equation 26 may be evaluated by substituting the function of Equation 5 for $I(T)$. Thus,

$$\int_{T_f}^{T_i} \left[1 - s_i \left(1 + \frac{K}{T_o - T} \right) \right] \frac{T_u - T}{T}\, dT =$$

$$(1 - s_i) \left[T_u \frac{T_i}{T_f} - (T_i - T_f) \right] - K s_i \left[\frac{T_u}{T_o} \ln \frac{T_i(T_o - T_f)}{T_f(T_o - T_i)} - \ln \frac{T_o - T_f}{T_o - T_i} \right] \quad (27)$$

Substitution of this in Equation 26 gives

$$W_3 = (C_s - C_j) \left[T_u \ln \frac{T_o}{T_f} - (T_o - T_f) - \frac{1}{I_f} \left\{ (1 - s_i) \left(T_u \ln \frac{T_i}{T_f} - (T_i - T_f) \right) - \right.\right.$$

$$\left.\left. K s_i \left(\frac{T_u}{T_o} \ln \frac{T_i(T_o - T_f)}{T_f(T_o - T_i)} - \ln \frac{T_o - T_f}{T_o - T_i} \right) \right\} \right] \quad (28)$$

The total energy required for the operation of the first idealized process is the sum

$$W = W_1 + W_2 + W_3 \quad (29)$$

In this idealization the formation and removal of ice are assumed to be simultaneous, so that the mass flow rate decreases throughout the transition from the initial freezing temperature, T_i, to the final temperature, T_f. The above computation of theoretical energy is not dependent upon removal of the ice in this manner, however. Ice formed at temperatures above T_f could, for example, remain in contact with the brine and be cooled to T_f before separation, the cooling being accomplished by perfect countercurrent heat exchange with previously formed ice.

Because this process is essentially reversible, the equations above provide a means of computing the minimum theoretical energy as a function of extraction ratio for saline water conversion.

Second Idealized Process

The second idealized process, illustrated in Figure 7, differs from the preceding process only in the freezing arrangement. In this case the incoming saline water is cooled to temperature T_i as before; then it is mixed with a large volume of brine at the exit concentration and the corresponding freezing temperature, T_f. Refrigeration machine R_1, which is of Type I, receives heat of crystallization at T_f so as to form ice at a rate corresponding to the mass flow rate of the incoming saline water and the extraction ratio. As R_1 and R_2 are Type I machines in series, the theoretical energy inputs per unit mass of ice formed are

$$W_1 = L_c \frac{T_o - T_f}{T_f} \quad (30)$$

and

$$W_2 = W_1 \frac{T_u - T_o}{T_o} \quad (31)$$

Addition of these two equations yields the theoretical energy input for freezing part of the process,

$$W_1 + W_2 = L_c \frac{T_u(T_o - T_f)}{T_o T_f} \quad (32)$$

Because the ice is formed isothermally in this process, the mass requiring auxiliary refrigeration over the range T_f to T_o is $(1 - C_j/C_s)$ per unit mass of ice formed, and the differential of sensible heat to be received by R_3 is

$$dH_3 = (1 - C_j/C_s)C_s\, dT = (C_s - C_j)\, dT \quad (33)$$

Refrigeration machine R_3 is of Type III with uniform reception of sensible heat

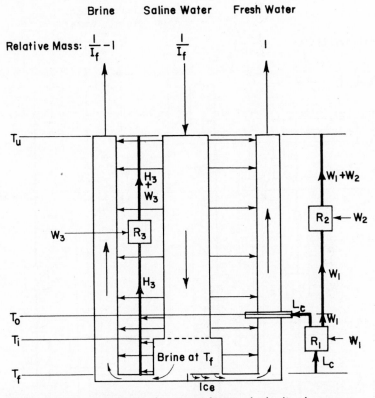

Figure 7.   Schematic diagram of second idealized process

over the range T_f to T_o, so modification of Equation 14 gives the theoretical energy input to R_3 as

$$W_3 = (C_s - C_i) \left[T_u \ln \frac{T_o}{T_f} - (T_o - T_f) \right] \qquad (34)$$

The total theoretical energy input for the second idealized process, per unit mass of fresh water product, is the sum of Equations 32 and 34:

$$W = L_c \frac{T_u(T_o - T_f)}{T_o T_f} + (C_s - C_i) \left[T_u \ln \frac{T_o}{T_f} - (T_o - T_f) \right] \qquad (35)$$

The theoretical energy at all extraction ratios, except $r = 0$, is greater for this process than for the first idealized process. This is due to the irreversibility introduced into the second idealized process by the mixing of saline water with brine at the exit concentration, and the consequent necessity of separating fresh water, in the form of ice, at the exit concentration instead of throughout the range from the inlet concentration to the exit concentration. More precisely, this irreversible internal mixing is accompanied by an increase in entropy, requiring a proportionately larger amount of energy input to effect the separation, in accordance with the second principle of thermodynamics.

Third Idealized Process

The third idealized process, illustrated in Figure 8, is a modification of the first to include irreversible heat transfer across finite temperature differences, and discharge of

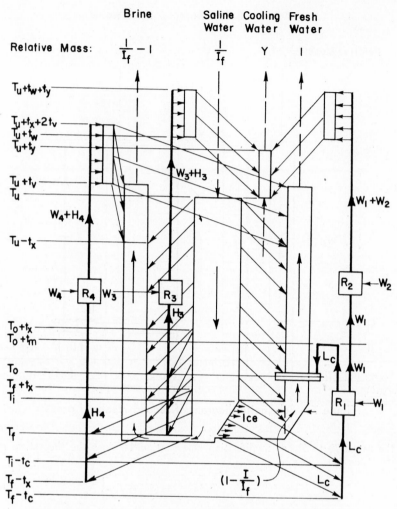

Figure 8.   Schematic diagram of third idealized process

waste heat to a finite stream of saline cooling water. The following temperature differences are assumed:

t_x, for countercurrent heat exchange
t_c, for reception of heat of crystallization
t_m, for discharge of heat of fusion to melting ice
t_w, for discharge of waste heat to saline cooling water
t_y, for temperature rise of saline cooling water
t_v, between temperatures of input and effluent streams

The general equation for theoretical energy input to R_1, per unit mass of ice, obtained by modification of Equation 21 to account for the increased difference between reception and discharge temperatures is

$$W_1 = -\frac{L_c}{I_f} \int_{T_f}^{T_i} I'(T) \frac{(T_o + t_m) - (T - t_c)}{T - t_c} dT \qquad (36)$$

By substitution of $I'(T)$ obtained from Equation 5 into Equation 36, the theoretical energy input to R_1 is

$$W_1 = \frac{K\, L_c s_i}{I_f} \int_{T_f}^{T_i} \frac{(T_o - T) + t_m + t_c}{(T_o - T)^2(T - t_c)} \, dT$$

$$= \frac{K\, L_c s_i}{I_f} \int_{T_f}^{T_i} \left[\frac{1}{(T_o - T)(T - t_c)} + \frac{t_m + t_c}{(T_o - T)^2(T - t_c)} \right] dT$$

$$= \frac{K\, L_c s_i}{I_f(T_o - t_c)} \left[\left(1 + \frac{t_m + t_c}{T_o - t_c}\right) \ln \frac{(T_i - t_c)(T_o - T_f)}{(T_f - t_c)(T_o - T_i)} + \frac{(t_m + t_c)(T_i - T_f)}{(T_o - T_i)(T_o - T_f)} \right] \quad (37)$$

When $t_c = t_m = 0$, Equation 37 reduces to Equation 22.

Refrigeration machine R_2 is of Type II with uniform discharge over the range $(T_u + t_w)$ to $(T_u + t_w + t_y)$, and operating in series with R_1. Modification of Equations 11 and 18 yields

$$W_2 = W_1 \left[\frac{T_u + t_w + 1/2 t_y}{T_o + t_m} - 1 \right] \quad (38)$$

In this process two refrigeration machines are employed for sensible cooling. Machine R_3 provides the supplementary cooling of the incoming saline water necessitated by the difference between the specific heats of ice and saline water, and machine R_4 provides the supplementary cooling necessitated by the temperature differential, t_x.

R_3 receives heat over the range T_f to T_o from incoming saline water in the range $(T_f + t_x)$ to $(T_o + t_x)$, and discharges heat uniformly over the same range as R_2. For each unit mass of ice produced, the mass fraction of incoming saline water between $(T_i + t_x)$ and $(T_o + t_x)$ which cannot be cooled by heat exchange with the unit mass of ice between T_i and T_o is $(1 - C_j/C_s)$. Below T_i the mass fraction of ice is a function of temperature, $[1 - I(T)/I_f]$, so that the mass fraction of saline water below $(T_i + t_x)$ which cannot be cooled by heat exchange with ice is $[1 - (C_j/C_s)(1 - I(T)/I_f)]$. If the condition $(T_f + t_x) < T_i$ exists, the mass of saline water to be cooled by R_3 decreases from T_i to $(T_f + t_x)$ and the expression for the mass fraction requiring cooling becomes $[(1 - C_j/C_s)(1 - I(T)/I_f) - I(T + t_x)/I_f]$. This latter expression may be used as the general expression throughout the operative range of R_3, if the following restrictions are observed: $I(T) = 0$ when $T \geq T_i$ and $I(T + t_x) = 0$ when $(T + t_x) \geq T_i$. When $t_x = 0$, the expression reduces to that used in Equation 25.

The differential equation for sensible heat received by R_3 is

$$dH_3 = \left[1 - \frac{C_j}{C_s}\left(1 - \frac{I(T)}{I_f}\right) - \frac{I(T + t_x)}{I_f} \right] C_s \, dT$$

$$= \left[C_s - C_j + \frac{C_j}{I_f} I(T) - \frac{C_s}{I_f} I(T + t_x) \right] dT \quad (39)$$

in which $I(T) = 0$ when $T \geq T_i$, $I(T + t_x) = 0$ when $(T + t_x) \geq T_i$.

Refrigeration machine R_3 is of Type IV, so substitution into Equation 15 gives the theoretical energy as

$$W_3 = (C_s - C_j) \int_{T_f}^{T_o} \frac{T_n - T}{T} \, dT + \frac{C_j}{I_f} \int_{T_f}^{T_i} I(T) \frac{T_n - T}{T} \, dT -$$

$$\frac{C_s}{I_f} \int_{T_f}^{T_i - t_x} I(T + t_x) \frac{T_n - T}{T} \, dT \quad (40)$$

in which $T_n = T_u + t_w + 1/2 t_y$, and the last integral exists only when $(T_i - t_x) > T_f$. When $t_x = t_w = 0$, Equation 40 reduces to Equation 26.

Substitution of the function of Equation 5 for $I(T)$ into Equation 40 gives the value of W_3 as

$$W_3 = (C_s - C_i)\left[T_n \ln \frac{T_o}{T_f} - (T_o - T_f)\right] +$$

$$\frac{C_i}{I_f}\left[(1 - s_i)\left(T_n \ln \frac{T_i}{T_f} - (T_i - T_f)\right) - K s_i\left(\frac{T_n}{T_o} \ln \frac{(T_o - T_f)T_i}{(T_o - T_i)T_f} - \ln \frac{T_o - T_f}{T_o - T_i}\right)\right] -$$

$$\frac{C_s}{I_f}\left[(1 - s_i)\left(T_n \ln \frac{T_i - t_x}{T_f} - (T_i - t_x - T_f)\right) - K s_i\left(\frac{T_n}{T_o} \ln \frac{(T_i - t_x)(T_o - T_f)}{T_f(T_o - T_i + t_x)} - \right.\right.$$

$$\left.\left.\ln \frac{T_o - T_f}{T_o - T_i + t_x}\right)\right] \quad (41)$$

in which the last term exists only when $(T_i - t_x) > T_f$.

Refrigeration machine R_4 receives sensible heat over the range $(T_f - t_x)$ to T_f from the total mass of saline water in the range T_f to $(T_f + t_x)$, and discharges heat uniformly over the range $(T_u + t_v)$ to $(T_u + t_x + 2t_v)$ into the effluent steams of brine and fresh water over the range $(T_u - t_x)$ to $(T_u + t_v)$.

Per unit mass of ice formed, the mass of brine to be cooled by R_4 is $\dfrac{1 - I(T + t_x)}{I_f}$ the variable being $(T + t_x)$ because the range of integration is $(T_f - t_x)$ to T_f. If $(T_f + t_x) > T_i$, the mass to be cooled between T_i and $(T_f + t_x)$ is $1/I_f$. The differential equation for reception of sensible heat by R_4 is thus

$$dH_4 = \frac{1 - I(T + t_x)}{I_f} C_s \, dT \quad (42)$$

with $I = 0$ when $(T + t_x) \geq T_i$.

This is also a machine of Type IV, so the theoretical energy is

$$W_4 = \frac{C_s}{I_f}\left[\int_{T_f - t_x}^{T_f} \frac{(T_u + 1/2 t_x) - T}{T} \, dT - \int_{T_f - t_x}^{T^*} I(T + t_x) \frac{(T_u + 1/2 t_x) - T}{T} \, dT\right] \quad (43)$$

in which T^* is the lesser of T_f and $(T_i - t_x)$. When $t_x = 0$, $W_4 = 0$, by virtue of a reduction of the range of integration to 0. Since t_v is not arbitrary, but dependent on a simultaneous solution of energy and heat balance equations, it is omitted from Equation 43 for convenience. Since t_v is relatively small, this introduces only a negligible error in W_4.

Substitution of the function of Equation 5 into Equation 43 gives

$$W_4 = \frac{C_s}{I_f}\left[(T_u + 1/2 t_x) \ln \frac{T_f}{T_f - t_x} - t_x - (1 - s_i)\left((T_u + 1/2 t_x) \ln \frac{T^*}{T_f - t_x} - \right.\right.$$

$$\left.\left.(T^* - T_f + t_x)\right) + K s_i \left(\frac{T_u + 1/2 t_x}{T_o - t_x} \ln \frac{T^*}{T_o - t_x - T^*} \frac{T_o - T_f}{T_f - t_x} - \ln \frac{T_o - T_f}{T_o - t_x - T^*}\right)\right] \quad (44)$$

in which T^* is the lesser of T_f and $(T_i - t_x)$.

The effluent exit temperature differential, t_v, may be computed by means of a heat balance. The heat capacity of the effluent streams between $(T_u - t_x)$ and $(T_u + T_v)$, per unit mass of product water, is equal to the heat discharged by R_4. Thus

$$(t_v + t_x)\left[C_s\left(\frac{1}{I_f} - 1\right) + 1\right] = W_4 + H_4 \quad (45)$$

which gives

$$t_v = \frac{W_4 + H_4}{C_s\left(\frac{1}{I_f} - 1\right) + 1} - t_x \quad (46)$$

The sensible heat, H_4, is obtained by integration of Equation 42, in which t_x may be omitted by taking the range of integration from T_f to $(T_f + t_x)$:

$$H_4 = \begin{cases} \dfrac{C_s s_i}{I_f} \displaystyle\int_{T_f}^{T_f + t_x} \left(1 + \dfrac{K}{T_o - T}\right) dT = \dfrac{C_s s_i}{I_f}\left[t_x + K \ln \dfrac{T_o - T_f}{T_o - T_f - t_x}\right], (T_f + t_x) \le T_i, \\[18pt] \dfrac{C_s s_i}{I_f} \displaystyle\int_{T_f}^{T_i} \left(1 + \dfrac{K}{T_o - T}\right) dT + \dfrac{C_s}{I_f}(T_f + t_x - T_i) \end{cases} \quad (47)$$

$$= \frac{C_s s_i}{I_f}\left[t_x + K \ln \frac{T_o - T_f}{T_o - T_i} + \frac{T_f + t_x - T_i}{s_i}\right], (T_f + t_x) > T_i$$

Upon substitution of values of W_4 and H_4 from Equations 44 and 47, respectively, Equation 46 may be solved for t_v.

Designating by Y the mass of saline cooling water per unit mass of product, a heat balance gives

$$Y = \frac{W_1 + W_2 + W_3 + H_3}{C_s t_y} \quad (48)$$

The sensible heat, H_3, is obtained by integration of Equation 39:

$$H_3 = (C_s - C_j)(T_o - T_f) + \frac{C_j}{I_f}\int_{T_f}^{T_i}\left[1 - s_i\left(1 + \frac{K}{T_o - T}\right)\right] dT -$$

$$\frac{C_s}{I_f}\int_{T_f}^{T_i - t_x}\left[1 - s_i\left(1 + \frac{K}{T_o - T - t_x}\right)\right] dT = (C_s - C_j)(T_o - T_f) +$$

$$\frac{C_j}{I_f}(1 - s_i)(T_i - T_f) - \frac{K C_j s_i}{I_f}\ln\frac{T_o - T_f}{T_o - T_i} - \frac{C_s}{I_f}(1 - s_i)(T_i - t_x - T_f) -$$

$$\frac{K C_s s_i}{I_f}\ln\frac{T_o - t_x - T_f}{T_o - T_i} \quad (49)$$

in which the last two terms exist only when $(T_i - t_x) > T_f$.

Fourth Idealized Process

The fourth idealized process, illustrated in Figure 9, is a modification of the second to include irreversible heat transfer across finite temperature differences, and discharge of waste heat to a finite stream of saline water. The notation for temperature differentials is the same as for the third idealized process.

Refrigeration machine R_1 is of Type I, and R_2 is of Type II with uniform discharge of heat, so that by simple modification of Equation 30,

$$W_1 = L_c \frac{(T_o + t_m) - (T_f - T_c)}{T_f - t_c} \quad (50)$$

and Equation 38 applies, giving

$$W_2 = W_1\left[\frac{T_n}{T_o + t_m} - 1\right] \quad (38 \text{ repeated})$$

Addition of these two equations yields the theoretical energy input, per unit mass of ice, for the freezing part of the process,

$$W_1 + W_2 = L_c \frac{T_n(T_o - T_f + t_m + t_c)}{(T_o + t_m)(T_f - t_c)} \quad (51)$$

From $(T_f + t_x)$ to $(T_o + t_x)$ the mass of saline water requiring auxiliary refrigeration by R_3, per unit mass of ice formed, is $(1 - C_j/C_s)$. This is received by R_3 uniformly over the range T_f to T_o. This machine is of Type IV with uniform reception and discharge of heat. Equation 33 gives the differential of sensible heat, so that Equation 16 becomes

$$W_3 = (C_s - C_j) \left[T_n \ln \frac{T_o}{T_f} - (T_o - T_f) \right] \qquad (52)$$

Refrigeration machine R_4 is also of Type IV, receiving heat over the range $(T_f - t_x)$ to T_f from $1/I_f$ mass units of saline water per unit mass of ice, and discharging over the range $(T_u + t_v)$ to $(T_u + t_x + 2t_v)$. The differential of sensible heat received by R_4 is thus

$$dH_4 = \frac{1}{I_f} C_s \, dT \qquad (53)$$

and, again applying Equation 16,

$$W_4 = \frac{C_s}{I_f} \left[(T_u + \tfrac{1}{2}t_x) \ln \frac{T_f}{T_f - t_x} - t_x \right] \qquad (54)$$

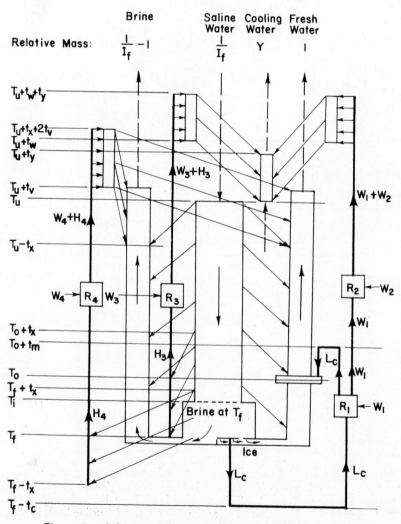

Figure 9.   Schematic diagram of fourth idealized process

The sum of Equations 51, 52, and 54 gives the total theoretical energy per unit mass of product. The temperature differential, t_v, has been omitted in Equation 54 for the same reason as given in the case of Equation 43. Equation 46 may be used to compute t_v with H_4 given by

$$H_4 = \frac{C_s}{I_f} t_x \tag{55}$$

Equation 48 may be used to compute Y with H_3 given by

$$H_3 = (C_s - C_i)(T_o - T_f) \tag{56}$$

Computations

Figure 10 shows some curves of theoretical energy *vs.* extraction ratio for the conversion of sea water by these idealized freezing processes. Values of constants and parameters used in computing these curves are listed in Table I, and the computed values are given in Tables II to V. The last two tables also list computed values of t_v and Y.

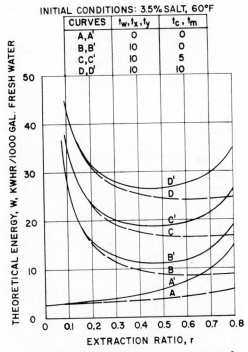

INITIAL CONDITIONS: 3.5% SALT, 60°F

CURVES	t_w, t_x, t_y	t_c, t_m
A,A'	0	0
B,B'	10	0
C,C'	10	5
D,D'	10	10

Figure 10. Theoretical energy curves for sea water conversion by idealized freezing processes

The lowest broken-line curve, A, in Figure 10 corresponds to the first idealized process, which is completely reversible. The other broken-line curves correspond to the third idealized process and illustrate the effect of the specified heat transfer temperature differentials. To be noted are the high values of the theoretical energy, approaching infinity as the extraction ratio approaches zero, introduced by a finite temperature differential, t_x, in the countercurrent heat exchange. This is due to the large cooling loads imposed on refrigeration machine R_4 at low extraction ratios. The curves are rather flat for extraction ratios in the range 0.4 to 0.8.

Table I. Summary of Assumed and Computed Values Used in Computations for Sea Water Conversion by Idealized Freezing Processes

K = 94.34° R
T_u = 519.69° R (60.00° F.)
T_o = 491.69° R (32.00° F.) s_i = 0.035
T_i = 488.27° R (28.58° F.) C_j = 0.50 B.t.u./lbm-° R
L_c = 143.4 B.t.u./lbm C_s = 0.94 B.t.u./lbm-° R
Basis of computations.   One lbm of fresh water product.   8333 lbm/1000 gal. fresh water

r	T_f, °R	I_f	$\dfrac{1}{I_f}$	s_f	H_3, B.t.u./Lbm[a] 1, 3	2, 4
0.0	488.27	0.0	∞	0.0350	1.50	1.50
0.1	487.89	0.0965	10.36	0.0387	1.78	1.67
0.2	487.41	0.1930	5.18	0.0434	2.11	1.88
0.3	486.80	0.2895	3.45	0.0493	2.57	2.15
0.4	485.99	0.3860	2.59	0.0570	3.18	2.51
0.5	484.85	0.4825	2.07	0.0676	4.06	3.01
0.6	483.14	0.5790	1.73	0.0831	5.42	3.76
0.7	480.28	0.6755	1.48	0.1079	7.79	5.02
0.8	474.58	0.7720	1.30	0.1535	12.66	7.53

[a] Numbers 1, 2, 3, 4 over last two columns refer to first, second, third, and fourth idealized processes, respectively.

Table II. Summary of Computed Values for Sea Water Conversion Utilizing First Idealized Process

(See also Table I)

r	$W_1 + W_2$, B.t.u./Lbm	W_3, B.t.u./Lbm	W, B.t.u./Lbm	W, Kw.-hr./ 1000 Gal.
0.0	1.06	0.08	1.14	2.79
0.1	1.13	0.09	1.22	2.98
0.2	1.19	0.10	1.29	3.15
0.3	1.27	0.11	1.38	3.37
0.4	1.36	0.12	1.48	3.61
0.5	1.48	0.13	1.61	3.93
0.6	1.63	0.14	1.77	4.32
0.7	1.84	0.16	2.00	4.88
0.8	2.16	0.21	2.37	5.78

Table III. Summary of Computed Values for Sea Water Conversion Utilizing Second Idealized Process

(See also Table I)

r	$W_1 + W_2$, B.t.u./Lbm	W_3, B.t.u./Lbm	W, B.t.u./Lbm	W, Kw.-hr./ 1000 Gal.
0.0	1.06	0.08	1.14	2.79
0.1	1.18	0.10	1.28	3.13
0.2	1.33	0.11	1.44	3.53
0.3	1.52	0.13	1.65	4.03
0.4	1.78	0.16	1.94	4.72
0.5	2.14	0.19	2.33	5.69
0.6	2.68	0.25	2.93	7.16
0.7	3.60	0.35	3.95	9.63
0.8	5.46	0.57	6.03	14.72

The lowest solid-line curve, A', corresponds to the second idealized process, in which the only irreversibility is that of internal mixing, and the other solid-line curves correspond to the fourth idealized process. At low extraction ratios the two sets of curves are almost coincident. At higher extraction ratios the curves for the second and fourth processes rise above those for the first and third processes, because of the increasing effect of the irreversible internal mixing with increasing extraction ratio. The curves for the fourth idealized process are seen to have minimums at extraction ratios approximating 0.5.

Table IV. Summary of Computed Values for Sea Water Conversion Utilizing Third Idealized Process

(See also Table I)

$t_x = t_w = t_y = 10° R$

r	W_3, B.t.u./Lbm	W_4, B.t.u./Lbm	H_4, B.t.u./Lbm	$t_c = t_m = 0$					$t_c = t_m = 5° R$				$t_c = t_m = 10° R$			
				t_v °R	W_1+W_2, B.t.u./lbm	W B.t.u./lbm	W Kw.-hr./1000 g.	Y	W_1+W_2, B.t.u./lbm	W B.t.u./lbm	W Kw.-hr./1000 g.	Y	W_1+W_2, B.t.u./lbm	W B.t.u./lbm	W Kw.-hr./1000 g.	Y
0.1	0.15	9.88	100.52	1.27	1.16	11.19	27.30	0.33	4.35	14.38	35.09	0.67	7.56	17.59	42.92	1.01
0.2	0.20	4.94	49.82	1.11	1.23	6.37	15.54	0.38	4.43	9.57	23.35	0.72	7.63	12.77	31.16	1.06
0.3	0.23	3.23	32.70	0.85	1.30	4.76	11.61	0.44	4.50	7.96	19.42	0.78	7.71	11.17	27.26	1.12
0.4	0.28	2.36	23.81	0.47	1.40	4.04	9.86	0.52	4.60	7.24	17.67	0.86	7.81	10.45	25.50	1.20
0.5	0.40	1.78	17.98	-0.17	1.52	3.70	9.03	0.64	4.73	6.91	16.86	0.98	7.93	10.11	24.67	1.32
0.6	0.54	1.32	13.25	-1.27	1.68	3.54	8.64	0.81	4.88	6.74	16.45	1.15	8.09	9.95	24.28	1.49
0.7	0.80	0.86	8.81	-3.33	1.89	3.55	8.66	1.15	5.11	6.77	16.52	1.46	8.33	9.99	24.38	1.80

Table V. Summary of Computed Values for Sea Water Conversion Utilizing Fourth Idealized Process

(See also Table I)

$t_x = t_w = t_y = 10° R$

r	W_3, B.t.u./Lbm	W_4, B.t.u./Lbm	H_4, B.t.u./Lbm	$t_c = t_m = 0$					$t_c = t_m = 5° R$				$t_c = t_m = 10° R$			
				t_v °R	W_1+W_2, B.t.u./lbm	W B.t.u./lbm	W Kw.-hr./1000 g.	Y	W_1+W_2, B.t.u./lbm	W B.t.u./lbm	W Kw.-hr./1000 g.	Y	W_1+W_2, B.t.u./lbm	W B.t.u./lbm	W Kw.-hr./1000 g.	Y
0.1	0.15	9.93	97.4	0.95	1.22	11.30	27.57	0.32	4.41	14.49	35.36	0.66	7.61	17.69	43.16	1.00
0.2	0.17	4.97	48.7	0.89	1.37	6.51	15.88	0.36	4.57	9.71	23.69	0.70	7.77	12.92	31.52	1.05
0.3	0.19	3.32	32.5	0.82	1.57	5.08	12.40	0.42	4.77	8.28	20.20	0.76	7.98	11.49	28.04	1.10
0.4	0.23	2.49	24.4	0.76	1.83	4.55	11.10	0.49	5.04	7.76	18.93	0.83	8.25	10.97	26.77	1.17
0.5	0.29	1.99	19.5	0.70	2.20	4.48	10.93	0.58	5.42	7.69	18.76	0.93	8.64	10.91	26.62	1.27
0.6	0.36	1.65	16.2	0.62	2.76	4.78	11.66	0.73	5.99	8.00	19.52	1.08	9.22	11.24	27.43	1.42
0.7	0.51	1.42	13.9	0.55	3.70	5.63	13.74	0.82	6.95	8.88	21.67	1.33	10.21	12.13	29.60	1.67
0.8	0.80	1.24	12.2	0.47	5.62	7.66	18.69	1.48	8.91	10.95	26.72	1.83	12.21	14.25	34.77	3.25

Energy values obtained from the curves of Figure 10 or by computation from the equations closely approximate the theoretical minimum values for saline water conversion by freezing processes at the specified values of constants and parameters. Any actual conversion process utilizing freezing will necessarily require considerably more energy than these minimum values for the same specified values of constants and parameters.

Nomenclature

C_j	=	specific heat of ice
C_s	=	specific heat of saline water
$c.p.$	=	coefficient of performance
H	=	sensible heat
H_3, H_4	=	sensible heat to refrigeration machines R_3 and R_4
I	=	ice fraction
i, f	=	subscripts denoting initial and final values
K	=	freezing point depression constant
L	=	heat of crystallization
L_c	=	latent heat of crystallization
q	=	heat
$\bar{q}$	=	amount of heat
r	=	extraction ratio
R_1, R_2, R_3, R_4	=	refrigeration machines
s	=	salt fraction
T	=	absolute temperature
T_o	=	melting temperature of ice
T_u	=	ambient saline water temperature
T_n	=	$T_n + T_w + \frac{1}{2}t_y$
$t_{x,c,m,w,y,v}$	=	temperature differentials
w	=	energy input
W_1, W_2, W_3, W_4	=	energy inputs to refrigeration machines R_1, R_2, R_3, R_4
Y	=	ratio of saline cooling water to fresh water product
Z	=	mass ratio of solute to solvent

Acknowledgment

The author expresses his gratitude to E. D. Howe, Director of the Sea Water Conversion Laboratory, University of California at Berkeley, for providing him with the opportunity of undertaking preliminary work on this paper during the summer of 1959, and to the Administration of St. Edward's University for providing the opportunity of subsequently completing it.

Literature Cited

(1) Lyman, J., Fleming, R. H., *J. Marine Research* **3**, 134–46 (1940).

RECEIVED for review July 7, 1960. Accepted July 15, 1960.

Water Purification by Zone-Freezing

WILLIAM H. MINK, GEORGE F. SACHSEL, and R. B. FILBERT, Jr.

Battelle Memorial Institute, 505 King Ave., Columbus 1, Ohio

The economics of purification of saline water by zone-freezing were investigated using analog simulation as a tool to optimize the design. Estimated costs for the process were found to be too high to make it competitive with other processes now under development.

For some time the United States Department of the Interior has been carrying out a program aimed toward the selection of an economical method of obtaining potable water from sea water. One method investigated at the Battelle Memorial Institute (1) is an adaptation of the zone-purification process which had previously been used satisfactorily in the purification of metals (3). In the process, as applied to purification of sea water, a narrow zone of water is frozen in a tube containing sea water. As this zone is made to traverse the length of the tube, the formation of ice crystals tends to concentrate the salt in the solution ahead of the crystals. This results in the concentration of the salt at one end of the tube and the depletion of salt at the other end.

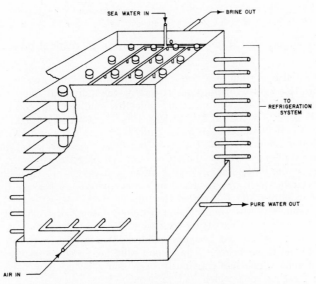

Figure 1. Vertical-tube zone-freezing unit

The Vertical-Tube Unit

Before costs could be estimated with any degree of accuracy for a possible large-scale operation, it was necessary to select some type of apparatus in which the process could operate in a continuous manner. The apparatus which Battelle believed would offer the greatest advantage from an economic and technical standpoint was the vertical-tube unit which is similar to the zone-void refiner described by Pfann (4) and is shown in Figure 1. In this unit a number of vertical tubes pass through closely spaced, insulated, horizontal plates. The spaces between the plates are connected by automatic valves to either the heating or the cooling part of a refrigeration system. It is thus possible to have any space between the plates be a melting or a freezing zone. Sea water is introduced near the top of the tubes. By selective operation of the valves, freezing and melting zones move upward through the tubes. Sea water passes down the tube and is subject to a zone purification each time it passes a freezing zone. It leaves the bottom of the tube as purified water, while the salt is concentrated in the form of brine at the top of the tube, where it is removed periodically by flushing.

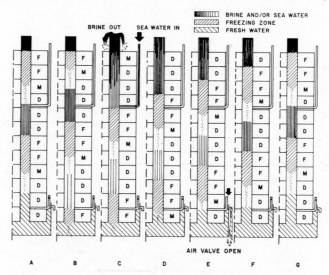

Figure 2. Schematic representation of vertical-tube process

The sequential operation of a two-stage, vertical-tube, zone-freezing unit is shown in Figure 2. In this figure, for purposes of clarity, the individual zones are shown large in comparison to the tube. In an actual unit the zone spacing would be a fraction of the tube diameter. In Figure 2,A, a single tube is shown as it might appear during operation. In the melting zone ice melts and the resulting water falls through an air space to the water below. Around the water is a dead zone and no heat is being transferred in either direction. Below the water is an ice plug formed by a freezing zone. The lower end of the bottommost ice plug melts, and water falls through an air space into the reservoir for pure water. However, since there is no passage for air into the tube, the level of pure water will rise in the tube as the ice melts.

At some time later the conditions shown in Figure 2,B, will exist in the tube. Operation of the automatic valves has shifted each zone upward one space. The top plug of ice melts as before and becomes smaller. Water falls from this zone through the air space to the water below. The second plug has in effect been moved upward, since the dead zone which had previously been above it has now become a freezing zone and the freezing zone which had previously been below it has now become a melting zone. At the bottom of the tube a third plug begins to form.

In Figure 2,C, which shows the tube at some time after that illustrated in Figure 2,B, the top plug has melted completely. The water in the top of the tube is concentrated to a salinity considerably above that of sea water, so that at this point the brine is flushed out and replaced with fresh sea water. The remainder of the tube operates as described previously.

As the zones continue to move upward as a result of the operation of the automatic valves, the plugs shown in Figure 2,D, also move upward. The water above the top plug becomes more concentrated because its volume is being reduced and because of the segregation action of freezing. This segregation action is the tendency to exclude salt from the ice formed, thus concentrating the salt in the liquid phase. Up to this point there has been no net downward flow of water.

Some time later the conditions shown in Figure 2,E, exist. The ice plugs continue to move upward as before. However, air is permitted to enter the bottom of the tube, so that as the bottom plug melts, the outside level of the reservoir is maintained within the tube, and purified water overflows.

When the air space has reached the desired volume as shown in Figure 2,F, the air inlet is closed and the plugs continue to move upward, concentrating the saline water.

In Figure 2,G, a cycle has been completed and the system is at the point shown in Figure 2,A.

The air space below each plug is necessary to obtain a net downward flow of water. The air space rises in the tube and is displaced by water as shown in Figure 2,C; in Figure 2,E, air displaces water.

Simulation of Operation of the Vertical-Tube Unit

To obtain both equipment and operating costs it was necessary to determine the optimum number of stages. The number of stages required to produce a given purity of water is in turn a function of the configuration and size of the vertical-tube unit, the segregation coefficient, and the extent to which the brine is concentrated (or converted) before discharge. Although mathematical relationships have been developed for the zone-void refiner (4), it appeared that the quantity of data required for optimization of the vertical tube unit could be obtained more efficiently by simulation on an analog computer. This was accomplished by simulation of each freezing zone individually and then by means of a programming relay connecting and disconnecting the proper zone at the proper time. A simplified block diagram of the computer setup is shown in Figure 3. The information obtained from the simulation was the salinity of the product water as a function of time. An actual tracing of the output of the computer is shown in Figure 4. By integrating the output it was possible to obtain an average value of product salinity for a given set of conditions. By obtaining product salinities for different sets of operating conditions it was possible to develop an expression correlating the concentration of salt in the output with different operating conditions. This relationship is shown in Figure 5, where the curves characterize a procedure to yield a product water of 500 p.p.m. salt from sea water with 35,000 p.p.m. of salt.

Experimental Studies

Before the curves of Figure 5 can be used, two things must be determined: the variation of the segregation coefficient, k, with the temperature of the coolant outside the tubes; and the time required to freeze a zone of ice in the tube (not needed for simulation, because it does not affect the product salinity) which affects the production rate from a given unit.

The effect of temperature difference on the segregation coefficient was determined experimentally. Although the segregation coefficient data vary with concentration, the effect is small in this type of system and was considered to have no significance in the economic study. Tubes ranging in size from 7/16 to 1 inch containing salt water were immersed in a constant temperature bath and the segregation coefficient was determined.

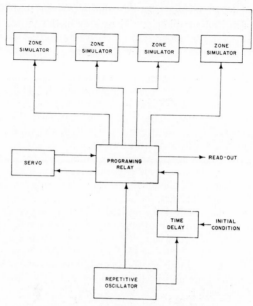

Figure 3. Simplified block diagram for
simulation of a four-stage vertical
tube zone-freezing unit

Figure 4. The instantaneous salinity out from a two-stage
zone-freezing unit

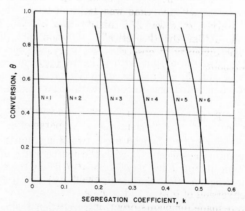

Figure 5. Conversion and segregation
coefficient required to produce water
with 500 p.p.m. salt for various
number of stages

It was found that, although tube size has no effect, the temperature difference has a large effect on the segregation coefficient, as shown in Figure 6.

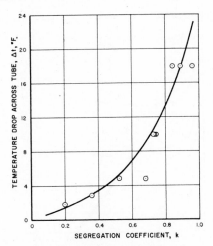

Figure 6. Effect of temperature difference on segregation coefficient

Using reasonable values of film coefficients and thermal conductivities, it can be shown that the time to freeze to the center of a tube is given approximately by:

$$T = \frac{3.2D^{1.88}}{\Delta t}$$

where

T = time required to freeze, hours
D = inside diameter of tube, inches
Δt = temperature difference between coolant and water, ° F.

As a check on the above equation, the time required to freeze in a 1-inch tube was determined experimentally. In one case, using a Δt of 17.8° F., the observed time was 13.4 minutes and the calculated time was 18.7 minutes. In another case, using a Δt of 9.7° F., the observed time was 27.5 minutes and the calculated time was 34.8 minutes. It can be seen that the theoretical calculation gives conservative values. This may be due to the difficulty of observing when crystal formation begins, and to the possibility of supercooling, both factors tending to reduce the observed freezing time.

Estimate of Costs

For optimizing the operating cost of the process, the variable operating cost (which is only that cost affected by the design and operating parameters of the vertical-tube unit) was determined as a function of number of stages and conversion using information from a heat exchanger manufacturer.

The variable operating cost is plotted in Figure 7 for units containing two to six stages. It can be seen from the curve that the lowest variable operating cost occurs at four stages, with a conversion of 0.13. Under these conditions the Δt should be 3° F.

Cost estimates were made for plants producing 100,000 gallons per day and 10,000,000 gallons per day of product water containing 500 p.p.m. of dissolved solids from sea water containing 35,000 p.p.m. of dissolved solids, using the procedure outlined by the Office of Saline Water (2). For the larger plant, a total of 77,000,000 gallons per day of sea water is required, of which 67,000,000 gallons per day are discharged as brine

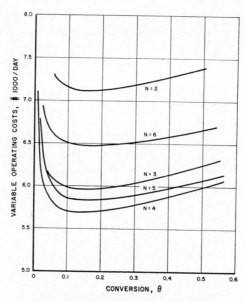

Figure 7. Variable operating costs for the
vertical-tube zone-freezing process

containing about 40,000 p.p.m. of dissolved solids. It was estimated that 387,000
kw.-hr. of electric power would be required per day. Capital costs are shown in Table
I and operating costs in Table II. Investment plays a large part in the operating costs;

Table I. Capital Costs for the Vertical-Tube Zone-Freezing Process

	Capital Costs, Dollars	
Item	10^5 gal./day plant	10^7 gal./day plant
Vertical-tube unit, installed	892,000	10,020,000
Standard engineering equipment, installed	636,000	52,940,000
Other plant costs	1,054,000	51,769,000
Working capital	57,000	2,420,000
Total investment	2,639,000	117,149,000
Unit investment, dollars/gal./day	26.40	11.70

Table II. Operating Costs for the Vertical-Tube Zone-Freezing Process

	Operating Costs, Dollars/Day	
Item	10^5 gal./day plant	10^7 gal./day plant
Power	27	2,710
Labor	103	3,227
Amortization	578	25,700
Other	251	10,504
Total	959	42,141
Cost per 1000 gallons of product water	9.59	4.21

it accounts for about 60% of these costs. Increasing the plant size beyond the 10,000,-
000-gallon-per-day capacity would result in only a slight decrease in the estimated
operating costs, since multiple units would be required and other costs would change
little. The possibility of better design does not hold much promise for reduced costs
either. The principal difficulty is that low freezing rates are required to obtain low

segregation coefficients. If the freezing rate is decreased enough to permit operation of a single-stage unit, the production rate from the unit approaches zero.

At the present time, the authors have no published cost data on other conversion processes obtained on the same basis as those presented here with which to compare the results. The estimated costs are, however, above the desired level set by the Office of Saline Water.

Literature Cited

(1) Himes, R. C., Miller, S. E., Mink, W. H., Goering, H. L., *Ind. Eng. Chem.* **51,** 1345 (1959).
(2) Office of Saline Water, U. S. Department of the Interior, "A Standardized Procedure for Estimating Costs of Saline Water Conversion," March 1956.
(3) Pfann, W. G., *J. Metals* **7,** 297 (February 1955).
(4) Pfann, W. G., *"Zone Melting,"* p. 119, Wiley, New York, 1958.

RECEIVED for review July 7, 1960. Accepted July 15, 1960. Work supported by the Office of Saline Water.

Saline Water Conversion by Freezing

HERBERT F. WIEGANDT

Cornell University, Ithaca, N. Y.

Favorable energy relationships and a convenient refrigeration cycle make freezing look attractive. Movement of a crystal bed by hydraulic forces combines adequate production with a simple washing procedure.

Investigations at Cornell University are based on process concepts in which an ice slurry is produced from saline water by evaporation of a suitable immiscible refrigerant. After washing, the ice crystals are melted by direct condensation on the ice of the compressed refrigerant vapors. Potable water is the product, and the immiscible refrigerant recycles to the process.

n-Butane and isobutane are the preferred economical refrigerants which allow the process to operate close to atmospheric pressures and thereby allow use of large-volume process equipment. Experimentally much use has been made of methylene chloride as a convenient refrigerant.

Energy Requirements

Although the minimum energy needed for the conversion of saline water to fresh water is the same for any isentropic process, the goal is to achieve this conversion efficiently in a real process, on a large scale, at low cost, and with easily maintained equipment.

The minimum work theoretically required at a specified salinity and temperature may be equated by a number of alternatives:

$-W_{rev}$ = reversible work in B.t.u. per pound of product

$$= \frac{RT}{M} \ln \frac{P_2}{P_1} \qquad \text{(distillation)}$$

$$= \frac{RT}{M} \ln \frac{A_2}{A_1} \qquad \text{(extraction)}$$

$$= \frac{\Delta Z}{778} \quad (\Delta Z = \text{feet of head across membrane}) \qquad \text{(osmosis)}$$

$$= 3560 \times C \times \Delta E \left(\Delta E = \text{voltage}; C = \frac{\text{pound equivalents removed}}{\text{pound product}} \right) \text{(electro-osmosis)}$$

$$= \frac{\Delta H_v \times \Delta T_{\text{BP rise}}}{T} \qquad \text{(distillation)}$$

$$= \frac{\Delta H_f \times \Delta T_{\text{F.P. depression}}}{T} \qquad \text{(freezing)}$$

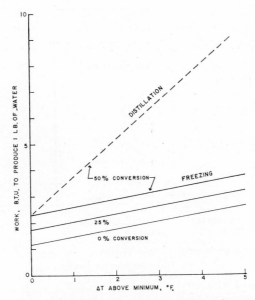

Figure 1. Energy penalty for driving force

In Figure 1 is singled out the most important reason why an actual freezing process may be competitive with distillation in energy requirements. This is by no means a complete energy comparison. Operating inefficiencies in the vapor recompression process in part actually become utilizable energy, whereas in freezing these inefficiencies result in an added refrigeration load.

Figure 1 represents single-stage conversions and a steady-state generation of ice or steam from a brine at the indicated conversion level. Intersections with the ordinate represent reversible conversion from brine at the indicated conversion level.

The freezing point depression at 50% conversion is 7.6° F. and the boiling point rise is 1.05° F. at the triple point. In order to achieve reasonable rates, it becomes necessary to operate between temperature limits which reach beyond the minimums of the freezing point depression or the boiling point rise. It is desirable to keep these driving force–temperature increments as small as possible for either distillation or freezing, but the penalty for each degree is over seven times greater for distillation than for freezing. A comparison of this kind could also be made for osmosis (flow pressure drop), electrodialysis (ohmic resistance), solvent extraction (concentration gradient), and critical pressure distillation (difference in countercurrent heat exchange temperature).

In Figure 2 are represented energy requirements over a wide range of design conditions. The British thermal unit per pound of product is the energy requirement at the compressor shaft. Total plant energy must still consider driver efficiency, liquid-pumping energy, and heat leaks. A number of balances which concern the optimum between plant investment cost and total energy cost indicate an over-all conversion level of 50% to be a good design basis.

In the first plot the importance of effective heat interchange in precooling the feed against the effluent product and concentrated brine streams is considered. The increase in energy requirements, as less effective feed precooling is done, affects mostly the secondary compressor. This is to be expected, when it is taken into account that the secondary compressor exists solely to allow the operation to proceed below ambient temperature by removing all the thermal inefficiencies at the lowest operating temperature and transferring them to cooling water available at 80° F. An interesting conclu-

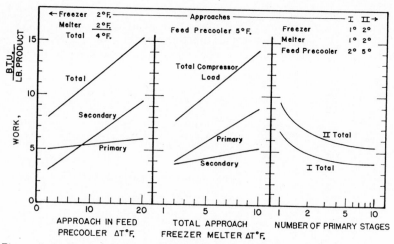

Figure 2. Refrigeration energy requirements. Influence of driving forces
on compressor loads

Sea water 80° F.   Compressor efficiency 80%
Total conversion 50%   Reflux 10%

sion that can be drawn is that if precooling is efficient, the secondary compressor is
relatively unimportant in the total energy requirements. It would be desirable, of
course, for the crystallization temperature to be above ambient temperature, thereby
allowing the secondary compressor to be eliminated entirely. Water is known to form
hydrates with numerous compounds, but unless the melting point of that hydrate is
above ambient temperature, a secondary compressor still is required. The maximum
possible gains, assuming good precooling, are marginal for all hydrates melting below
ambient temperature. There is actually a slight penalty because the latent heats of
fusion, based on the mass of water, are a little greater for hydrates than for ice. It
would seem that the most common criticism of the freezing-to-ice cycle—namely, operating below ambient temperature—represents a minor engineering hurdle.

In the second plot, the energy required by the primary compressor is shown to be
sensitive to the pressure in the evaporator-freezer and condenser-melter. Because both
the evaporation and condensation are by direct contact of the refrigerant with water or
ice, the opportunity exists for realistic achievement of a low over-all driving force.
Experimentally, the evaporation has been found to occur so rapidly that a rate measurement has not been practical. The melting of the ice is more of a problem because the
condensate film is a heat transfer barrier. However, the barrier is a fluid and not a
stationary wall as in a distillation unit, wherein steam is condensed against water or
boiling water.

In the third plot, the importance of achieving 50% conversion in stages is shown.
The upper curve considers temperature approaches that may reasonably be expected
in a large installation; the lower curve assumes conditions which are so optimistic that
no practical design is envisioned which achieves them. The interesting observation to be
made is that the difference in energy requirements between a realistic design and an
"ultimate" design is less than 3 B.t.u. per pound of product. A comparable gain can
be made simply by use of two primary compressors, assuming conversion to 25% in the
first flash chamber and further conversion of the resulting brine to an over-all 50%
conversion level in the second flash chamber. If a very large plant were to call for two
primary compressors, this advantage could be realized without penalty.

Distillation and flash-freezing processes both require the condensation of vapors.

The volume of these vapors must be recognized in the design of vessels. For direct condensation of vapor on ice and for vapor-recompression distillation, the volume is also important in the compressor design. Figure 3 compares the volumes of vapor generated for each pound of product. The fairly high operating pressure makes propane to propane hydrate the system with the least generated gas volume among the systems considered.

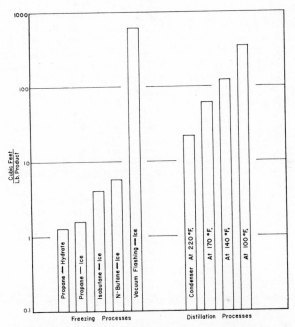

Figure 3. Volume of gas flow to compressor

The three hydrocarbons being discussed all form hydrates. Their hydrate melting points are above 32° F., and the hydrate is the stable solid phase. On flash evaporation in the absence of backmixing, ice forms so much more rapidly than the hydrate that the liquid hydrocarbon is gone before a measurable amount of hydrate forms. In a process arrangement in which hydrate formation is encouraged by refrigerant evaporation from a hydrate-water slurry, the pressures for the higher-temperature hydrate cycle would be slightly greater and the volumes correspondingly less. The comparison could also have been represented in Figure 3 for isobutane and n-butane hydrates. Whether or not condensation and ice melting can be accommodated without the formation of the more stable hydrate under sustained operating conditions remains to be tested. In the case of n-butane the question is academic, because its hydrate melts at less than 34° F., which is economically below the condensation temperature of the n-butane from the primary compressor.

The formation of an ice slurry by vacuum flashing of water benefits from the high latent heat of evaporation of water. The large volume vapor represented in Figure 3 is a consequence of water vapor pressures at the operating temperature of about 3.5 mm. of mercury. These pressures and volumes pose engineering problems of a nature different from those using hydrocarbon refrigerants.

Distillation processes have a degree of flexibility not available to freezing processes in the choice of an operating temperature. The almost vertical ice-water line in the temperature-pressure phase diagram for water indicates essentially a fixed operating temperature. Similarly this is true for the hydrate-water line in the hydrate systems. The effect on vapor volume resulting from the relationship between vapor pressure and boiling point is indicated in Figure 3. Even at 220° F. this volume is four times greater than that from the process using *n*-butane. In order to establish the engineering possibilities of a process using an immiscible solvent, an experimental unit was constructed following a number of bench-scale experiments (*1, 2*).

Experimental Unit

Figure 4 is a diagram of the experimental unit. In its operation the two-phase feed of brine and methylene chloride enters the flash column. Ice slurry forms in the upper part of the column as the methylene chloride vaporizes, and the slurry is transferred by the slurry pump to the glass tee at the bottom of the separation column. In the glass tee, the ice floats into the separation column, where it is washed and removed. The brine recycles from the bottom of the separation unit to the ice generator by joining a stream of fresh feed and liquid refrigerant.

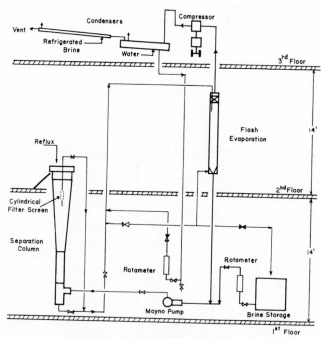

Figure 4. Pilot plant arrangement

The flashed refrigerant vapors are de-entrained by a section of York mesh located near the top of the generator and flow to a Stokes, Model H-149, Microvac compressor. Condensation follows in a refrigerant condenser, which serves also for surge storage of refrigerant. The refrigerant condenser vents into a refrigerated secondary condenser through which inert leakage gases escape from the system. Pressures in the vapor space of the ice generator and at the bottom of the separation column are indicated by manometers. The rates of refrigerant addition to the feed line and salt-water feed addition just prior to the slurry pump are read from rotameters.

The ice generator consists of two vertically assembled 5-foot sections of 6-inch borosilicate glass pipe. The refrigerant and brine mixture jets toward the wall near the top of the column. The refrigerant flashes off immediately, leaving the ice slurry to slide down the walls. A large wall area is provided to allow time for the small amount of methylene chloride hydrate which forms to decompose. Although metastable at the column pressure, the hydrate which does form decomposes slowly. At the bottom of the generator, a metal cone directs the slurry into a line leading to a Moyno L-3 slurry pump. The maximum bottom ice discharge rate is 65 pounds per hour. A rate above this results in plugging of the cone. This has proved to be the capacity limitation of the ice generator and the unit.

The ice floating into the separation section rises and adds to the existing bed. Some recycle water is routed through a significant portion of the bed and out through a screened probe mounted inside the bed. This flow of water serves to compact the bed and furnishes a pressure drop through the bed which aids the upward movement of the ice. The maximum rate of rise of the ice bed from the water in the 6-inch glass separation column is greater than the 65 pounds per hour that can be supplied from the generator.

The upper portion of the ice bed emerges as a drained bed. A proper balance of feed rate, spent-brine discharge rate, and rate of outflow through the probe permits the column liquid level to be maintained at a desired distance above the probe screen. The drained bed is washed with a small amount of reflux (10% or less of the ice rate) to yield a product of less than 300 p.p.m. in salt content.

Hydraulic-Piston Bed

An analysis of the hydraulic forces which are responsible for the movement of the porous ice bed so that countercurrent flow of liquid occurs through the upper part of the bed is presented in Figure 5. A total ice-bed height of 30 feet is considered with

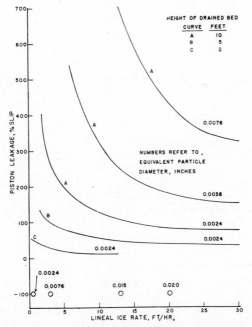

Figure 5. Piston flow bed hydraulic characteristics

co-current flow of water for a distance of 20 feet from the bottom. Vertical filter screens or leaves which allow the ice bed to slip by are located at this level. The flow of liquid above the screens may be countercurrent if the hydraulic forces are adjusted appropriately. The bed is considered as a porous piston, and the flow up through the bed and out the screens is referred to as piston leakage and represented as slip. Numerically, slip is the ratio of the lineal water rate relative to the lineal ice rate. The curves labeled

A represent a case in which the ice bed rides with 10 feet of its height out of the water. The particle diameters refer to equivalent diameters as defined by the Carmen-Kozeney equation which equates particle diameter to the filter properties of a bed. Because small particles give poor filterability, there will be less piston leakage for beds made up of fine particles than for those of coarse particles. Likewise, the drainage properties of the bed from the top to the screen are affected by particle diameter. If it is assumed that the minimum pressure at the screen were to be the same as the pressure above the bed—in other words, full gravity drainage—then the maximum lineal ice rate is established for each equivalent particle diameter. Calculations based on the filtration behavior of the bed and on calorimetric determinations of porosity indicate the approximate relationship:

$$V_{max} = 1.56 \times 10^6 D_p{}^2$$

$$V_{max} = \text{maximum lineal ice rate, feet per hour}$$

$$D_p = \text{equivalent particle diameter, inches}$$

Ice velocities greater than V_{max} will result in salt water accompanying the product ice. The conclusion to be drawn is that at the maximum ice rate which allows downflow washing by gravity drainage, the percentage slip is greater for beds of large ice particles, but the maximum ice rate is also greater for large particles. There is an optimum, which has not yet been established, between obtaining a high production rate per unit bed area and minimizing the costs of recycling the piston-leakage water.

Crystal Growth

With flash evaporation of solvent from a sprayed mixture of solvent and brine the crystals have a D_{eq} of 0.0024 inch. Although little control of crystal size is possible by the spray technique, the allowable lineal ice-production rate is 9 feet per hour with these crystals. This is completely satisfactory for an economical plant.

It is recognized that decreasing the cooling rate will allow larger crystals to form when the cooling results from the evaporation of an immiscible liquid. Plates 3 × 3 mm. in cross section were readily achieved by evaporation of butane with the pressure regulated for an evaporation temperature less than 1° F. below the crystallization temperature and with poor mixing.

In Figure 5 the points plotted at −100% slip indicate the ice rates for gravity rather than for hydraulic-piston movement of the ice bed. The ice projection or drainage height for these points is only 1 foot. If ice is rising from a solution, the solution is exhibiting a total reverse slip relative to the ice bed, although in a column the ice moves upward and the solution is stationary to the observer. For gravity operation a D_{eq} of 0.015 inch would be adequate if a minimum of wall friction were encountered. Further study is required which considers the problem of achieving the large crystals at reasonable rates. To avoid the difficulties which result from the change in freezing point with conversion, it becomes necessary either to operate with a high rate of recycle or to devise an evaporator having a high degree of backmixing.

Melting

The melting of slush ice by bubbling butane vapors into a concentrated ice slurry gave a volumetric U of 3200 B.t.u./hr., cu. ft.,° F. In a dumped ice bed the heat transfer is less effective, very likely because of the channeling and the inability for the condensing vapors to come in contact with more than the outside surface of wet ice clumps. Despite a volumetric U of only 2000 to 2500 B.t.u./hr., cu. ft., °F., the low pressure drop and simplicity of condensing the refrigerant in a large chamber charged with dumped ice make this procedure attractive.

Office of Saline Water Pilot Plant

Planned for the winter of 1960 is a 35,000-gallon-per-day pilot plant to study and demonstrate the feasibility of saline water conversion with the use of butane as a refrigerant. The Blaw-Knox Co. will test both the Rotocel extractor and the hydraulic-piston bed for effectiveness in ice washing. Figure 6 is a sketch of the freezer-washer-melter unit for the hydraulic-piston operation.

Figure 6. Proposed 35,000 gallon-per-day sea water conversion pilot plant unit

Acknowledgment

The assistance of graduate and undergraduate students who contributed to the study is gratefully acknowledged. They include R. D. Bradford, Juan Carrere, Roger Fisher, Robert Givey, Edward Godleski, Charles Krutchen, Donald Leonard, Che-Yu Li, Jay Markley, Landon Nichols, and John Slack.

Literature Cited

(1) Bradford, R. D., Fisher, R. K., "Demineralization of Saline Water by Freezing," Senior Project Rept., School of Chem. Eng., Cornell University, Ithaca, N. Y., June 1, 1957.
(2) Wiegandt, H. F., "Saline Water Conversion by Direct Freezing," Nat'l Acad. Sci., U. S., Washington, D. C., Publ. 568, 377 (1958).

RECEIVED for review July 7, 1960. Accepted July 17, 1960. Work supported by Office of Saline Water, U. S. Department of Interior.

A 15,000-Gallon-Per-Day Freeze-Separation Pilot Plant for Conversion of Saline Waters

CYRUS M. BOSWORTH

Research and Development Division, Carrier Corp., Syracuse, N.Y.

ALLEN J. BARDUHN

Chemical Engineering Department, Syracuse University, Syracuse, N.Y.

DEWEY J. SANDELL, Jr.

Research and Development Division, Carrier Corp., Syracuse, N.Y.

Results from operation of a 300-gallon-per-day plant were extrapolated to a 15,000-gallon plant which began making ice in October 1959. Since presentation of the paper in April 1960, the plant has operated at design capacity for periods of 1 to 2 days and previous cost estimates of 60 cents to $1.00 per 1000 gallons appear to be attainable.

The chemical and petrochemical industries have utilized distillation, freezing, ion exchange, electrodialysis, selective membrane, and hydrate processes for a number of years to separate certain species or components from a multicomponent solution in their refining operations. Recent emphasis has been placed on developing and modifying these basic processes to obtain fresh water from brackish and sea water supplies.

The need for greater water supplies is evident; however, in addition to the requirement for developing a method for conversion, a paramount factor is that it be done inexpensively to allow usage for domestic, industrial, and possibly agricultural needs.

Freezing processes have been investigated more actively since the feasibility of direct freezing and simplified wash-separation of ice particles from the brine has been established in small scale operations.

Sea water containing 35,000 p.p.m. (3.5%) of solids is representative of many saline water supplies in the earth. It contains a number of ion species, molecules, and chemical complexes dissolved in water. It is possible and practicable to separate a portion of this water from the solution by lowering the temperature and causing the water to form into ice crystals. An equilibrium freezing curve for sea water (Figure 1), plotted from an early publication of Thompson and Nelson (6), shows the equilibrium freezing temperature in degrees Fahrenheit as a function of per cent solids content in sea water. For example, the 3.5% sea water begins to yield ice crystals at 28.5° F. and continues to increase ice content in the ice-brine mixture until 17.2° F. is reached. At

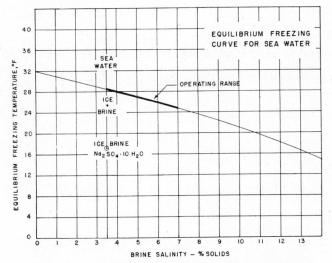

Figure 1. Equilibrium freezing curve for sea water

this temperature sodium sulfate decahydrate crystals also begin to form. Only 73% of the water is frozen out above this temperature.

The freeze-separation process which has been developed at Carrier Corp. since 1956 operates in the range of 3.5 to 7.0% solids or freezing temperatures of 28.5° to 25° F. Ice-brine separation takes place at temperature levels of 25° to 32° F. from concentrated brine at the bottom of the column to pure ice at the top.

Several design variations are possible for a direct freeze-separation process. The one reported utilizes the evaporation of water directly in an evacuated freeze chamber to form ice crystals and concentrated brine. Separation of ice from brine does not use any mechanical devices, such as centrifuges, but simply a counterflow wash column of ice being moved by applied hydraulic forces.

The results of a 300-gallon-per-day experimental unit have been utilized to design a 15,000-gallon-per-day pilot plant. Design parameters and calculations are elaborated in the following sections.

Pilot Plant Design

Prior to the completion of the design of a 15,000-gallon-per-day pilot plant, an experimental program was carried out in the laboratories to evaluate a 300-gallon-per-day freeze-separation system. The design of this freezer and column evolved from previous experimentation in small glassware components. Results of the early testing and the design of the 300-gallon-per-day process were published in 1957 (1). The present paper extends the results of this evaluation of a direct freezing–continuous wash separation process to the design and preliminary operational phases of a 15,000-gallon-per-day pilot plant.

A major objective of the larger pilot plant is to determine if extrapolation of the design parameters from operating results of the 300-gallon-per-day plant is valid when scaled upwards 50 to 1 to a 15,000-gallon-per-day facility. In the design of the pilot plant, flexibility of each major component has been paramount. The determination of the best of several methods for introducing the saline water into the freezer, height of column necessary for adequate ice-brine separation, permeability of ice bed, rates of ice production, minimum wash water, and power requirements are but a few of the important variables which must be evaluated carefully to qualify the technical feasibility of the process and thence to yield the economic potential.

Detailed results are elaborated in progress reports (2).

Flow Sheet and Mass Balances. Figure 2 represents a flow sheet of the 15,000-gallon-per-day pilot plant. The four major components are the freezer, the wash-separation column, the ice melter, and the vapor-handling device. The other essential components are the deaerator, which removes air from the saline water before it enters into the evacuated freezer; the auxiliary refrigeration system, which removes heat leakage into the system and thermal inefficiencies of the process; an ice scraper, pumps, controls, and instruments.

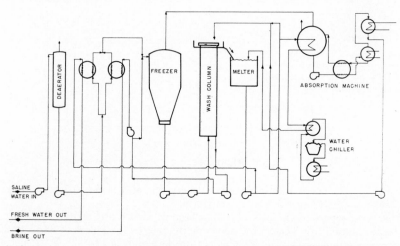

Figure 2. Diagram of process flow

The main process streams may be followed by referring to the flow sheet.

Fresh sea water feed is first deaerated and then precooled by heat exchange against the two product streams, brine and fresh water product. It enters the freezer at about 37° F., is cooled further to 25° F. by evaporation, and is partially frozen. Because the freezer is maintained at 3.3 mm. of mercury pressure (25° F.), the brine concentration is 7%, and half of the water in the sea water is removed. The slurry is diluted by recycle brine that has been filtered in the separation column.

The water vapor leaving the freezer is absorbed by a concentrated lithium bromide solution. The dilute absorbent solution is pumped from the absorber through heat exchangers to the generator, where it is boiled. The vapor leaving the generator is condensed with cold sea water and this distilled water flows back to the separator, where it is used for washing the ice. The absorbent solution, after being concentrated in the generator, is cooled in the heat exchangers and flows back to the absorber by gravity.

The ice-brine slurry is pumped to the bottom of the separation column, where ice and brine are initially separated by filtering through a screen. The ice crystals are still surrounded by concentrated brine, which is removed by washing. Water containing relatively few dissolved salts replaces this brine around the ice as the ice flows upward through the column.

As the ice reaches the top of the column, the water adhering to the ice crystals contains less than 1000 p.p.m. of salt. This ice is scraped into a tank, where it is melted by recycled fresh water. The effluent of this tank is called "melt water" and is divided into three streams. The largest stream flows through tubes in the absorber, where it picks up the heat of absorption. This same melt water stream flows through a chiller, in which it is cooled slightly by the auxiliary refrigeration system to preserve heat balances. It then flows back to the melt tank and melts more ice. The second stream is used for washing the ice and is recycled from the melt tank to the top of the column, part of which returns to the melt tank adhering to the ice. The third stream is the product water, which flows through the heat exchangers cooling the inlet feed and thence back into the storage tank.

Part of the brine leaving the bottom of the column is returned to the freezer to dilute the slurry and part flows through the heat exchangers to cool the inlet feed and thence to waste.

Mass balances and heat balances of the components are present in Table I.

Table I. Mass and Heat Balances for Pilot Plant

	Material Balance, Lb./Hr.		Heat Balance,[a] B.t.u./Hr.	
	In	Out	In	Out
Deaerator	12,800	12,800	410,000	410,000
Sea water precoolers				
Sea water feed	12,800	12,800	410,000	74,800
Fresh product	6,400	6,400		153,800
Waste brine	6,400	6,400	−42,300	139,100
Total			367,700	367,700
Freezer				
Sea water feed	12,800		74,800	
Brine	26,400		−175,000	
Slurry	119,773	158,100	−1,126,800	−2,163,000
Vapor		873		936,000
Total	158,973	158,973	−1,227,000	−1,227,000
Column				
Slurry	110,500		−1,505,000	
Brine		104,970		−694,000
Ice		5,630		−811,000
Water	5,527	5,427		
Total	116,027	116,027	−1,505,000	−1,505,000
Melter				
Ice	5,527		−796,000	
Water	182,627	188,154	984,000	188,000
Total	188,154	188,154	188,000	188,000
Absorber				
Vapor (water)	873		936,000	
Lithium bromide	18,310	19,183	347,700	223,000
Water	177,100	177,100	177,100	1,237,800
Total	196,283	196,283	1,460,800	1,460,800
Generator				
Lithium bromide	19,183	18,310	1,300,000	1,421,000
Vapor (water)		873		990,000
Steam	1,142		1,317,000	
Condensate		1,142		206,000
Total	20,325	20,325	2,617,000	2,617,000
Condenser				
Vapor (water)	873		990,000	
Water		873		50,600
Cond. water	182,100	182,100	6,010,000	6,949,400
Total	182,973	182,973	7,000,000	7,000,000
Chiller—evaporator water	177,100	177,100	1,239,000	884,000
Condenser water	21,500	21,500	924,000	1,379,000
Total			2,163,000	2,263,000[b]

[a] Basis for calculation of heat balances is enthalpy of liquid water at 32°F. = 0 B.t.u./lb.
[b] Unbalance due to efficiency of refrigerating system.

Vapor-Removal System. Water vapor may be removed from the freezer by several means: a compressor, a steam ejector, a condenser, or absorption into a low vapor pressure solution. A water vapor compressor does not easily permit variable capacity; a steam ejector is not economically feasible; a wet condenser which had been used in the 300-gallon experimental plant is not as economical as an absorption cycle. Therefore, a steam-heated absorption machine utilizing lithium bromide solution was chosen to remove the vapor from the pilot plant freezer.

Energy input is a direct function of the rise in temperature or saturation pressure of the water vapor evaporating in the freezer and condensing in the absorber. By keeping this temperature rise low, the efficiency of the system is improved. According to the process design, the absolute pressure in the freezer is 3.3 mm. of mercury. Only 0.1-mm. pressure drop through the vapor lines is allowed. This low pressure may be maintained with either a concentrated absorbent solution at moderate temperature (70° F.) or a moderately dilute solution at a lower temperature, 40° F. The design conditions chosen were a compromise for the desired flexibility (Table II).

Table II. Absorber-Design Conditions

	Temp., °F.	Pressure, Mm. Hg	Lithium Bromide Concn., Wt. %	Flow, Lb./Hr.
Water vapor	24	3.2	...	873
Cioncentrated absorbent	59	...	52.5	18,310
Dluted absorbent	53	2.5	50.5	19,183
Melt water entering	33	...	...	177,100
Melt water leaving	40.2	...	...	177,100

The absorption machine chosen for the pilot plant is nominally a 140-ton refrigeration unit. The design load is only 70 tons of ice per day, but the larger machine was specified because the vapor volumes are greater than those at normal air conditioning temperatures. A standard unit was modified by removing the chilled water circuit, the evaporator (because the freezer is the evaporator), and the purge system. The number of heat exchangers was increased to permit closer temperature approach.

Any leakage of noncondensables into the vacuum system is purged through the absorber by a three-stage ejector. The condenser-generator, which is at a higher pressure, is also purged but at the suction of the second stage of the ejector.

Freezer. Rather than a conventional indirect freezing process where the ice is formed on a chilled metallic surface, the freezer is direct. The heat of fusion is removed by evaporation of water at low pressure.

Previous experimental results indicated that the heat transfer rates were high and that considerable ice may be produced with a small driving force, if sufficient interphase area is available.

A freezer to produce 100 pounds of ice per hour was designed and operated prior to the design of the pilot plant freezer. This freezer before insulation is shown in Figure 3. It is 18 inches in diameter and 7 feet high. The purposes of the tests were to determine if ice could be produced continuously and removed continuously, and what the relationships were between ice production rates and driving force for various configurations at different areas.

Ice adheres to all surfaces unless wetted by a continuous moving film. Projections which interrupt the film are also areas for ice formation and adhesion. This problem was overcome by lining the inside of the freezer with sheet plastic and flowing a film of brine down the sides of the freezer. These modifications allowed the freezer to produce ice continuously for extended periods.

The mechanism of forming ice in salt water by removing vapor is complex. It involves three phases in which the transfer of mass and energy takes place. Heat is removed at the gas-liquid interface by evaporation. In the immediate vicinity of the

Figure 3. Three hundred–gallon freezer

ice and at the evaporation areas, there is a higher salt concentration than in the bulk of the liquid. A possible illustration of the process is as follows:

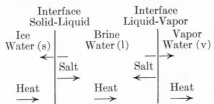

There is diffusion of salt away from both the solid-liquid interface and the vapor-liquid interface, in each case toward the brine. Water moves counterflow to the salt. Heat must transfer from solid to liquid to gas through stagnant films at the solid surface and through the turbulent liquid. An additional resistance to the formation of ice exists at the ice surface, where water molecules must orient themselves and find positions of low energy before being incorporated into the crystal lattice. When inadequate ice surface or foreign particles exist in the freezer, nucleation may control or affect the rate of ice production.

No study has been made to discover which of the several resistances is important, but a simple rate equation can be written which states that the rate of the over-all process is some function of the extent of departure from equilibrium. The function is likely to be approximately linear in the departure, unless the intrinsic crystal growth rate or the nucleation rate is controlling, because the mass and heat transfer rates are usually linear over small ranges of temperature or pressure. The departure from equilibrium is the driving force and can be measured by either a temperature or a pressure difference. The temperature difference between that of the bulk slurry and the equilibrium vapor temperature is measured experimentally to $\pm 0.2°$ F. and lies in the range of $0.5°$ to $2°$ F. under normal operating conditions.

The rate of ice production is thus a function of ΔT. If the function is assumed to be linear,

$$\text{Rate} = k_f(\Delta T - a) \qquad (1)$$

The proportionality constant, k_f, is not a heat transfer coefficient but rather an unknown combination of intrinsic rates of heat and mass transfer and crystal growth. In any case, k_f will be affected by the extent of interfacial area between phases, the degree of agitation, the properties of the brine, the size of the ice particles, the general design of the freezer, and the ice concentration in the slurry present in the freezer. The quantity a is added to allow for any driving force lost through metastability or slow nucleation.

Several devices were tested in the freezer for presenting area for evaporation and ice formation. Fine sprays produce large quantities of ice but because large volumes of vapor are also formed, the salt water is entrained in the vapor. Coarse sprays are not entrained, but very small crystals are formed because of the small residence time for crystal formation. Wetted plastic surfaces were tested, but an area relationship could not be developed because of variable ice adherence. The three configurations most successful are sketched in Figure 4: sprays pointing downward, a nozzle pointing upward to a surface for impingement, and a submerged nozzle. The purpose of the latter two configurations was to allow the drops a longer time for ice formation before reaching the bottom of the freezer.

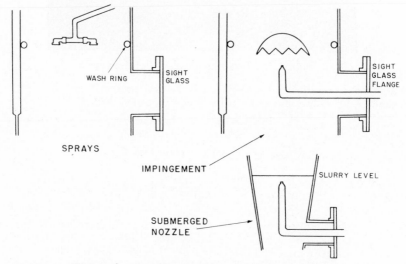

Figure 4.   Liquid distribution systems in freezer

Metastability with respect to ice crystal formation was not apparent in this freezer, probably because particulate matter in the salt solution induced nucleation. Nevertheless, more ice may be produced for a given pressure difference and surface when the slurry is recycled. The ice in the flowing slurry presents more surface and precludes the necessity of high driving forces to induce nucleation. Also, the size of the ice crystals is increased by recycle of slurry.

Actual area for ice formation is difficult to measure, but total ice production was measured at varying temperature difference. Figure 5 plots the rate of ice production in pounds per hour with different configurations. More ice is produced when the slurry is recycled.

A method was devised for recycling the slurry that had the advantage of a long time for contact, and at the same time was a means of slurry agitation. It was simply to return cold filtered brine from the bottom of the separation column through a nozzle partly submerged in the slurry at the bottom of the freezer. The clear brine entrains slurry, maintains violent agitation, and forms a fountain.

From the results of using two spray heads or one submerged nozzle to produce 100 pounds of ice per hour at a temperature difference of 1.2° F., a design was made for a

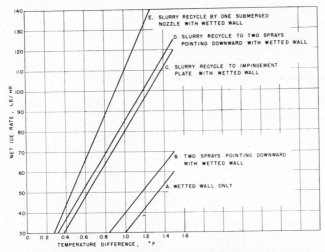

Figure 5. Ice-production rate in 300-gallon unit

freezer to produce 5000 pounds of ice per hour or enough for 15,000 gallons of fresh water per day. The pilot plant freezer is four times in diameter and twice as high and has the same shape. The freezer can be equipped with 35 submerged nozzles or 75 spray heads. It is coated with a smooth polyethylene lining. A flow of 50 gallons of brine per minute to the sides of the freezer maintains a flowing film.

The freezer operates at 3 mm. of mercury absolute pressure and vacuum tightness is essential to its successful operation.

Separation of Ice from Brine. Brine must be rather completely separated from the mass of small ice crystals formed in the freezer before the ice can be melted to produce fresh water. In the Carrier process this is accomplished by countercurrent washing with fresh water in a vertical moving bed called the wash-separation column. In this column the ice-brine slurry is introduced at the bottom, where much of the brine is removed by filtration. The remaining bed of ice crystals is pushed vertically upward through the column by hydraulic forces and is freed of its salt content by the countercurrent stream of fresh water. The ice is continuously harvested at the top of the column. Figure 6 shows a schematic view of the wash column in operation.

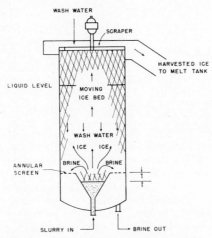

Figure 6. Wash-separation column

Hydraulics. The incoming slurry may contain from 1 to 10% ice suspended in brine, depending on its circulation rate. As the slurry flows into the lower part of the column, it encounters the bottom side of the packed ice bed and the pump pressure forces the brine upward through the bed until it reaches the top of the cone. The brine flow is then upward and radially outward and eventually downward through the horizontal annular screen. The ice in the slurry deposits on the underside of the bed, thus tending to make the interface between the packed ice and slurry move downward. In steady-state operation, however, this interface is stationary because the bed moves upward at the same linear rate at which ice is deposited on its underside. The thickness, t, as shown in Figure 6 adjusts itself to such a value that the pressure drop through this thickness creates a force equal to that necessary to push the bed upward. For a thickness less than t the motive force is insufficient to move the column and for a thickness greater than t the force is more than necessary and the ice bed accelerates upward. The net downward force is equal to the weight of the ice bed plus wall friction less the buoyant force. The buoyant force depends mainly on the liquid level in the column and the frictional force at the wall is negligible in columns of large diameter.

It is important to be able to predict at just what level of t in the inlet cone the slurry begins to consolidate into an ice bed with brine flowing through it. If the zone at which consolidation begins is well below the level of the screens, packed ice may back up and fill the inlet pipe. The pressure drop through the ice packed in the inlet cone is important for specification of the pumping head required.

The above process description allows t to be calculated, if the properties of the ice bed and brine are known. A force balance for steady-state operation yields the following relations for any inlet section geometry:

$$t = \frac{F B_o g_c}{\mu Q} \tag{2}$$

$$\Delta p = \frac{Q \mu}{B_o g_c} \int_0^t \frac{dt}{A} \tag{3}$$

where

F = upward force required to support and move the ice column upward
A = cone cross section (variable)
p = fluid pressure
t = distance measured downward from screen to ice-slurry interface
Q = brine flow rate, vol./time
μ = brine viscosity
B_o = packed ice permeability, (length)^2

Equation 2 shows that the depth of the consolidated ice in the inlet section is independent of the shape and size of the inlet, but Equation 3 shows that the pressure required to force brine through this thickness t of ice does depend on these factors. Calculated values of t range from $1/2$ to 16 inches for various operating conditions, but these values have not been checked by observation.

Effects of Properties of Ice Bed. The size and shape of the ice particles affect the properties of the bed strongly. The ice produced by the direct freezer is in the shape of flat disks, either circular or oval in shape, similar to those reported by Rose (5) and Umano (7).

In the 300-gallon-per-day plant the mean ice particle sizes have been calculated from measurements of ice bed permeability and porosity made on the ice harvested at the top of the column. From these results the important design parameters can be calculated, such as particle diameters, linear ice velocities, residence time of ice in the column, frictional losses in the wash water flowing down the column and in brine flowing toward the screens in the bottom of the column, and the fraction of voids occupied by air above the liquid level in the column. Typical ranges for some of these measured or calculated quantities are shown in Table III from measurements in the 12-inch diameter column.

Table III.   Design Parameters of Separation Column

Quantity	Symbol	Range of Values	Units
Ice bed porosity	ϵ	0.38–0.44	Dimensionless
Ice bed permeability	B_o	$0.3 – 1.4 \times 10^{-6}$	Sq. cm.
Fraction of ice in harvested product	p	0.55–0.65	Dimensionless
Equivalent particle diameter	d_e	60–120	Microns
Air volume per unit bed volume (above liquid level)	a	0.04–0.06	Dimensionless

The equivalent diameters given in Table III are those of a sphere having the same surface area as the particle. Larger diameters and higher permeabilities were observed when slurry was recycled to the freezer. Large particle size leads to several advantageous effects, such as:

1. High permeability of ice bed to wash water.
2. Less brine entrainment by the ice.
3. Good distribution of brine and wash water in the column.

A disadvantage of large particle size was pointed out by Wiegandt (8), who stated that the resulting high permeability may lead to excessive bed thicknesses t, required to get the necessary force for moving the ice bed upward.

Washing. As ice moves upward through the column, it behaves as an unconsolidated porous medium and carries brine with it, held by viscous and capillary forces. The flow is entirely laminar, because the Reynolds number based on particle diameter is always less than 0.05. The brine is carried thus at the surface and in the fillets between the particles. The downward flowing wash water moves between. the particles and mixes with the brine mainly by molecular diffusion. Salt will diffuse from the brine to the wash water.

The liquid level is held in the column at some distance below the top to allow the ice to drain before being harvested. Harvested ice carries about an equal weight of dilute brine, which may be as high as 1000 p.p.m. When this mixture is melted, the salt concentration is 500 p.p.m. or less. For every pound of ice made in the freezer there is thus produced about 2 pounds of gross fresh water product. One pound of this, or at most 1.05 pounds, is returned to the column as wash and the remainder is the fresh water product from the plant.

A theory of the washing action has been studied which proposes that the brine moving upward and the wash water moving downward may be considered as two separate phases between which transfer of salt takes place. Because the flow always is laminar, the two streams will be mixed mainly by molecular diffusion. Furthermore, the equilibrium condition is particularly simple, as it requires only that salt concentrations be equal in each stream.

It is assumed that the rate of salt transfer is proportional to the difference in the average salt concentration of the two passing streams at any level in the column; the equations for describing this system may be set up and solved directly with no recourse to graphical analysis.

The additional assumptions are made:

1. Wash water is introduced at the freezing temperature of the product.
2. The ratio W/B is constant throughout the column height.

In an adiabatic column in which there is 7% salt in the brine at the bottom and essentially no salt at the top, some ice will form as the bed moves upward through the vertical concentration gradient, and this will affect the rate, B, but this effect is small and is ignored below. Following the nomenclature in Figure 7, in the differential height, dL, the rate of salt transfer is

$$kSdL\,(C_b - C_w) = BdC_b = WdC_w \qquad (4)$$

where

W = wash water rate, lb./hr.
B = adhering brine rate at top of column, lb./hr.
L = height of column above screens, feet
H = height of a salt transfer unit, feet
k = mass transfer coefficient, lb. salt/(hr.) (unit volume of bed)
S = cross section area of column, sq. feet
C_T = salt concentration in adhering brine at top of column, lb./lb. or p.p.m.
C_W = salt concentration in wash water at top of column, lb./lb. or p.p.m.
C_B = salt concentration in entering brine at bottom of column, lb./lb. or p.p.m.
C_b = salt concentration in brine at any point in column, lb./lb. or p.p.m.
C_w = salt concentration in wash stream at any point in column, lb./lb. or p.p.m.

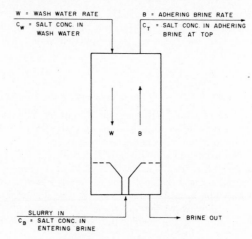

Figure 7. Wash theory

A salt balance around the top of the column gives

$$W(C_w - C_W) = B(C_b - C_T) \tag{5}$$

Combining 3 and 4 to eliminate C_w yields:

$$\frac{kS}{B}(dL) = \frac{dC_b}{C_b(1 - B/W) - C_W + (B/W)C_T} \tag{6}$$

Let

$$\frac{W - B}{W} = r = \text{the net wash ratio}$$

Then integrate 6 from $L = 0$ to $L = L$

and from $C_b = C_T$ to $C_b = C_B$

This yields

$$\frac{kSL}{B} = \frac{1}{r} \ln \left[\frac{rC_B + (1 - r)C_T - C_W}{C_T - C_W} \right] \tag{7}$$

This may be rearranged to

$$\frac{C_T - C_W}{C_B - C_W} = \frac{r}{e^{\frac{kSLr}{B}} - (1 - r)} \tag{8}$$

The left member of 8 may be interpreted as the unaccomplished fractional concentration change and given the symbol U. Thus

$$U \equiv \frac{C_T - C_W}{C_B - C_W} \tag{9}$$

The term B/kS may be interpreted as the height of a transfer unit and given the symbol H. Thus

$$H \equiv \frac{B}{kS} \tag{10}$$

In its most convenient forms Equation 7 may now be written:

$$\frac{L}{H} = N \equiv \frac{1}{r} \ln \left[1 + r \left(\frac{1}{U} - 1 \right) \right] \tag{11}$$

$$U = \frac{r}{e^{Nr} + r - 1} \tag{12}$$

and the right side of Equation 11 may be interpreted as the number of transfer units accomplished.

Equation 12 has been plotted (4) and the curves show that adequate washing of ice can be accomplished with values of r which are small and positive, zero, or even slightly negative. A value of r equal to zero means that none of the ice produced need be consumed for washing purposes and negative values of r mean that fresh water product may be produced at a rate greater than ice is harvested from the column. Under these conditions, the height of the column necessary to reduce the fresh water product to 500 p.p.m. is excessive, but net wash ratios of around 1.05 give very reasonable designs.

Design Data. The basic necessities in designing a wash-separation column are to:

1. Provide adequate cross-sectional area to allow ice to move upward and wash water to flow downward simultaneously.
2. Provide adequate height (ice retention time) for salt to transfer from ice surface to wash water and yield a final product containing 500 p.p.m. of salt or less.
3. Distribute ice properly at the entrance in the bottom of the column.
4. Provide adequate area for brine entering the bottom to flow to the screens without excessive pressure drop.
5. Provide good distribution of the wash water at the top and prevent channeling in the rest of the column.
6. Assure that consolidated ice at the bottom of the column does not back up to inlet lines or charge pump.

To provide the basic information necessary to fulfill the above requirement and design a 15,000-gallon-per-day pilot plant, a freezer and wash column with a capacity of 300 gallons per day were built and tested for more than a year. Extensive bench-scale tests were made previous to this. The results reported in Table IV were taken on the 300-gallon-per-day unit and are typical of those used to design the 15,000-gallon-per-day unit.

Table IV. Selected Operating Results for Wash Column

(12-inch diameter, 300-gallon wash column)

	Ice Production, Lb./Hr.		% Ice in Product	r, Net Wash Ratio	% Ice Lost to Wash	Salt Content, P.P.M.		No. of Transfer Units, N	Height of One Trans. Unit, Ft., H
Run	Wet	Dry				Brine in	Melted prod.		
I-5	79	54	69	−0.05	−4	75,400	1540	25	0.44
II-1	155	99	64	−0.12	−7	63,000	2750	19	0.58
II-3	227	126	55	+0.08	+6	60,000	600	20	0.56
II-4	218	124	57	+0.24	+24	65,000	250	14	0.79
II-6	201	114	57	0.16	14	65,000	225	20	0.55
II-7	133	86	65	0.01	0	70,000	425	49	0.23
III-2	132	85	65	0.12	6	70,000	770	13	0.83
III-3	75	56	75	0.13	5	62,000	275	17	0.65

The items to note are: A separation column 12 inches in diameter can wash at least 125 pounds of ice per hour, the column can be operated to give satisfactory product when only 0 to 5% of the ice is used for wash water, and the height of a transfer unit is about 0.55 foot and this does not appear to be a function of ice, brine, or wash water rates. More complete experimental results on this column are available (2–4).

In designing the 15,000-gallon-per-day wash column certain basic assumptions were made:

1. The properties of the ice bed are the same in large and small units—e.g., the permeability of the ice is about 1.0×10^{-6} sq. cm.
2. The height of a transfer unit is 0.55 foot.
3. The theory of washing explained above holds.
4. The allowable ice rate in the column is 130 lb. per hr. sq. ft.

The column of the pilot plant is 7.5 feet in diameter and is 18 feet above the slurry distributor. It is made in sections, so that different slurry distributors may be tested and the height may be 6, 12, or 18 feet. The bottom section is constructed of Monel and the two upper sections are coated to reduce ice adhesion. The column is instrumented with thermocouples and pressure taps at 2-foot intervals.

The first slurry distributor to be tested is a simple cone 8 inches in diameter at the base and 4 feet at the top. A horizontal screen is in the annular space around the cone.

Melter. A heat balance shows that 180 gallons per minute of 40° F. water is sufficient to melt 5000 pounds of ice per hour. Even though good agitation provides very high melting rates, a higher water circulation rate is necessary in order not to approach temperature equilibrium too closely. The final design of the melter was based on a melt water flow of 350 gallons per minute at 40° F. and a nominal retention time of 3 minutes using a 1-hp. agitator. The aluminum tank holds 1000 gallons.

Deaerator. The deaerator was designed to reduce the amount of air dissolved in the feed to a value equivalent to 0.005 cc. of oxygen per liter of salt water feed. It is a two-stage unit. The feed at 65° F. is sprayed into a vacuum of 41.4 mm. of mercury and then flows over a packed bed of ceramic Raschig rings maintained at a pressure of 16 mm. Very little liquid is flashed, so the feed is cooled less than 1° in the deaerator.

The deaerator is of Monel construction, 18 inches in diameter and 18 feet high. The packed bed height is 12 feet.

Chiller for Auxiliary Refrigeration. The calculated load on the auxiliary refrigeration is about 350,000 B.t.u. per hour. A 40-ton refrigeration unit was chosen for this service. Before ice is produced in the freezer, and while ice fills the column, the total refrigerating load is taken by the chiller and therefore a unit larger than 350,000 B.t.u. per hour is required.

Other Auxiliaries. The inlet feed coolers are conventional marine shell and tube heat exchangers, three in each bank. One bank is counterflow to the brine and the other is counterflow to the product water. Final temperature approach is in the order of 10° F.

The scraper at the top of the column is designed with two cutting blades and two rakes which transport the shaved ice to the chute to the melt tank. A stainless steel pipe nozzle header is part of each of the four arms of the scraper. Wash water is supplied through a hollow shaft to the headers and is sprayed onto the top of the ice (see Figure 8).

Pumps are standard bronze centrifugal pumps, except those in vacuum service, which have double rotary seals.

Instruments and Controls. Liquid levels in several of the tanks are automatically controlled with pneumatic instruments. Flows of several of the process streams are controlled and some are recorded. Temperatures of the feed and melt water are automatically controlled; temperatures are recorded by two 16-point potentiometer recorders. Pressures are measured at several points in the system but all are manually

Figure 8.   Ice production at 15,000-gallon pilot plant

controlled and manually recorded. Both an Alphatron and a Zimmerli gage are used for pressure measurements in the millimeter range.

Summary and Conclusions

A 15,000-gallon-per-day pilot plant was designed in 1958 and fabricated and assembled in 1959. Figure 9 is a view of the pilot plant, including auxiliaries required for operation at Syracuse, N. Y. Results from operation of a 300-gallon-per-day plant

Figure 9.   Fifteen thousand-gallon pilot plant

were extrapolated successfully to the 15,000-gallon pilot plant, which began making ice in mid-October 1959. Modifications of the piping and of the separation column have resulted in successful operation of the plant at design capacity for periods of 1 to 2 days. Several of the important design variables will be correlated from the operational experience of the pilot plant at Syracuse. The pilot plant has since been moved to Wrightsville, N. C., for continuing operation on natural sea water which will permit evaluation of the reliability of the process.

Results from the pilot plant should permit extrapolation of this design to larger capacities.

The standard procedure for estimating costs of saline water conversion prepared by the Office of Saline Water, United States Department of the Interior, has been used to prepare estimates of the owning and operating costs per 1000 gallons of fresh water for this freeze-separation process (*2, 4*). These estimates have included a number of methods for handling the water vapor—i.e., absorption, compression, etc.—and for capacities of 100,000 to 10,000,000 gallons per day. They indicate a potential of $0.60 to $1.00 per 1000 gallons. However, these estimates need the validation of pilot plant and demonstration production plant results prior to assurance that the economics will be realized even for plants of very large capacity.

The operating results of the subject pilot plant will be published in a future paper.

Acknowledgment

The authors express appreciation to the project team, Sal Carfagno, Samuel Moore, and the technicians for vigorous effort in assembly and operation of the pilot plant at Syracuse. C. M. Ashley conceived the original idea of the process and assisted generously by consultation.

Literature Cited

(1) Ashley, C. M., Bosworth, C. M., Proceedings of Symposium on Saline Water Conversion, November 1957, pp. 385–92, Office of Saline Water, U.S. Dept. Interior, in cooperation with Natl. Acad. Science–Natl. Research Council, **NAS-NRC-568** (1958).
(2) Carrier Corp., Eng. Repts. **8, 12, 14, 15, 23** to Office of Saline Water, Bimonthly Progress Reports under Contract 14-01-001-86.
(3) Carrier Corp., Research and Development Progress Rept. **23**, Office of Saline Water, under Contract 14-01-001-86.
(4) *Ibid.*, Rept. 32.
(5) Rose, Arthur, Hoover, T. B., Saline Water Research and Development Progress Rept. **7**, under contract to Office of Saline Water, No. 14-01-001-69.
(6) Thompson, T. G., Nelson, K. H., *Sears Foundation J. Marine Research* 13, No. 2, 166–82 (1954).
(7) Umano, Shuji, Hiratuka Branch of Government Chemical Industrial Research Institute, Tokyo, Hiratuka City, Kanagawa Prefecture, Japan, 1959, unpublished data.
(8) Wiegandt, H. E., Progress Repts. 3 and 4 to Office of Saline Water, May–October 1959.

RECEIVED for review July 7, 1960. Accepted July 15, 1960. Project sponsored by Office of Saline Water, U.S. Department of the Interior.

Scale Deposition on a Heated Surface

J. T. BANCHERO[1] and KENNETH F. GORDON

Department of Chemical and Metallurgical Engineering, University of Michigan, Ann Arbor, Mich.

Scale formation was followed visually in an apparatus which approximated conditions in evaporators producing potable water. The time required for appearance of scale was investigated with and without boiling under a variety of solution and surface temperatures, concentrations, and flow rates. Results with aqueous solutions of lithium carbonate, calcium sulfate, calcium hydroxide, and sodium sulfate, all of which possess inverted solubility curves, gave gentle curves when plotted as per cent supersaturation against the logarithm of the time for scale to appear with a parameter of concentration. For a given supersaturation a lower concentration (and necessarily higher wall temperature) resulted in more rapid formation of scale than a higher concentration. The time for scale formation was independent of liquid velocity between 2 and 10 feet per second and ranged from 2 to 360 minutes with supersaturations from 90 down to 5%.

One of the simplest methods of recovering potable water from sea water is distillation. The technology is well understood, with much experience available from both civilian and armed service applications.

The formation of a tenacious scale which decreases the heat flux by providing an additional thermal resistance reduces the economic attraction of sea water distillation. The undesirable scale is removed and controlled by awkward and expensive chemical or mechanical means. This may well become a serious factor in the large scale production of potable water from the sea. A contact stabilization method has been used (*2*) where much of the scale is deposited in a bed of contact material outside rather than inside the evaporator. The circulation of a suspension of seed crystals of the scale-forming constituent through the sea water evaporator, so that the scale would be deposited on these crystals rather than on the heating surface, was suggested by Badger and Banchero (*1*) and application of this technique has been checked experimentally by Standiford, Sinek, and Bjork (*6*). The costs of control of calcium carbonate and magnesium hydroxide scale have been reported as 40 cents per thousand gallons with citric acid (*3*)

---

[1] Present address, Department of Chemical Engineering, University of Notre Dame, Notre Dame, Ind.

and 12 cents with ferric chloride (5). With sulfuric acid the cost might drop to 3 cents per thousand gallons. The desired total cost for potable water delivered at a large plant would be about 50 cents per thousand gallons.

The Symposium on Saline Water Conversion (4) provides background information. Neville-Jones (5) and Badger and Banchero (1) cover scale prevention knowledge and practice with many references to the literature.

Types of Scale

Calcium sulfate, which exists in sea water in ionic form, has a reverse or inverted solubility curve above about 37° C.—that is, solubility decreases with increasing temperature.

In distillation the water closest to the heating surface is hottest and it is there that calcium sulfate is least soluble. Thus, calcium sulfate deposits, forming an adhering film that increases the thermal resistance and decreases the heat flux. The scale is continuously deposited until the tubes are cleaned or become plugged. For scale deposition the local concentration must be at least saturated in calcium sulfate. At 100° C. this occurs in concentrated sea water at a concentration 3.1 times that of ordinary sea water. A plant has been successfully operated continuously without calcium sulfate deposition by taking only part of the available water from the sea water, so that the liquid in the evaporator is never more than 1.8 times the concentration of sea water and the wall temperature is below about 250° F. (6). This imposes technical and economic limitations on distillation plants. Similar considerations hold for plants distilling brackish water containing calcium sulfate.

While the reverse solubility curve of calcium sulfate is often the main reason for scale deposition in fresh water boilers and in brackish water distillation, when the sea water is not chemically treated the cause is chemical rather than physical. Sea water contains bicarbonate ion. On heating, the bicarbonate ion reacts with water to form carbonate ion plus carbon dioxide, which tends to be evolved as a gas as shown in the equations

$$2HCO_3^- \rightarrow CO_3^{-2} + CO_2 \uparrow + H_2O$$
$$Ca^{+2} + CO_3^{-2} \rightarrow CaCO_3 \downarrow$$
$$H_2O + CO_3^{-2} \rightarrow 2OH^- + CO_2 \uparrow$$
$$Mg^{+2} + 2OH^- \rightarrow Mg(OH)_2 \downarrow$$

The increased amount of carbonate ion present causes the supersaturation of calcium carbonate, which comes out of the solution. As the carbon dioxide is least soluble at the temperature of the hot metal surface, the calcium carbonate has its greatest supersaturation at the surface and therefore tends to deposit there.

In turn, the carbonate ion reacts with water to form hydroxide ion and more carbon dioxide is evolved. The increased concentration of hydroxide ion makes the solution supersaturated with respect to magnesium hydroxide. The magnesium hydroxide will have the greatest supersaturation at the temperature of the hot metal, where it too will deposit. By suitably altering the concentration factor or the temperature of the sea water being distilled, either magnesium hydroxide or calcium carbonate can be made to be the main constituent of the scale. While other materials are deposited, these two can make up 98% of the scale (2), and can be prevented from depositing by controlling the pH with acidic materials. Citric acid and ferric chloride have been used successfully. Sulfuric acid has been used in the Wrightsville Beach, N. C., sea water distillation pilot plant operated by W. L. Badger Associates. The same pilot plant has shown that the seed recycle technique could prevent calcium carbonate and magnesium hydroxide scale (6). It has not yet been applied successfully to the prevention of calcium sulfate in that pilot plant.

The objective of the present continuing investigation is to obtain a better knowledge of the mechanism and limits of scale formation on a heated surface to provide a sound basis for developing methods of scale prevention.

Experience indicated that results from laboratory bench experiments might not be directly comparable to those of production plants. It was necessary to design an experimental system resembling tubes of an operational evaporator. It is hoped that future work will allow an acceptable correlation between simpler laboratory bench runs and the experimental system used.

Apparatus

Scale deposition was investigated with and without boiling in an apparatus designed to approximate to some extent conditions in commercial evaporator tubes, yet in which observation of scale formation is possible.

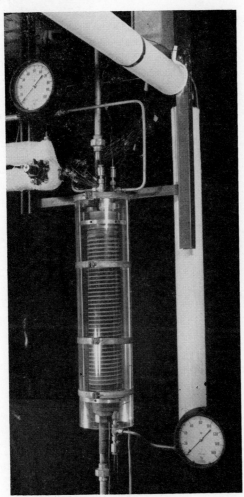

Figure I. Test section

As seen in Figures 1 and 2, the equipment consists of a copper cylinder 3.8 inches in diameter, in which a quarter-inch-diameter helical groove was cut on the external surface. On the outside, there is a close-fitting precision-bore glass tube, through which the solution flowing in the groove can be seen and the scale deposition followed visually. Appropriate safety shielding of steel plate and safety plate glass is used rather than that shown. An inflated spiral gasket, resting in a $3/16 \times 3/16$ inch groove parallel to the $1/4$-inch solution groove, maintains the solution flow in its helical path, preventing

Figure 2. Calcium sulfate scale deposited on hot
upper end of groove

short circuiting or bypassing. By means of an internal helix (not shown) a counter-current stream of hot water under pressure heats the solution being investigated. The internal helix is a quarter-inch, semicircular groove cut on the outside of a 3.1-inch-diameter copper hollow cylinder which is shrunk-fit inside the 3.8-inch cylinder. The internal, hot-water helix groove rests directly under the inflatable gasket groove, so that 18 thermocouple wells of $1/_{16}$-inch diameter could be cut to the surface of the scaling solution groove and sealed with $1/_{16}$-inch-long plugs shrunk-fit and finished to give a smooth surface. The surface temperature of the hot-water groove is obtained through eight thermocouple wells cut in the internal cylinder. Thermocouples led through the hollow internal cylinder allow measurement of the appropriate copper surface tempera-tures along the whole path length of each groove.

The solution under study flows in a 37-foot-long helical path of semicircular cross section which has a copper circular edge and a straight edge of glass. Thermocouples in the wall and the flowing stream allow good measurement of the various temperatures. The solution of interest flows upwards in the external helical groove, while the hot water flowing countercurrently and internally supplies the heat to the solution. Thus the solution enters cold at the bottom and leaves hot at the top. Its exit temperature is fixed by the inlet hot water temperature and relative flow rates. The hot water also determines the temperature at the metal wall of the solution helix and, hence, the super-saturation there.

The equipment contains three separate fluid systems: the scaling solution circulation system, the heating water circulation system, and the constant temperature circulation system. The solution is prepared in a 500-gallon stainless steel tank with a heating jacket. It is pumped by a variable speed, Moyno, stainless steel slurry pump through a stainless steel Cuno Autoclean filter, then through a rotameter to the helix test section. A needle valve after the helix test section allows control of the pressure in the test section. From the test section, the solution goes through a cooler to the spent solution tank and either is discarded or returned to the 500-gallon tank. A 55-gallon stainless steel tank of distilled water whose temperature is controlled by a heating-cooling coil is connected to the inlet of the slurry pump, so that the test section may be brought to thermal equilibrium before the salt solution is run through it. After a run, this distilled water can be used to dissolve the scale in the test section if necessary.

The constant temperature circulation system consists of another 55-gallon drum of water maintained at the desired temperature by a thermostat. Water is pumped from the drum through the jacket of the large solution tank and the test section. This allows close temperature control of the solution entering the test section.

The hot water used to control the temperature in the helical test section is heated by steam in a shell and coil heat exchanger. The hot water temperature in the exchanger outlet line controls the steam flow. From the exchanger the hot water flows to a 12-gallon high pressure surge tank, where the fine control of the temperature is obtained by electrical heaters. The water is then pumped to the helix test section through a rotameter and returned to the heater.

Procedure

To establish the final steady-state temperatures, a run was started by having distilled water at the temperature of the inlet solution flowing through the outer grooves with heating water passing through the internal helix. At time zero the distilled water was turned off and the solution of known concentration turned on at the same temperature and flow rate as the distilled water. By observation the elapsed time until the beginning of scale formation was noted. With temperatures and concentrations known, the per cent supersaturation at the exit end of the helix could be calculated and, as the scale always occurred at the exit end, it was taken to be the per cent supersaturation for the run.

A typical deposit of calcium sulfate can be seen in Figure 2. On continuing the run the scale deposit increased, causing very high pressure drops, and in some cases the equipment became plugged with scale.

The initial step was to study systems with reverse solubility curves to learn the general pattern of the onset of scaling which would be of value for understanding the sea water system. Calcium sulfate, lithium carbonate, sodium sulfate, and calcium hydroxide have reverse solubility curves in water, are readily available, and are soluble to an extent that neither visual observation of scale nor chemical analysis would be a problem.

The behavior of solutions of each substance was explored in the helix, lithium carbonate solution being the last used. The effect of concentration level was then examined with the solution in the equipment, lithium carbonate. It was discarded and replaced with calcium sulfate, which is being studied more intensely. It is hoped that the results of these runs will be correlated with those from pilot plants and operational plants distilling sea water.

Analyses

The lithium carbonate concentration was measured by acidimetric titration with methyl orange indicator. The calcium sulfate and calcium hydroxide concentrations were determined by titration with disodium dihydrogen Versenate [the disodium salt of (ethylenedinitrilo) tetraacetic acid], with added magnesium chloride. A buffer of ammonium chloride in ammonium hydroxide was employed. The indicator was Eriochrome Black T. A special high purity calcium carbonate in hydrochloric acid was used as a standard. Because of the high concentration of sodium sulfate it was convenient to analyze by evaporation, ignition, and weighing, all with appropriate precautions.

Results

A convenient correlation of the helix data is on a plot of supersaturation against the logarithm of the time for scaling. From the initial results (Figures 3 to 6) it is seen that, for a given concentration, the data could be represented as a gentle curve or a straight line. An arrow indicates a run stopped before scaling.

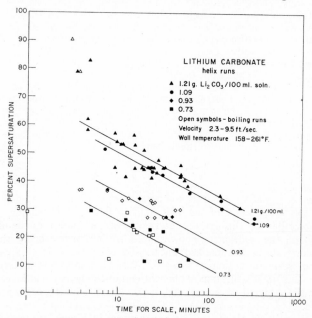

Figure 3.   Data for lithium carbonate

Lithium Carbonate. Using the helix, 77 runs were made with the lithium carbonate system in water, yielding the results shown in Figure 3. During a run all temperatures were held constant, but were varied from run to run, with the wall temperature covering the range 158° to 261° F. Concentration has a definite effect on the time for scaling, when the data are correlated by using per cent supersaturation. With a low concentration a higher temperature is required for a given supersaturation than at a higher concentration. The results for the low concentration runs might be showing the effect of the higher temperature and lower viscosity of the solution. The deviation of the points at 78 to 90% supersaturation and very short times could be a reflection of a time lag in the system. The points at 45% supersaturation are taken to determine the effect of velocity. Fourteen runs made under apparently identical conditions (except for velocity) show that velocity has no effect (Figure 7). The scatter is probably due to uncontrolled variation in the copper surface.

In Figure 3 the open symbols are for runs in which there was active boiling, while the solid symbols are for those where boiling was prevented by maintaining an appropriate back pressure on the system. Although the data scatter, it is surprising that no effect of boiling is apparent. This may be misleading, for the vapor bubbles could prevent any small particles of scale formed by boiling from being seen, the scale being apparent to the eye only after it has deposited in modest amounts. The per cent supersaturation was calculated on the basis of the concentration of the feed solution, without attempting to account for any change due to boiling. It is not possible to estimate the local concentration and supersaturation and judge if their use would raise the points

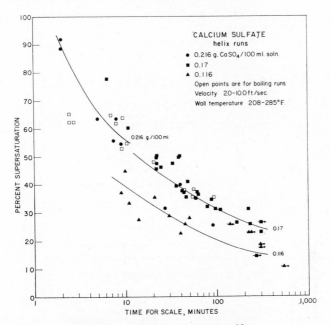

Figure 4. Data for calcium sulfate

for boiling sufficiently to indicate a difference between boiling and nonboiling runs. Such a difference would show boiling runs depositing scale more slowly than nonboiling runs at the same local per cent supersaturation.

Calcium Sulfate. The results of the 65 runs for this system (Figure 4) show a similar pattern—namely, a gentle curve with the coordinates used, scatter of data giving a band rather than a line, deviation from a straight line at very high supersaturations, apparently no great difference between boiling and nonboiling runs, and an effect of concentration with the lower concentration (and higher temperature) giving a lower time for scale formation. Here the supersaturation was calculated with respect to the hemihydrate. The wall temperature covered the range 208° to 285° F.

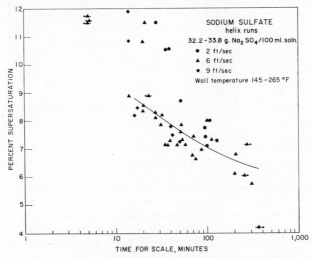

Figure 5. Data for sodium sulfate

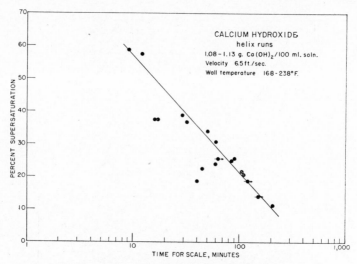

Figure 6. Data for calcium hydroxide

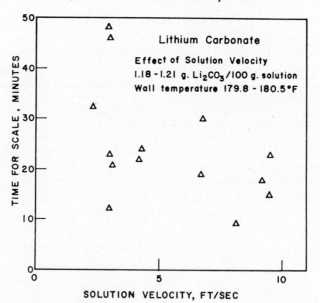

Figure 7. Effect of velocity on lithium carbonate deposition

Sodium Sulfate. With this system, 49 runs of up to 6 hours' duration were made, showing the usual behavior with no appreciable effect of velocity over a 4.5-fold range. Here the wall temperature was from 145° to 265° F. at the point of scale formation.

Calcium Hydroxide. Nineteen scaling runs were made in the helix using 1.1 mass % calcium hydroxide in water at a velocity of 6 feet per second. The data show the normal trend. The wall temperature at the scaling point was from 168° to 238° F.

Velocity. From Figures 5, 7, and 8, it is seen that for the sodium sulfate, lithium carbonate, and calcium sulfate systems velocity does not affect the time required for the appearance of scale.

Temperature Level. As the formation of scale will be influenced by the kinetics

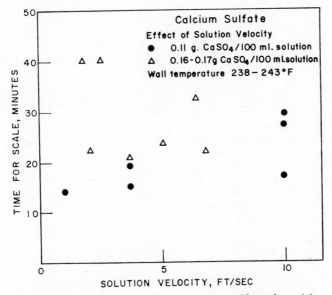

Figure 8.   Effect of velocity on calcium sulfate deposition

of ions going from the solution to the scale and by the surface diffusivity of the scaling components as well as the bulk diffusivity, wall temperature might be an important factor in determining the scaling time, aside from its effect on supersaturation.   While the previous correlations employing supersaturation were satisfactory, it is of interest to see the data plotted as a function of wall temperature.   Figure 9 shows that the data for lithium carbonate can be represented by a straight line.   Because the bulk tempera-

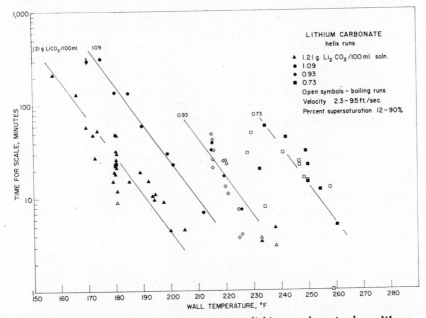

Figure 9.   Effect of wall temperature on lithium carbonate deposition

ture of the flowing solution was not varied greatly, a plot using temperature difference between the wall and bulk solution rather than the wall temperature gave a similar correlation. Similar plots may be drawn for the other systems.

Conclusions

The greater the supersaturation, the less the time required for scale formation. For a given concentration the data can be represented by a gentle curve on a plot of per cent supersaturation against the logarithm of the time for scaling.

At a given supersaturation the concentration level has an effect on the time for scaling. With a lower concentration, and necessarily higher temperature for a given supersaturation, the scale will form faster than at a higher concentration.

The time for scale formation is independent of liquid velocity between 2 and 10 feet per second.

For the lithium carbonate and calcium sulfate solutions operation with boiling apparently does not cause earlier visible scaling than with nonboiling conditions, other things being equal. Possibly scale is formed earlier but is obscured by the vapor bubbles.

Acknowledgment

The authors are indebted to the Office of Saline Water, which supported this study with a research contract. The able work of a number of chemical engineering students in building the equipment and making the runs is acknowledged with pleasure. The authors appreciate and value the discussions with W. L. Badger and F. C. Standiford, both of whom contributed a number of most useful suggestions and ideas, especially during the design of the equipment.

Literature Cited

(1) Badger, W. L., Banchero, J. T., "Symposium on Saline Water Conversion," Natl. Acad. of Sciences–Natl. Research Council, Pub. 568, 44 (1958).
(2) Langelier, W. F., Caldwell, D. H., Lawrence, W. B., Spaulding, C. H., Ind. Eng. Chem. 42, 126 (1950).
(3) Langelier, W. F., Caldwell, D. H., Lindholm, G. F., Final Rept. to Engineer Research and Development Laboratories, Contract DA-44-009-Eng-193, Institute of Engineering Research, University of California, Aug. 15, 1952.
(4) "Symposium on Saline Water Conversion," Natl. Acad. of Sciences–Natl. Research Council, Pub. 568 (1958).
(5) Neville-Jones, David, "Symposium on Saline Water Conversion," Natl. Acad. of Sciences–Natl. Research Council, Pub. 568, 35 (1958).
(6) Standiford, F. C., Sinek, J. R., Bjork, H. F., "Scaling in Sea Water Evaporators," A.I.Ch.E. Meeting, Washington, D. C., December 1960.

RECEIVED for review July 20, 1960. Accepted July 21, 1960.

Evaporation of Sea Water in Long-Tube Vertical Evaporators

F. C. STANDIFORD, Jr., and H. F. BJORK

W. L. Badger Associates, Inc., Ann Arbor, Mich.

An inexpensive, dependable method of producing fresh water from saline sources is becoming increasingly important throughout the world as fresh water requirements grow and supplies decrease. Use of a falling-film long-tube vertical multiple-effect evaporation system in conjunction with a sludge recirculation technique has prevented scale formation from sea water evaporation at operating temperatures up to 250°F. Pilot plant test runs of over 1500 hours have been made. Pilot plant results translated to the design of a 1,000,000-gallon-per-day demonstration plant indicate fresh water costs of $1.00 per 1000 gallons. Ultimate costs for 15,000,-000-gallon-per-day production will be 35 cents per 1000 gallons of fresh water.

The late W. L. Badger's 40 years' experience with commercial evaporators in the chemical industry has provided the basis for the economic production of fresh water from sea water. Five years ago, those familiar with sea water evaporation practice could predict minimum possible water costs no lower than about $1.60 per 1000 gallons. In 1955, the Office of Saline Water, U. S. Department of the Interior, commissioned W. L. Badger and Associates to study the minimum cost of making fresh water from sea water by using evaporator techniques of the chemical industry. Because previous estimates of water cost had been several times above the Office of Saline Water's goal, several optimistic assumptions served as a basis for this study:

That the highest performance evaporator could be used for sea water. By performance was meant heat transfer coefficient not in B.t.u./hr./° F./sq. ft. but in B.t.u./ hr./° F./dollar of installed cost. For a long time, the long-tube vertical (LTV) evaporator has best fitted this description, at least under favorable operating conditions, such as at relatively high temperature differences (usually), and with little scale formation.

That the evaporator could be made as efficient as economically justifiable. Thermal efficiency of an evaporator is increased by multiple-effect operation, by recompression of the vapor, by a combination of these, and by a number of other design features. While sea water evaporators had rarely been made with more than three effects, commercial evaporators of six and seven effects are common and ten-effect evaporators have been used.

That the LTV evaporator could be kept free of scale, at little or no cost for scale prevention, at temperatures as high as 250° F. In 1955, no satisfactory method of scale prevention was proved for sea water evaporators, scale was most severe at the highest temperatures, and about 220° F. was the highest temperature that had been used.

That the evaporator could be made as large in capacity as practical and could take up as much room as necessary. Although a "large" evaporator turned out to be small in terms of municipal water requirements, it would be several orders of magnitude larger than most sea water evaporators, which were built small, compact, and easily operable for shipboard and military use.

That the evaporator could be fabricated primarily or completely from steel.

Preliminary Estimates

On the basis of these assumptions, plant designs and cost estimates were prepared that showed considerable economic promise (3). Two basic types of flowsheet were considered. One used exhaust steam from a power plant, at a price, to heat a multiple-effect LTV evaporator having a capacity of about 17,000,000 gallons per day. Water cost was estimated at 23 cents per 1000 gallons when the steam cost was adjusted to give the same power cost as would be incurred by a conventional power plant that expanded the steam to high vacuum. The other type of flowsheet was similar, except that the powerhouse turbine drove a vapor compressor instead of a generator. The compressor served a number of LTV evaporator bodies, making a thermocompression evaporator, and the turbine exhaust was used to heat a multiple-effect LTV evaporator. The capacity of the plant was also about 17,000,000 gallons per day. Because the only power generated was for use in driving plant auxiliaries, all costs were chargeable to the production of water. Table I shows the capital cost of the plant as estimated in 1955 and Table II shows the annual operating cost.

Table I.   Capital Cost of 17,350,000-Gallon-per-Day Combination Thermocompression–10-Effect Sea Water Evaporation Plant

Boiler	$1,020,000
Turbine-generator	170,000
Turbine-vapor compressor	925,000
Evaporators	2,425,000
Heat exchangers	991,000
Pumps	138,000
Piping	305,000
Instruments	40,000
Total installed process equipment	$6,014,000
Site development	70,000
Office, shop, and lab	135,000
Weatherproofing	300,000
Engineering	481,000
Contingencies	600,000
Total plant cost	$7,600,000

Table II.   Annual Operating Cost of 17,350,000-Gallon-per-Day Combination Thermocompression–10-Effect Sea Water Evaporation Plant

Interest, 3% of total capital	$ 228,000
Insurance, 1% of total capital	76,000
Depreciation, 5% of total capital	380,000
Maintenance, 3% of equipment cost	180,000
Labor, $2.50 per man-hour	138,000
Fuel, $0.30 per million B.t.u.	991,000
Total	$1,993,000

Equivalent to $0.328 per 1000 gallons or $106.90 per acre-foot

Plants of this size were considered about the largest that could be built as single units. Smaller plants could easily be built, but the reduced efficiencies of pumps, turbines, and compressors and the inability to reduce labor costs made the water cost from small plants appreciably higher. Figure 1 is an estimate prepared in 1955 of the water cost from various sizes of these combination multiple-effect, thermocompression LTV plants. These estimates were prepared before the Office of Saline Water's "standard estimating procedure" was available, but later estimates made on the basis of this procedure gave substantially the same water costs, if the assumptions listed above were true.

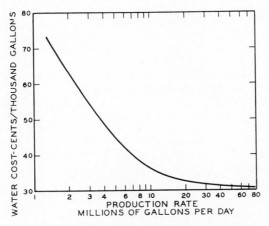

Figure I. Effect of plant size on water cost

Pilot Plant Investigation

The cost estimates were so promising that the Office of Saline Water financed a pilot plant program to test these optimistic assumptions. This pilot plant is located on the site of the International Nickel Co. Test Station at Wrightsville Beach, N. C. It was designed by W. L. Badger Associates, Inc., and was erected and has been operated for the past $2^1/_2$ years by them under subcontract from the Whiting Corp. (1). The pilot plant contains an LTV evaporator, donated by the Swenson Evaporator Co., Division of the Whiting Corp., that has tubes of the dimensions that would probably be used in a full scale plant. There are seven of these tubes, each 2 inches in outside diameter by 24 feet long, and insulated from each other and from the shell, so that different tube materials can be tested without the complication of galvanic corrosion. The LTV evaporator is instrumented so that it can be run under any desired conditions of feed rate, feed temperature, boiling point, and steam flow. This makes it possible to duplicate operating conditions that would be met in any effect of a multiple-effect evaporator or in a thermocompression evaporator.

Because the feed to one effect in this type of evaporator is the partially concentrated sea water discharged from another effect, it was necessary to have a source of partially concentrated sea water for the pilot plant. Rather than trying to store previously concentrated sea water, with the possible result that some of the potential scale might deposit on storage, sea water is concentrated continuously in one or two forced-circulation evaporators which can be operated single or double effect, as necessary, and can provide sea water feed to the LTV at any desired concentration.

Heat Transfer. The first series of tests were made to measure heat transfer coefficients and thereby confirm the operating conditions that had been predicted for the various effects in the production plants. The LTV evaporator can be built to operate in one of two ways. Most such evaporators have the liquid feed at the bottom. The liquid rises in the tubes, is heated, and begins to boil, and the vapor formed creates such high velocities in the boiling section that high transfer coefficients are obtained in the boiling section. The other method of operation involves feeding liquid to the tops of the tubes as a film, so that boiling takes place for practically the full length of the tube. The pilot plant evaporator was built so that it could be operated either way.

The first tests used rising flow through the tubes. It was found that, under conditions of low temperature difference and with feed practically at the vapor head boiling point, as would be expected in the production plant, heat transfer coefficients were low. The primary controlling variables were temperature and temperature difference. Even at high temperature differences between steam and boiling liquid, heat transfer coefficients were only about 150 B.t.u./hr./sq.ft./° F. at low temperature and about 500 in the same units at high temperature. Pressure drop measurements indicated that most of the tube length was filled with nonboiling and therefore relatively slow-moving liquid and that this was most pronounced at low temperature and low temperature difference. Consequently, all subsequent work was done with falling-film operation to eliminate this hydrostatic head that prevented boiling in most of the tube length.

The tests under falling-film conditions gave heat transfer coefficients that were practically the same as those used in preparing the original plant designs and cost estimates. The coefficient depended mainly on boiling temperature and varied from 350 to 400 at about 100° F. to 700 to 800 at 250° F. Subsequent tests under conditions that would be met in a 12-effect evaporator operating between an initial boiling point of 250° F. and a final boiling point of 125° F. gave coefficients that varied as shown in

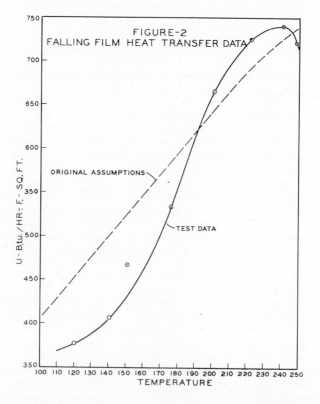

Figure 2 (2). These coefficients were determined when the following tubes were installed in the evaporator: 2 copper, 1 Admiralty, 1 Ampco Grade 8, 2 aluminum brass, and 1 cupronickel. Each tube was 2 inches in outside diameter and 24 feet long, and had a 0.109-inch wall. The dashed curve of Figure 2 shows the heat transfer coefficients that were assumed in preparing the original estimates. In these tests, temperature differences were obtained from pressure measurements using manometers or calibrated gages and were corrected for boiling point elevation of the concentrated sea water. Areas were based on the inside diameter of the tubes. The amount of heat transferred was calculated both from steam consumption (measured by a calibrated drip tank) corrected for superheat, condensate subcooling, and calibrated heat losses from the steam chest and from evaporation rate (measured by another calibrated drip tank), sensible heat change, and calibrated heat losses from the vapor side. Material balances usually checked within 3% and heat balances within 8%.

Scale Prevention. The scale normally formed on heat transfer surfaces of sea water evaporators consists of calcium carbonate, magnesium hydroxide, and/or calcium sulfate. The first two form as a result of the breakdown of bicarbonate in sea water, which is initially saturated with calcium carbonate. Calcium sulfate scale forms purely as a result of its inverted solubility curve. Sea water is not saturated with calcium sulfate and an economically reasonable amount of fresh water can be recovered from sea water without exceeding saturation with calcium sulfate. However, at the start of this investigation, the solubility of calcium sulfate in sea water was not accurately enough known to tell whether 30, 50, or 80% of the water content could be removed at various temperatures without encountering calcium sulfate scale.

The original plant designs and cost estimates were not made without having plans for combating scale formation. Two rather inexpensive possibilities were proposed. One involved the use of acid to prevent calcium carbonate and magnesium hydroxide scale. If the carbon dioxide that is lost when bicarbonate decomposes is replaced by nonvolatile acid, the pH can be kept low enough to prevent formation of these alkaline scales. This method was adopted at about the same time by the military, using citric acid. The cost of using this acid amounted to about 50 cents per 1000 gallons of distilled water—more than the total cost of water from the proposed plants. However, it was felt that in large land-based plants, sufficiently close control could be attained to permit the use of cheap sulfuric acid. Even if all the bicarbonate broke down to carbon dioxide, the cost of acid required amounted to only about 2 cents per 1000 gallons. This method of scale prevention would not introduce enough sulfate ion, compared to that already present in the sea water, to affect the solubility of calcium sulfate appreciably. The chief disadvantages of this method, besides acid cost, were that it could not by itself prevent calcium sulfate scale formation and that it might require operation at pH's slightly below neutrality, thus increasing corrosive tendencies.

The other method of scale prevention proposed, and incorporated in the original plant designs and cost estimates, involved a seeding technique. If some of the scaling ingredient is going to precipitate, it will deposit on the heating surface if no other surface is available. However, it would prefer to deposit on crystals of its own kind. By providing seed crystals of the scaling ingredient in suspension in the liquid, it was hoped that all precipitation could be induced to occur on these seeds rather than on the heating surface. This practice had been completely successful for the prevention of calcium sulfate scale formation in the salt industry. In practice, this method of scale prevention would involve incorporation of scale solids in the sea water to make a dilute slurry and recovery of these solids from the waste sea water concentrate. The seeds would be continuously added to by precipitation of the scaling ingredient in the sea water, thereby making up for minor mechanical losses of solids. Thus the only cost for this method of scale prevention would be the cost of equipment required to separate the solids from the concentrated sea water and return them to the feed. It was hoped that this method would work both for calcium sulfate, which deposits by one mechanism, and for calcium carbonate and magnesium hydroxide, which deposit by another mechanism. This method of scale prevention would have the additional advantage that evaporation would be conducted under alkaline conditions, where corrosion should be less severe.

As the acid method of scale prevention had already been proved by others, only a few trials were made to determine the approximate limiting conditions for LTV evaporators. Week-long tests were made using sulfuric acid to determine the extent to which equilibrium pH could be exceeded. The tests were made under the following conditions, which were at the time thought to represent the most severe that would be encountered without calcium sulfate depositing:

Boiling point, ° F.	192
Temperature difference, ° F.	8 to 10
Feed temperature, ° F.	190
Feed concentration	2.35 times normal sea water

In the first run, acid feed rate was gradually reduced without immediate evidence of scale formation and then was cut off entirely. Heat transfer coefficients started to drop immediately and at the end of the week the tubes were coated with calcium carbonate scale. In this first run, the pH entering the evaporator was 8.3 and leaving it was 8.4. Langelier, Caldwell, and Lawrence have measured the equilibrium pH above which a sea water concentrate is supersaturated with respect to calcium carbonate and magnesium hydroxide (4). Under the conditions of this test, the following conditions were encountered:

	LTV Feed	LTV Blowdown
Concentration factor	2.46	2.88
Total alkalinity, p.p.m. $CaCO_3$	159	145
Equilibrium pH, $CaCO_3$	6.8	6.8
Equilibrium pH, $Mg(OH)_2$	7.8	7.8
Actual pH	8.3	8.3

It was evident that, under conditions of this test, calcium carbonate scale would form if the equilibrium pH were exceeded by 1.5 pH units.

In the second test, the acid free rate was adjusted to maintain an LTV blowdown pH of 7.5. The acid was fed to the forced-circulation evaporator preceding the LTV, so that the additional time available permitted evening out fluctuations in acid feed rate. Under these conditions, some of the total alkalinity was lost and the LTV operated under the following scaling environment:

	LTV Feed	LTV Blowdown
Concentration factor	2.31	2.70
Total alkalinity, p.p.m. $CaCO_3$	73.7	83.1
Equilibrium pH, $CaCO_3$	7.2	7.1
Equilibrium pH, $Mg(OH)_2$	7.85	7.8
Actual pH	7.51	7.52

When operated under these conditions for a week, no scale was evident, either by a decrease in heat transfer coefficients or by examination at the end of the run. Thus, it is apparent that scale can be prevented by this mechanism when the equilibrium pH is exceeded by something more than 0.3 to 0.4 and less than 1.5 pH units. All heat transfer tests were made with use of acid for scale prevention. In these tests, the pH was kept below the equilibrium pH in order to be on the safe side, and no scaling was ever detected. As evident from the above data, the pH required is not so low as to involve operation under acidic conditions, where accelerated corrosion might be expected.

The next series of tests was made to prove out the seeding method of scale prevention. The first test was made under the same conditions as for the acid trials. Once the mechanical problems of recycling the seeds in the pilot plant were solved, it was found possible to prevent scale formation completely, if the evaporating liquid contained 0.5% calcium carbonate solids. The solids were made initially by slowly adding soda ash to sea water.

The first trials at higher temperature were unsuccessful in preventing scale formation. These trials were made under conditions such that calcium sulfate scale might be expected (concentration factor of 3.3, boiling points of 205° and 255° F.). A slurry of calcium carbonate was tried first, in the hope that this would also serve as seeds for the calcium sulfate. Heat transfer coefficients dropped rapidly and a heavy scale was found on all tubes at the end of the run. The next trials therefore used a mixed slurry of calcium carbonate and calcium sulfate. Two crystal forms of calcium sulfate might be expected as scale—hemihydrate and anhydrite. Both were tried as seeds, using purchased materials (U. S. Gypsum Hydrocal White for hemihydrate and the Snow White filler for anhydrite). Trials with hemihydrate resulted mainly in the cementing shut of all drains, stagnant pockets, etc., where the temperature was below 180° to 190° F., the transition temperature of hemihydrate to gypsum in these solutions. Trials with a mixed slurry of calcium carbonate and anhydrite always resulted in scale formation, although the scaling rate was tantalizingly low in some runs.

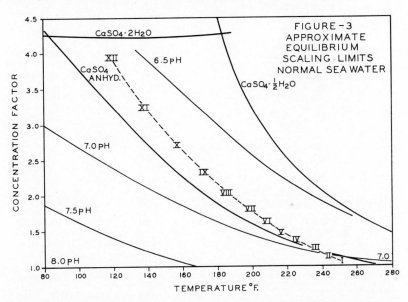

The inability to control calcium sulfate scale formation led to a more thorough investigation of solubility limits of calcium sulfate in sea water concentrates (5). The current "best guess" as to solubility of the different crystal forms of calcium sulfate is shown in Figure 3. Anhydrite is so inert that it is almost never encountered as scale in evaporators. The main difference between this solubility diagram and previous estimates (4) is a much higher solubility limit for gypsum or hemihydrate at temperatures below 212° F. Figure 3 indicates that concentration factors of more than 4 can be achieved if the evaporator is operated in such a manner that high concentrations are reached only at low temperatures. This corresponds to recovery of over 80% of the water under conditions such that calcium sulfate solubility is not exceeded and hence no scale can form from this source. Such conditions can be achieved by use of a forward-feed evaporator in which unconcentrated sea water enters the first, or hottest, effect and is then passed from effect to effect until concentrated sea water is pumped from the last, or coolest, effect and discarded. Typical conditions for a 12-effect forward-feed evaporator are plotted in Figure 3. Also plotted in this diagram are the equilibrium pH's for the acid method of preventing calcium carbonate and magnesium hydroxide scale, assuming that no carbonate alkalinity has been lost. Forward-feed operation results in relatively mild pH conditions—much milder than for a backward-feed evaporator, where the high concentrations are reached at high temperatures.

By adopting a forward-feed flowsheet, it became possible to ignore the calcium sulfate scale problem. However, it was still necessary to prove that the alkaline scales could be prevented at temperatures up to 250° F. The first trial was made at 250° F. with raw sea water feed and a calcium carbonate slurry. The evaporator scaled rapidly and analysis showed the scale to be magnesium hydroxide. The next run was therefore made under the same conditions, except that a magnesium hydroxide slurry was used. This slurry was made before the run started by slowly adding caustic soda to the initial dilute calcium carbonate slurry until the solids contained about 50% magnesium hydroxide. During the 200 hours of the run, the magnesium hydroxide content of the solids gradually increased to over 95% and no scale formed in the tubes.

Table III. Summary of Operating Conditions for All Sludge Runs

Run No.	Feed Temp., °F.	Evap. Temp., °F.	Disch. Concn. Factor	Temp. Diff., °F.	Sludge Used	Hr. Operation	Type of Scale	Reason for Termination
LWBB–1	190	192	2.75	8	$CaCO_3$	6.5	. . .	Mech. trouble
–2	190	192	2.75	8	$CaCO_3$	46	Trace, 2 alloy tubes	Burst filter cartridges
–3	190	192	2.75	7	$CaCO_3$	22	. . .	Burst filter cartridges
–4	190	192	2.75	5.5	$CaCO_3$	44	?	Plugged feed controller
–5	190	192	2.75	7.5	$CaCO_3$	210	None	. . .
–6	187	192	2.75	13	$CaCO_3$	150	None	. . .
–7	194	204	3.3	11	$CaCO_3$	162	$CaSO_4$	. . .
LWBC–1	250	255	3.3	14	$CaCO_3 +$ $CaSO_4{}^a$	52	$CaSO_4$	Descaling
–2	250	255	3.3	14	$CaCO_3 +$ $CaSO_4{}^a$	33	?	Plugged piping
–3	250	255	3.3	14	$CaCO_3 +$ $CaSO_4{}^a$	26	$CaSO_4$	Descaling
–4	250	255	3.3	10	$CaCO_3 +$ $CaSO_4{}^a$	33	$CaSO_4$	Descaling, low solids
LWBD–1	200	205	3.0	11	$CaCO_3 +$ $CaSO_4{}^a$	16	$CaSO_4$	Descaling, plugged piping
–2	195	200	3.5	13	$CaCO_3 +$ $CaSO_4{}^b$	168	$CaSO_4.$ $^1/_2H_2O$	(No scale-steel tube)
LWBE–1	250	250	3.5	13	$CaCO_3 +$ $CaSO_4{}^b$	141	$CaSO_4$	Plugged orifices
–2	250	250	3.3	13	$CaCO_3 +$ $CaSO_4{}^b$	154	$CaSO_4.$ $^1/_2H_2O$	Hurricane
LWBF–1	225	250	1.0	9.5	$CaCO_3$	133	$Mg(OH)_2$	. . .
–2	250	250	1.2	9.5	$Mg(OH)_2$	200	None	. . .
LWBG–1	250	250	1.7	7	$Mg(OH)_2$	170	$CaSO_4.$ $^1/_2H_2O$	. . .
–2	250	250	1.7	7	$Mg(OH)_2$	141	None	Power failure
LSBH–1	130	120	3.0–5.7	13	$Mg(OH)_2$	238	None	. . .
LWBI–1	236	220	2.0	8	$Mg(OH)_2$	167	None	. . .
LWBJ–1	203	186	2.3	7	$Mg(OH)_2$	160	None	. . .
LWBG–3a	250	250	1.6	7–8	$Mg(OH)^2$	593	$CaSO_4.$ $^1/_2H_2O$	Descaling, over-concentrated
–3b	250	250	1.6	7–8	$Mg(OH)_2$	1001	None	. . .

[a] $CaSO_4$ solids were $CaSO_4.^1/_2H_2O$ (Hydrocal White, U. S. Gypsum Co.).
[b] $CaSO_4$ solids were $CaSO_4$ (insoluble) (Snow White filler, U. S. Gypsum Co.).

Subsequent runs were made, using this same magnesium hydroxide slurry, at lower temperatures and higher concentration factors and all were successful as long as conditions were under the hemihydrate and gypsum solubility curve of Figure 3. A final run of 1594 hours' duration was made to prove this method of scale prevention under the most severe conditions that might be encountered—250° F. and a concentration factor just under the hemihydrate solubility curve. In the first 593 hours, poor control allowed concentrations to exceed hemihydrate solubility at times and a hemihydrate scale formed slowly. This was removed by rinsing with sea water and the run continued under more careful control for another 1001 hours with no scale formation whatsoever.

Table III summarizes the runs that proved the efficacy of the seeding method of scale control for the demonstration plant (1). This work is being continued at still higher temperatures (up to 300° F.), but it has been found impossible to keep below the calcium sulfate solubility curve. Consequently, the attack is again being concentrated on use of seeding for prevention of calcium sulfate scale. If this work is successful, it should permit development of evaporators that could operate at still higher temperatures, thereby making practical use of more effects with a consequent saving in steam; design of evaporators to concentrate sea water to or beyond the point where it is saturated with sodium chloride, making possible the recovery of by-products; and design of evaporators for brackish waters high in calcium sulfate.

Corrosion. The tubes in the LTV evaporator were installed with Swenson rubber grommet packing commonly used for Karbate tubes in acid evaporators. This both insulated the tubes from galvanic corrosion and allowed nondestructive removal for weighing. Corrosion rates were estimated both from weight loss of the tubes and from International Nickel Co. test spools located both in the vapor space and immersed in the liquid in the blowdown tank.

The first set of corrosion results was promising, even though the data were taken during the time the first heat transfer runs were made, using excess acid (pH's down to 3), and the time the tests of the acid method of scale prevention were under way. Corrosion rates from INCO test spool data were as follows (in inches per year):

Material	Vapor	Liquid
Steel	0.016–0.027	0.010–0.021
Cast iron	0.009–0.016	0.008–0.030
Admiralty	0.001	0.001–0.003
Copper	0.001	0.002–0.004
Aluminum brass	0.001	0.001–0.002
90/10 cupronickel	0.001	0.001–0.003
Aluminum	0.001	0.004–0.006

The next sets of spools were exposed during the early sludge runs, which were made under alkaline conditions where corrosion should have been much less severe. The results were as follows:

Material	Vapor	Liquid
Steel	0.057–0.062	0.030–0.044
Cast iron	0.016–0.021	0.031–0.032
Admiralty	0.002	0.001–0.003
Copper	0.002–0.003	0.002–0.011
Aluminum brass	0.001	0.001
90/10 cupronickel	0.001	0.001
Aluminum	Perforated	

The fact that steel and cast iron suffered by far the greatest corrosion under supposedly the mildest conditions indicated an extraneous influence. This could only have been atmospheric corrosion; the evaporator was shut down and the samples were exposed to the air far oftener when the early sludge runs were made—runs which sometimes lasted only a day or two each.

A set of spools exposed during the 1594-hour demonstration run showed the following corrosion rates:

Material	Vapor	Liquid
Steel	0.0164	0.0031
Cast iron	0.0147	0.0022
Admiralty	0.0018	0.0015
Copper	0.0016	0.0019
Aluminum brass	0.0015	0.0002
90/10 cupronickel	0.0009	0.0003

Even though the test spools were exposed to the atmosphere after 508, 593, and 1093 hours, corrosion rates for steel and cast iron were acceptably low, especially for samples immersed in the liquid.

Corrosion rates for the tubes themselves were even lower, presumably because they were continuously coated with flowing liquid when the evaporator was in operation. The only tube materials that showed any change in weight greater than the experimental error were the steel and aluminum tubes. The aluminum tubes showed such poor corrosion resistance that some tubes failed during the short time of the tests. The steel tubes showed weight losses equivalent to 0.01 inch per year during the later sludge runs. Steel tubes used during the 1593-hour demonstration run showed no weight loss. There was some evidence of pitting of the tubes used during the first 593 hours, but no pits deeper than 0.001 inch were found in tubes used during the last 1001 hours. These good results could be attributed to the practically continuous operation after the calcium sulfate scale problem of the first 593 hours was overcome.

These corrosion data indicate that deaeration of the sea water is essential to long life of steel sea water evaporators. Where reasonable corrosion allowances can be made, as in piping, vapor heads, etc., steel is the most practical material of construction. Its only uncertain application is for the evaporator tubes, which must be made thin for good heat conduction. Only long runs in a continuously operating plant can prove whether or not steel is the most satisfactory material for tubes.

Demonstration Plant

The pilot plant work has proved that the initial assumptions were not as optimistic as we had feared nor as impossible as others had predicted. It was shown that:

The cheapest type of commercial evaporator could be used for sea water.

This LTV evaporator could be operated under such conditions that the high heat transfer coefficients initially assumed could be attained.

This type of evaporator could be kept free of scale, at little or no cost, and at temperatures as high as 250° F.

The evaporator could be built primarily of steel.

Early in 1959, the Office of Saline Water's demonstration plant program was inaugurated. This process, which showed the greatest economic promise, was chosen for the first of the five demonstration plants, which is now under construction near Freeport, Tex. W. L. Badger Associates, Inc., provided the process design and architect-engineering services for this plant (2), which will have a capacity of 1,000,000 gallons per day and will use a 12-effect falling-film LTV evaporator. Evaporator operating conditions will be as shown in Figure 3. Operating conditions will be below the solubility curve of calcium sulfate hemihydrate, so that only the alkaline scales need be dealt with. Provisions have been made to use the seeding method as the basic means of scale prevention for the alkaline scales. These provisions include the installation of a thickener-clarifier to remove solids from the concentrated sea water blowdown and a mixer to reincorporate these solids in the feed.

Because pilot plant work indicated that deaeration of the sea water was important for corrosion prevention, a deaerator has been incorporated in the flowsheet. This deaerator will use a small part of the vapor from the eleventh effect to strip out oxygen from sea water feed that has been partially preheated, so that it will be at its boiling point under conditions in the deaerator.

A forward-feed evaporator is not efficient when the feed is cold, unless the feed is preheated in some manner almost to the boiling point in the first effect. Otherwise, a considerable proportion of the prime steam must be used to preheat the feed and thus is unavailable to evaporate water. In the demonstration plant, feed will be preheated by two sets of heat exchangers. One set will obtain heat by cooling of the condensate from each effect of the evaporator. The first of these will cool first-effect condensate, the second will cool combined first- and second-effect condensate, and so on to the last one, which will handle the combined condensate from all effects, cooling the distilled water as close as practical to the incoming sea water temperature. These condensate coolers will not provide all of the heat needed for preheating the feed; the remainder will be supplied by condensing vapor bled from each effect of the evaporator in another series of heat exchangers. The sea water feed will pass alternately through a condensate cooler, a vapor condenser, another condensate cooler, etc., so that heat can be recovered at the highest temperature level possible. Figure 4 is a model of the plant,

Figure 4. Demonstration plant for sea water conversion

showing disposition of evaporators, heat exchangers, clarifier-thickener, deaerator, and other auxiliary equipment. A simplified flow diagram of the plant is shown in Figure 5.

This demonstration plant will normally operate at a first-effect boiling point of 250° F., a last-effect boiling point of 120° F., and a discharge sea water concentration factor of 4. The primary control of the process is accomplished by automatic control of steam flow rate, sea water flow rate, and last-effect vacuum. No control is needed for temperature or pressure in the individual effects and heat exchangers, since these achieve their own levels, influenced only by the proportioning of the equipment. The demonstration plant is rather heavily instrumented to permit close surveillance of operating conditions and carrying out of special tests.

To increase the value of the demonstration plant, features have been incorporated to permit operation under other than demonstration conditions. It will be possible to operate the evaporator at first-effect temperatures up to 300° F., thus almost doubling plant output if calcium sulfate scale can be prevented, and to use the acid method of scale prevention in place of the sludge method. Provisions have been made for later installation of a vapor compressor, which would convert the plant to a combination multiple effect–thermocompression system. This would add about 15% to plant output and would permit performance evaluation of vapor compressors in sea water service.

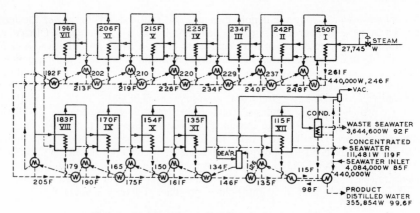

Figure 5. Flowsheet for demonstration plant

——————— Steam
— — — — Sea water
- - - - - - Condensate
F. Temp., ° F.
W. Flow, lb./hr.

It will also be possible by relatively minor piping changes to convert the forward-feed evaporator to backward feed, which might be more favorable if the calcium sulfate scale problem can be solved. Except for tubes, pump shaft sleeves, impellers, etc., the plant will be built exclusively of steel and cast iron. Tube materials will be evaluated by tubing different evaporator effects and heat exchangers with steel, admiralty metal, aluminum brass, and 90/10 cupronickel. The copper alloy tubes will be used exclusively in the final condenser and in the few heat exchangers that are in contact with nondeaerated sea water.

These experimental features add to the expense of the basic demonstration plant, in both operating and capital cost. The principal increase in operating cost results from the use of 160-p.s.i. steam from Dow at 45 cents a thousand pounds instead of 30-p.s.i. steam at 40 cents. The higher steam pressure was chosen to permit tests at temperatures up to 300° F. The extra capital costs result from the use of alloy tubes in most of the effects and heat exchangers, and provisions for increased production if 300° F. operation becomes possible, and for acid treatment and backward-feed operation. Badger's cost estimate was $1,374,000 for the entire plant. Of this $205,000 was chargeable to experimental features and factors of safety made necessary by the fact that this plant, the first of its kind, was to be built on a competitive-bid, guaranteed-performance basis. The actual low bid for the entire demonstration plant was $1,246,000, including all buildings, services, site development, and initial operation through a satisfactory performance test. The low bidder, Chicago Bridge and Iron Co., is now in the process of erecting the plant, which is due for completion in April 1961.

The out-of-pocket operating cost of this demonstration plant should be about $0.85 per 1000 gallons of distilled water, based on steam and power requirements both by W. L. Badger Associates, Inc., estimates and by the low bidder's guarantees. This water cost includes steam and power costs, estimated contract maintenance costs, and labor costs that include the increased supervisory labor needed during the demonstration and test phases of the program, projected to economic conditions that will probably exist in 1963.

When interest, insurance, and depreciation costs of the basic plant (one that does not include the test features, etc.) are added and the labor requirement is reduced to that to operate a normal production plant, the total water cost is about $1.04 per 1000 gallons, again based on projected 1963 costs. If the costs shown on Figure 1, which were estimated in 1955, were projected to 1963 conditions, the total water cost would be

$0.98 per 1000 gallons. If the demonstration plant had included a thermocompression stage, as did the plant on which the 1955 estimates were based, the demonstration plant would have shown even lower costs.

Conclusions

Estimates of reasonable costs of evaporating sea water to produce fresh water were made in 1955 by W. L. Badger Associates, Inc., on the basis of certain assumptions. These assumptions were proved in a pilot plant program in North Carolina conducted by Badger and Swenson Evaporator Division of Whiting Corp. for the Office of Saline Water. The results were so promising that the process was chosen by Office of Saline Water for its first demonstration plant. This 1,000,000-gallon-per-day plant was designed by W. L. Badger Associates, Inc., and is now under construction by Chicago Bridge and Iron Co. The cost of water from this plant will be about $1.00 per 1000 gallons, in agreement with the 1955 predictions. Those same predictions showed that in a plant of reasonable size (over 15,000,000 gallons per day), water costs could be brought down to about $0.35 per 1000 gallons.

Pilot plant work is still under way in North Carolina, in an attempt to increase even further the operating temperatures and sea water concentrations at which scale formation can be prevented. If such proves possible, water costs even lower than those originally predicted should be achievable.

Acknowledgment

The authors are indebted to the Office of Saline Water for supporting the work presented in the paper. Allen Cywin, J. J. Strobel, and E. A. Cadwallader of that office were particularly helpful in their untiring efforts with the program. The cooperation of the International Nickel Co. in providing space, services, and technical assistance is highly appreciated. The continued efforts of C. E. Sech, Jr., J. R. Sinek, and R. G. Reimus of W. L. Badger Associates, Inc., are also acknowledged with due appreciation. The Swenson Evaporator Division of the Whiting Corp. is deserving of special thanks for providing equipment and valuable technical assistance.

Literature Cited

(1) Badger Associates, Inc., W. L., Office of Saline Water, U. S. Dept. Commerce, R. & D. Report 26, OTS Publ. 161290 (1959).
(2) Badger Associates, Inc., W. L., Office of Saline Water, U. S. Dept. Interior, Specif. 195 (1960).
(3) Badger, W. L., Standiford, F. C., Natl. Acad. Sci.–Natl. Research Council, Publ. 568 (1958).
(4) Langelier, W. F., Caldwell, D. H., Lawrence, W. B., *Ind. Eng. Chem.* 42, 126–30 (1950).
(5) Standiford, F. C., Sinek, J. R., paper to be presented at AIChE Meeting, Washington, D. C., December 1960.

RECEIVED for review August 8, 1960. Accepted September 20, 1960.

Centrifugal Phase-Barrier Recompression Distillation

K. C. D. HICKMAN and W. J. HOGAN[1]

Aquastills, Inc., Rochester, N. Y.

J. A. EIBLING and W. L. BUCKEL

Battelle Memorial Institute, Columbus, Ohio

A 15,000-gallon-per-day Hickman still at Wrightsville Beach, North Carolina, is operated primarily for studies on over-all performance and on scaling and corrosion characteristics. A laboratory still at Columbus, Ohio, has been used for basic studies of the parameters that influence the evaporating and condensing heat transfer coefficients of a rotating surface. With the laboratory unit over-all heat transfer coefficients of the order of 3000 B.t.u./hr. sq. ft./°F. are routinely obtained at moderate rotational speeds. The estimated cost of distilling 50,000 to 100,000 gallons per day with the Hickman process is between $1.75 and $1.20, depending mainly on the useful life assigned to the evaporator. The household-size Aquastill has a capacity of 500 gallons per day, with an average power consumption of 1500 watts. Costs are estimated as $1.50 ± 0.50 for power, with a total of $4.00 ± 1.00 per 1000 gallons over a 10-year period, including amortization and repairs.

This paper brings together three phases of the study of centrifugal phase-barrier compression distillation (*3–6, 8*): the field test of the large multirotor unit known as the No. 5 still, built by the Badger Manufacturing Co. and now installed at the Sea Horse Institute in North Carolina; the experiments on the No. 4 research-type still at the Battelle Memorial Institute, which culminated in conceptual designs for larger machines, the concepts being contributed from Columbus and Rochester; and the development at Aquastills, Inc., of an automatic still of household size (*7*). Sequentially, the development has also seen three stages: to demonstrate the basic concept (1952–4), to determine parameters and reduce to practice (1954–9), and to equate with the dollar sign (1957 onward).

The No. 5 Badger-Hickman Still

Designed and fabricated by the Badger Manufacturing Co. under contract with the Office of Saline Water, this still, shown in Figures 1 and 2, was assembled and

---

[1] Present address, Arthur D. Little, Inc., Cambridge, Mass.

Figure 1.   No. 5 Badger-Hickman still installed at International
Nickel Co. test facility, Wrightsville Beach

shop-tested in Cambridge, Mass., on sea water trucked in from Gloucester.   The still
was then dismantled and transported to Harbor Island, North Carolina, where it was
reassembled under Badger direction on the test premises of International Nickel Co.
After surviving near-zero weather in which sea water congealed inside and outside
the apparatus, a series of tests was conducted by personnel of Battelle Memorial Institute during 1958.   In December of that year the machine was put on a stand-by
basis, pending results of the fundamental studies on the No. 4 still being conducted at
Columbus.

Construction.   The centrifugal phase barrier, A, Figure 2, comprises eight pairs
of conical sheet copper rotors 0.064 inch thick, manifolded on a cage formed of stainless
steel rings and vertical struts (not shown).   Feed water is supplied by a central pipe,
C, and a series of lateral stationary nozzles.   After passing over the inside surface of
the rotor, the greatly evaporated feed—now residue—passes out through peripheral
ports into two downspouts, D, integral with and on opposite sides of the rotor assembly, whence it is flung into the base of the still casing at P.   A supporting member,
F, forms a lid or skirt to isolate, at least partially, the steam in space P from the rest
of the still.   Steam evolved by the feed water is manifolded through stationary and
moving "spiders," past the upper rotor bearing into the motor-driven centrifugal steam
compressor, H.   The compressed steam flows down the outside of the rotor assembly,
and after condensing on the convex sides of the rotors the distillate is flung against
the walls of the casing down which it falls, to be collected by the gutter, U, at the base
of the still.

Designed for operation in a warm climate, the approach heat exchangers, pumps,
piping, and flanges on the still were spread widely, with little means for protection, so

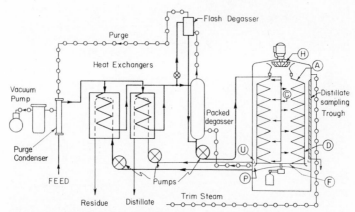

Figure 2. Diagrammatic elevation and flowsheet for No. 5
Badger-Hickman centrifugal recompression still

A. Sheet copper 8-pair rotor assembly
D. Downspout for collecting residue
F. Lower rotating support plate
H. Centrifugal steam compressor
P. Residue discharge jets
U. Distillate collection gutter

that the heat losses suffered in an inclement test situation were heavy. This was compensated by admission of steam from a boiler.

Still Operation. Functionally, the still operated satisfactorily, though there were certain mechanical troubles not basically inherent in the design. The struts securing the downspouts snapped, the upper bearing housing required replacement, and the vacuum seal on the blower shaft failed from time to time. The still was given many runs between minor repairs, but delivered only 68% of the predicted yield from sea water (17,000 instead of 25,000 gallons per day).

Described in detail elsewhere, the method for testing involves measurement of still temperatures and ΔP, the pressure differential before and after the steam compressor—i.e., inside and outside the rotor. From the measured temperature of the outside steam and presupposing absolute steam purity and absence of superheat, the temperature of the inside steam is computed by reference to steam tables, thus providing the temperature differential, ΔT, from which the over-all heat transfer coefficient, U, is derived. Where the boiling point of the feed-residue solution differs from pure water, a correction for mean boiling point elevation (BPE) is made. Ideally, and experimentally under the best conditions, this method is accurate, with a reproducibility within 1%. Fluctuations are indicative of lack of and varying steam purity; and unwarranted trends over a wide range of ΔP suggest a zero point error in reading the differential manometer. Typical No. 5 distillation data, some of them of less than desirable reproducibility, are given in Table I.

The performance ranges and the best performance for the two most different feeds —distilled water and sea water—are summarized in Table II. The ranges are not to be averaged and the best performances are not to be considered freaks; they are merely the nearest approach to an optimum evidently never yet reached.

Temperature Dependence. Early experiments with laboratory stills and a variable-speed steam compressor had shown that heat transfer and yield increased with temperature. The No. 5 compressor has a fixed speed and, since the specific volume of the steam decreases as temperature increases, the compressor was evidently starved for steam and operated in the unstable region when run at evaporator temperatures above 125° F. However, a trend toward increasing performance persisted,

Table I. Typical Operating Data for No. 5 Badger-Hickman Still

Date	7/10/58	5/23/58	4/10/58	5/23/58	4/12/58	10/21/58	12/9/58	12/15/58	12/17/58	12/19/58
Reading number	1	1, 2	8, 9	3, 4	18, 19	1, 2	7, 8	6	1, 2	1
Condensing temp., ° F.	105.0	110.5	120.5	130.0	140.0	125.5	140.2	135.2	125.0	140.0
Rotor speed, r.p.m.	400	400	400	400	400	400	400	400	400	400
Type of water	Sea	Sea	Sea	Sea	Sea	Sea	Sea	Fresh	Fresh	Sea
Feed, lb./hr.	16,230	14,050	14,467	15,540	13,130	18,740	21,370	23,240	22,200	22,140
Residue, lb./hr.	12,520	9,849	9,850	10,200	7,884	13,280	15,530	14,470	15,120	15,600
Distillate, lb./hr.	3,710	4,201	4,617	5,340	5,246	5,460	5,840	8,770	7,076	6,540
F/D ratio	4.38	3.35	3.13	2.91	2.51	3.43	3.66	2.65	3.14	3.39
Trim steam, lb./hr.	80	56	108	94	106	90	370	140	164	260
Purge withdrawal, lb./hr.	141	54	42	100	52	118	143	124	112	174
Temp. difference (corrected for BPE), ° F.	3.74	3.84	3.67	4.08	3.96	4.11	4.24	5.23	4.70	4.25
Net coefficient of heat transfer, U, B.t.u./(hr.)(sq. ft.)(° F.)	1,600	1,725	2,010	2,050	2,090	2,100	2,200	2,610	2,350	2,440
Power, kw.										
Rotor	9.7	7.7	8.6	8.9	8.7	10.1	12.8	12.4	12.0	13.2
Blower	20.5	23.1	26.5	31.0	34.0	23.6	27.8	36.0	29.0	31.4
System	35.5	36.2	41.0	46.0	48.6	40.0	46.7	54.1	46.9	52.0
Auxiliaries (by difference)	5.3	5.4	5.9	6.1	5.9	6.3	6.1	5.7	5.9	7.4
Kw.-hr./1000 gal. distillate	84.0	75.8	77.0	76.0	79.5	64.5	70.1	51.4	55.2	67.1
Lb. dist./blower kw.-hr.	181.0	182.0	174.5	172.0	154.3	232	210	244	244	208

Table II. Range and Best Performance Data for No. 5 Badger-Hickman Still

	Range	Best Performance Fresh water feed	Best Performance Sea water feed
Feed water rate, gal./hr.	1136–2875	2855	2247
Distillate rate, gal./hr.			
Fresh water feed	698–1075	1050	
Sea water feed	445– 700		655
Trim steam added, lb./hr.	54– 290	140	90
Purge steam subtracted, lb./hr.	46– 194	124	118
Condensing temp., ° F.	105– 144.8	135.2	125.5
Temp. differential, $\Delta\Gamma$, ° F.	5.23	5.23	
Temp. corrected for BPE, ° F.	3.67		4.11
Net heat transfer coefficient, U = B.t.u./(hr.) (sq. ft.)(° F.)		2610	2100
Total kw.-hr./1000 gal., for installation		51.4	64.5
Blower only, kw.-hr./1000 gal.		34.3	36.1

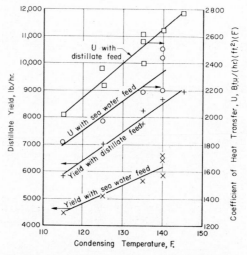

Figure 3. Dependence of yield and heat transfer coefficients with operating temperature of Badger-Hickman still

as shown in Figure 3, where condensing temperature is plotted against yield and heat transfer coefficient.

Continuous Run for 72 Hours. The "best performance" conditions were chosen for a continuous run of 72 hours on sea water, to determine fall in yield and onset of scaling, if any, and form a base line for future modifications to the still. The condensing temperature was held at 125° F., with sea water feed rate at 35 gallons per minute. Readings were taken at hourly intervals for the first 24 hours and then every other hour. The starting yield of 5800 pounds decreased to 5600 pounds per hour by the third hour and averaged this rate to the finish 3 days later (see Figure 4). Because the steady average negatived any suggestion of scale formation, at least in 72 hours, the initial fall of 4% in yield must be attributed to other causes, such as the attainment of equilibrium with the gases dissolved in sea water, as discussed further below. In summary, the 72-hour run was successful mechanically, functionally, and in freedom from scale and suffered only in that the yield was 70% of specification.

Analysis of Performance. It is basic to this research to learn why the yield of the No. 5 still is depressed. Two primary factors could contribute: lack of complete wetting of the rotors and uneven spreading of the feed water; and air leakage, with or

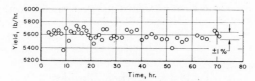

Figure 4. Yield of No. 5 still during 72-hour sea water run

Condensing temperature. 125° F.
Feed rate. 18,000 pounds per hour
Rotor speed. 400 r.p.m.
Starting date. Sept. 8, 1958

without accumulation of condensable vapors other than water in the still. A third dependent factor would be a progressive mismatching of the steam compressor to its load as the steam supply was reduced.

Wetting of Rotors. Boiling Point Elevation. When water is projected at a small angle (0° to 25°) at a rotating plate, part of the water makes permanent contact and part may glance or splash away. If the plate faces upward, the lost fraction may rejoin the spread fraction further out; if it faces downward, the splashings fall away permanently and in the case of an oppositely facing rotor pair will fall onto and wet the lower rotor. With equal feed supplies, an upper rotor will be starved and a lower rotor will be oversupplied. The situation was not recognized nor was compensation made in the No. 5 still runs.

Even with this unequal distribution there may be little effect on yield of distillate from a substantially fresh water feed; hence the high output of the still from distilled water feed. With sea water, 3 to 4% NaCl equivalent, the average or effective boiling point elevation becomes unequal on the two rotors. Thus if a 50% cut is secured and the lower rotor receives twice the feed of the upper, the average residue concentrate of 7% brine from 3.5% feed could be an actual 10% from the upper periphery and 5% from the lower, supposing equal rates of distillation. Actually because of the different elevations of boiling point (1.1° and 1.8° F.) the rate of evaporation from the upper rotor decreases while that from the lower rotor increases but less than proportionally because of the added thickness of the feed layer. Later experiments at Columbus on the No. 4 machine suggest that this situation existed in the No. 5 still.

Another adverse spreading factor is associated with the spokes that form the supporting cage of the rotor assembly and interfere 8 times per revolution with the passage of feed streams from nozzles to rotors. A separate mathematical study (5) shows that the feed streams should be directed at 30° from normal in the direction of travel, to produce a minimum of 10% interruption of the water.

Interference from Noncondensable Gases. Foreign gas in the still comprises air from mechanical leaks and traces of dissolved gas that have survived the degasser. The effectiveness of the degasser was tested by measuring dissolved oxygen, according to the ASTM procedure which yielded the data of Table III.

Table III. Interference from Noncondensable Gases

	Oxygen, P.P.M. by Weight	
	Example 1	Example 2
In sea water, before entry to system	7.0–8.0	7.0–8.0
In preheated feed water before entry to degasser	2.04	2.18
In feed water, after degasser, before still	0	0
In residue stream, from still	0	0

Evidently less than $1/_{350}$ of the air dissolved in the sea water reaches the still. Two other types of gas could have survived the degasser—carbon dioxide and suspected "semivolatiles." The carbon dioxide would be carried into the still as dissolved bicarbonate, to be liberated under the prevailing heat and vacuum. A material balance of carbon dioxide in feed and residue streams made by E. A. Cadwallader (5) showed that carbon dioxide was substantially absent from the steam (Table IV).

Table IV. Carbon Dioxide

	G./Liter
In sea water feed	0.188
In residue	0.274
In residue, adjusted to feed volume	0.190
CO_2 liberated	0.000

In confirmation, the addition of alkali to the feed water did not alter the yield of distillate.

As to the suspected semivolatiles, Armstrong and Boalch (2) described the detection and partial identification of volatile organic matter in concentrations of 5 to 20 p.p.m. in littoral sea water. The lower aliphatic acids, alcohols, aldehydes, and amines are mentioned. Now, the countercurrent degasser, so effective for eliminating air, could increase the concentration of these substances in a sea water feed by continually redissolving them in the liquid leaving from the bottom of the degasser, until a new equilibrium concentration was secured which permitted them to escape at the top of the degasser as fast as introduced by the raw water. This situation can be changed by altering the degasser. In the present instance, and in all our stills transferred to sea water feed, the fall in yield after the first 1 to 3 hours to a new steady level, to be departed from only by reventilation of the still, can be ascribed to the semivolatile artifacts in sea water.

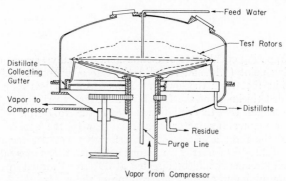

Figure 5. No. 4 still as received at Battelle Memorial Institute

Leakage of outside air, chiefly through the steam compressor shaft seal and the pipeline from the trim steam boiler, and measured by collection from the vacuum pump exhaust, varied between 0.25 and 0.60 pound per hour. These quantities of air, mingling with an average of 5500 pounds per hour of steam leaving the compressor, provide a steam feed at the bottom of the rotating condenser containing 45 to 110 p.p.m. of air. The purge steam withdrawn at the base, ranging from 50 to 140 pounds per hour, acquires all the inleakage and thus leaves containing 1700 to 12,000 p.p.m. or an average of 0.5% of air. The concentration of noncondensable gas against the surface of the lower rotors is likely to be much higher, so that a serious blanketing effect, with consequent loss of yield, is inevitable. This checks with the findings on the No. 4 still at Battelle, where 0.1% of foreign gas in the steam reduced the rate of distillation by 30%.

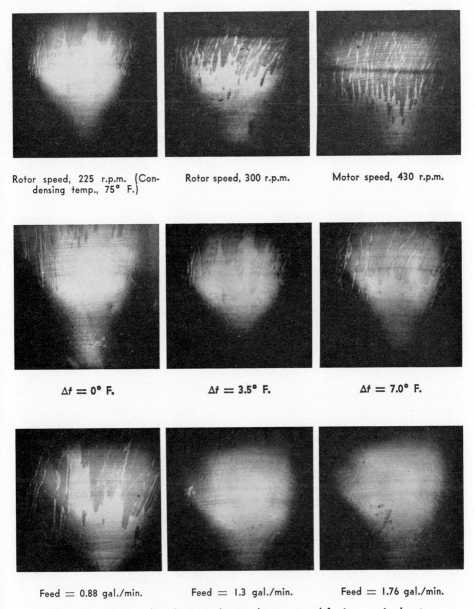

Rotor speed, 225 r.p.m. (Condensing temp., 75° F.)   Rotor speed, 300 r.p.m.   Motor speed, 430 r.p.m.

$\Delta t = 0°$ F. $\Delta t = 3.5°$ F. $\Delta t = 7.0°$ F.

Feed = 0.88 gal./min.   Feed = 1.3 gal./min.   Feed = 1.76 gal./min.

Figure 6. Water distribution obtained on upward-facing conical rotor

Upper row. Influence of rotor speed. Condensing temperature 110° F. Temperature difference 4° F. Feed supply rate 0.88 gallon per minute
Center row. Influence of temperature difference. Condensing temperature 75° F. Rotor speed 225 r.p.m. Feed supply rate 0.88 gallon per minute

Summary and Forecast. The incidental mechanical difficulties, inseparable from a first model of a device—in this case chiefly rotary seal leakage—should be readily correctable. The depression of yield of the still to 30 to 35% less than design maximum is accounted for quantitatively by gross inleakage of air, presence of sea water semivolatiles, and incomplete wetting of the rotor surfaces. It is fair to suppose that these items can be corrected if the facilities are made available.

Fundamental Studies with No. 4 Still

The objectives of this phase of the program were to determine the maximum heat transfer coefficient that may be expected with a rotating surface and to devise an inexpensive method of packing such surfaces into a vapor compression still. The model available for this study was the No. 4 Badger-Hickman still, shown in diagrammatic elevation in Figure 5, as received and before various modifications were made.

Evaporating Film. The No. 4 still was placed in operation at Battelle on March 25, 1958. Earlier tests by Cameron and Hickman (6) were repeated to verify the performance and acquaint the operators with the still. Observation of the rotors under continuous or stroboscopic illumination showed that the feed water does not always completely cover the evaporating surface, often breaking into a rivulet flow near the rims of the conical rotors. Increasing the flow or reducing the rotor speed would give complete spreading but with lower rates of heat transfer. Examples of rivulet formation on a conical rotor 16° from horizontal are shown in Figure 6. If these rivulets persisted during the operation of a still, much of the surface would be inactive.

The construction of Figure 5 accommodated feed water on the inside of a rotor pair. To improve observation and experimental accessibility, the turntable system was improved, as in Figure 7, so that rotors of different slope could be fitted and viewed without obstruction. It was soon found that a completely flat rotor would spread water as well as, if not better than, the previous conical variety and at the same time would permit many more rotors to be manifolded into a given container.

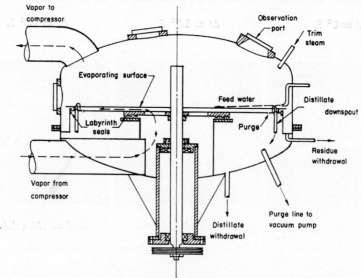

Figure 7. No. 4 still with altered drive and labyrinth steam seal, adapted for multiple-nozzle feed

The flat-plate experimental rotors were $4\frac{1}{2}$ feet in diameter and were completely wetted by a centrally applied feed stream of volume dictated by the realized rate of distillation. Central application, however, involved an unnecessarily thick layer of water near the center, offering a correspondingly low rate of heat transfer. Comparisons were made between a single central feed and from two to 16 peripheral feed nozzles which projected water inward at a small angle at progressive annular regions from center to edge, as suggested in Figure 8. Data for fresh water fed to a flat plate with either one central or eight and 16 peripheral jets are shown in Figure 9, where the multiple feed registers higher yield and heat transfer.

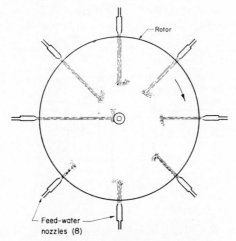

Figure 8.   Multinozzle   peripheral feed injection

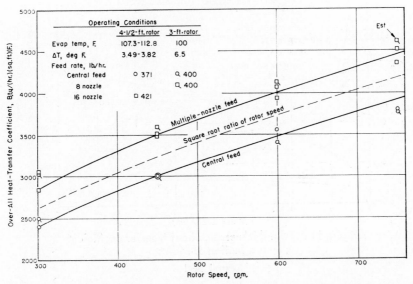

Figure 9. Effect of multinozzle vs. central feed on still performance

In a practical still a stack of annular flat plates with a large diameter central channel for the compressed steam would replace a single complete flat plate (Figure 10 shows the No. 4 still modified to take multiple rotors), and here a multiplicity of feed nozzles for each surface becomes less important. Figure 11 illustrates calculations of film thickness and heat transfer coefficient for a central feed on a flat rotor without a center hole. Adding a center hole would amount to removing the region of lowest heat transfer. Data obtained by operating the No. 4 multirotor column with both an eight-nozzle feed system and a two-nozzle system showed that for salt water feed the yield resulting from the multiple-nozzle feed system was only 2 or 3% higher than the yield obtained with the central feed system.

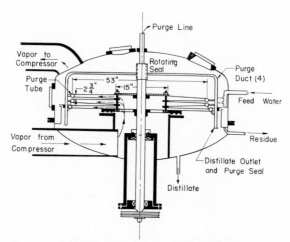

Figure 10. Multiple rotor assembly in No. 4 still

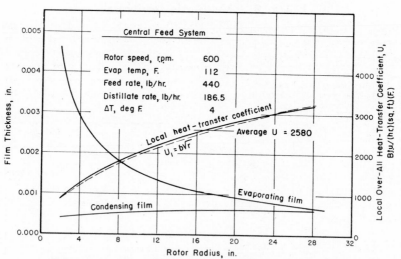

Figure 11. Film thickness and heat transfer coefficient as a fuction of radius

Central feed

Condensing Film. With the thermal resistance of the evaporating film reduced to a minimum and the resistance of the rotor fixed as a small fraction of the whole, the only factor remaining for improvement is the condensing film. Two general methods are available for reducing the thickness of this film—chemical inducement of dropwise condensation or fitting mechanical dams or slingers to the condensing side of the rotor, so that each element of condensate travels only a short distance before removal. Figure 12 shows the heat transfer coefficients that were obtained with fresh water feed from eight nozzles and dropwise condensation.

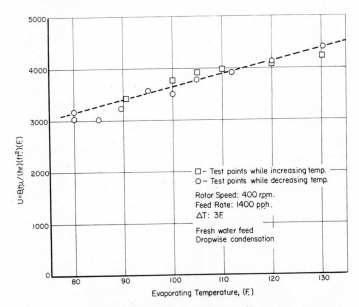

Figure 12. Relation of heat transfer coefficient to temperature with dropwise condensation on rotor

Purge System. The importance has been stressed of preventing noncondensable gases entering the still and removing as economically as possible—i.e., with as little working steam as possible—the gases that do gain entrance. Because of the relatively low diffusion rate of air in steam, air is continually being driven to form an obstructive layer at the condensing surface. Under conditions of laminar flow, the obstructive layer is pushed outward toward the rims of the rotors and it is from this terminal position that the gas can most economically be removed.

Figure 13 shows a cross-sectional view of the rim-purge system which has been tried in the No. 4 still. Some of the purge steam appears to be condensed in the rim tube and returns part of the heat to the still. Through the use of this type of purge system, it is expected that purge rates as low as 0.1% of the total vapor flow may be realizable, in contrast to the 2 to 3% lost from the No. 5 still. Further measurements suggest that if the vapor entering the condensing cavity contains less than 10 p.p.m. of noncondensable gas, the effect on condensation will be negligible if the rim-purge system is employed.

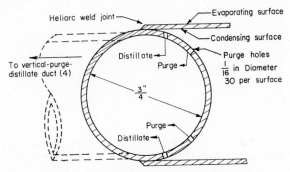

Figure 13. Peripheral rotor closure, with rim-purge facilities

Cost Study

The cost of producing potable water from sea water with vapor compression stills using the centrifugal barrier heat transfer principle has been estimated, making the following assumptions:

The heat transfer coefficient for a still operating at 110° F. evaporating temperature, with a feed-distillate ratio of 2.5 to 1, and with a rotor speed of 400 r.p.m., is 3000 B.t.u./(hr.) (sq. ft.) (° F.).

Heat transfer coefficient increases 5% with every 10° F. increase in evaporating temperature.

The useful life of the rotating assembly is 5 years. All other components of the still have a 20-year life.

Figure 14 shows an assembly drawing of a 20-rotor still upon which the cost study was based. The "installed" cost of the rotor area was estimated at about $23 per sq. foot. This value may be adjusted up or down as the capacity requirements change. The larger the number of rotors required, the lower the unit cost of the evaporator. Twenty rotor pairs should produce 65,000 gallons per day, 30 rotor pairs about 100,000.

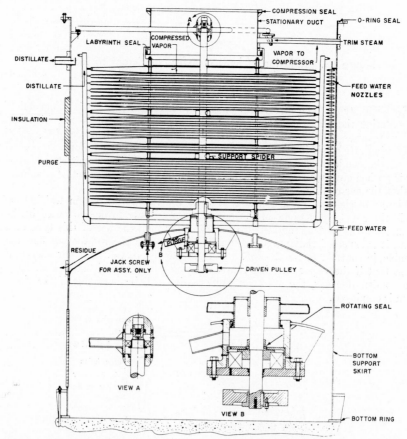

Figure 14. Conceptual design for large centrifugal compression still with flat-plate rotor construction and outside feed

Figure 15 shows the results of the cost calculations. The curves show minimum operating costs of $1.28, $1.31, and $1.40 per 1000 gallons for evaporating temperatures

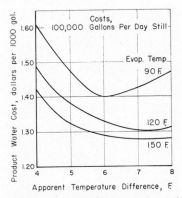

Figure 15. Variation of total product water costs within expected limits of construction and operating conditions

of 150°, 120°, and 90° F., respectively. The capital costs are $1.70, $1.72, and $1.80 per gallon per day. Although operation at 150° F. offers a slight advantage over 120° F., this may be only superficial, in that operation at the higher temperature may require special reinforcement of the rotor because of the higher pressure differentials. The cost per square foot of evaporator surface is based upon a first layout and not a refined design; therefore it may be possible to reduce these evaporator costs somewhat. Another point to consider is the useful life of the evaporator. The assumption of a 5-year life is not supported in any way by experimental data. In fact, so far as is known, no corrosion studies have been made with the type of flow and heat transfer conditions present in the centrifugal still.

Small, Automatic Rotary Compression Still

Design requirements called for a still to supply an average household (250 to 500 gallons per day); be sized to pass through a door 26 inches wide; be thermally self-sufficient—i.e., stay at operating temperature without additional heat—and start and stop on demand without supervision. The Aquastill (9) meets these specifications on the laboratory floor and in the field on noncorrosive waters. For prolonged use on sea water, changes will be required in construction materials for the steam blower and residue extraction pumps.

The development has passed through five previous models to the Type D still, shown in Figure 16 with a diagrammatic elevation, simplified in detail, in Figure 17.

Housed between two mild steel dished heads which are held closed on gasket by atmospheric pressure, the rotor is fabricated from five sheet copper spinnings fastened to a conical base plate, 6, which rotates on a shaft, 7, projecting from the "clockwork" speed changer, 8. A high speed impeller, 9, also driven by the speed changer, co-operates with members 5 and 6 to form a single-stage steam compressor integral with the rotor. The input shaft of the speed changer, projecting outside the still, is driven by the motor, 10, through the friction clutch, 11. The crude water, fed on demand through the solenoid valve, 12, and regulating valve, 13, passes to a flat-plate heat exchanger of authors' design, to recover sensible heat from the effluent streams. The warmed feed water then enters the degasser, where it "explodes" into the prevailing vacuum and is washed by the "purge" steam which leaves the distilling region. Con-centrated purge steam accumulates in the inside of the inner peripheries of the rotor assembly, 5, 6, and escapes through pipes 17, either back into the newly generated steam or by a devious path directly into the degasser. From there the foreign gases flow to the heat exchanger, where they lose most of the admixed steam and emerge by

Figure 16. Household-size Aquastill

Capacity 400 gallons, 500 gallons per day from brackish or sea water

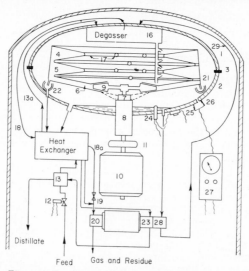

Figure 17. Operating diagram of Aquastill

pipe 18 and valve 19 to join the residue stream entering pump 20, which discharges both gases and residue to waste.

The pure water cycle begins with the condensation of steam on the inner surfaces of rotor 5, 6. Distillate passes out of peripheral parts 21 into gutter 22, and flows into the heat exchanger, 14, and out to the extraction pump, 23. The distillate is now forced through the regulator valve, 13, where it adjusts the incoming feed stream to give a desired preset distillate-residue ratio, and then to use or storage. A small space heater (600 watts), 24, and thermostat, 25, cooperate with the thermally lagged outer casing and the steam bleed valve, 19, to maintain a selected operating temperature under diverse conditions of ambient and feed water temperatures. A vacuum-operated switch, 26, and electrical control box, 27, complete the essential features of the still.

Operation. Water is placed in the machine to fill the pipelines and extraction pumps and the casing to the normal overflow level. With the lid in place and the operating current "on" the extraction pumps begin to create vacuum, further securing the lid; the space heater is also warming the still. When the pressure has fallen to about 23 mm. of mercury, the vacuum switch starts the rotor motor, rotor, and steam impeller and energizes valve 12, which admits a slow stream of feed water. When the moving parts have reached full speed—the rotor 1400 r.p.m. and impeller 12,000 r.p.m.— the electric load ranges from 1000 down to 400 watts for the rotor motor, depending on the residual gas pressure, 250 watts for the extraction pump motor, and 600 watts for the heater, a total of 1.5 to 2.0 kw., all of which is dissipated within the unit to liberate 5000 to 6800 B.t.u. per hour, rapidly warming the machine. Within a few minutes the pressure falls to 25 to 27 inches of mercury while the temperature rises to 118° to 120° F., and as soon as the pressure corresponds exactly with that of saturated steam at the temperature within the casing—for instance, 26.83 inches (1.56 p.s.i.a.) and 117° F.—distillation starts. The stream of distillate which begins to flow through valve 13 progressively increases the admittance of feed and the still rapidly passes into full operation.

Thus from a cold start at atmospheric pressure and without intervention by the operator distillation is in full swing in less than 45 minutes. The space heater is now in intermittent use, merely to "float" the still at the chosen operating temperature. Both load and capacity increase considerably with the temperature, so that the setting of the thermostat controls the output of the still. The constant electrical load of the still is now of the order of $(1200 + 200 + \eta 600) \pm 100 \approx 1500 \pm 100$ watts. Factor η is the proportion of time, less than unity, that the heater is energized and the factor ± 100 allows for the selected still temperature and the nature of the feed water, brackish or strongly saline. A breakdown of the energy requirements is shown in Table V.

Table V. Performance Variation on Aquastill Models C and D

Date 1960	Type of Still	Evaporation Temp., °F.	Feed–Distillate Ratio	Distillate, Gal./ 24 Hours	Power Consumption[a]		Nature of Feed Water
					Kw.	Kw.-hr./ 1000 gal.	
2/10	C-3	108	1.40	440	1.12	61.2	Rochester tap water
		115	1.37	495	1.20	58.9	Rochester tap water
		126	1.26	520	1.28	59.5	Rochester tap water
5/11		124		505	1.26	60.2	Rochester tap water
		122		460	1.17	61.4	Tap water + detergent[b] (Joy)
		120		480	1.19	60.3	Tap water only
		124		540	1.31	58.4	Tap water + 1:4000
		123		530	1.29	58.3	2-(2-aminoethylamino) ethanol
				480	1.20	60.5	Tap water only
3/8	D-3	109	1.80	508	1.15	55.2	Tap water
		113	1.42	530	1.16	53.9	Tap water
		119	1.55	582	1.30	53.8	Tap water
		123	2.00	450	1.14	61.4	Tap water + 3% NaCl
		122	1.56	595	1.30	52.9	Tap water alone
3/16		118	2.11	430	1.08	60.8	Tap water + 3.7% NaCl[c]
		118	1.60	545	1.21	53.5	Tap water alone
		121	1.43	630	1.34	51.4	Distilled water
		119	1.53	580	1.27	52.8	2-(2-Aminoethylamino) ethanol, 1:4000

[a] Power taken by still proper, including rotor and compressor but not extraction pumps and intermittent space heater.

[b] Sudsy dish water.

[c] Higher value for 3.7% NaCl in comparison with previous 3.0% NaCl due to acid clean of still.

Quantitative Data. The best investigative tool has proved to be the recording wattmeter. Because of the self-contained nature of the unit, with single motor for rotor and compressor, the power-yield ratio—e.g., kilowatt-hours per 1000 gallons— is constant for any given still and setting and is reproducible within 0.1 to 0.2%. Even trifling changes in quality of water or manner of operating change the power-yield ratio. A given still in a given degree of cleanliness, adjusted for a given kind of feed water, supplied at a fixed ratio of distillate to residue, may yield from 420 to 500 gallons per day according to temperature, but the power index will stay constant within 0.5%. Let any significant variable other than temperature be changed and the power index also changes; all of which furnishes a powerful tool for studying and improving still performance. It is instructive to make small chemical additions to the feed water—alkali, acid soaps, for instance—and note the small but definitely reproducible changes in the power index, as recorded in Table V. Variations in performance of a particular still, the D-3, with increasing salinity of feed water, are shown in Figure 18. The values plotting the dotted traces were obtained with a Model C unit and show the progress that has been made since May 1959, when the earlier still was tested. Table VI lists a breakdown of the power usage of a typical Aquastill, by parts.

Table VI. Power Requirements of Aquastill, Model C

	Drive Motor, Watts	Typical Yield, G.P.D.	Typical, Kw.-Hr./1000 Gallons		
			Still only	Still, pumps	Still, pumps, heater[a]
Drive motor, idling	180	. . .			
+ speed changer, idling	205	. . .			
+ rotor and impeller, idling in high vacuum	400	. . .			
Complete assembly, idling at operating temperature and pressure[b]	750	. . .			
Active distillation					
Tap water feed, casing temp., 120° F.	1250	500	60	69.8	77
Sea water feed, 120° F.	1150	400	69	81.0	90
Sea water feed, 128° F.	1250	430	70	78.9	87

[a] Taken as constant 150 watts. In warm climates heater is not used and a steam-line thermostat controls still temperature.

[b] At 120° F., just sufficient air admitted to block distillation.

Qualitative Data. Stills Models B, C, and D have been operated daily on the test floor in Rochester for $2\frac{1}{2}$ years. The longest nonstop run was 500 hours, terminated by failure of a speed changer. Though fluctuating during the run, the yield on Lake Ontario feed water was the same at the finish as at the start, 470 gallons per day. Scale was found on most of the top rotor spinning, but little appeared on the inner facing feed surfaces. Sea water has been imported from the North Carolina coast and run in limited quantities. Simulated sea water, from 3.5% solution of "driveway" salt, has been employed routinely for checking yield vs. salinity. Only recently, however, have rotors been available with all-copper construction suitable for tests on sea water. Preliminary indications are that the cast aluminum steam impellers show too rapid corrosion from entrained brine spray to be operated safely. Suitable materials changes are now being made.

Summary and Conclusions

With the exception of the chemical processing of aqueous solutions, the exploratory phase of centrifugal barrier compression distillation is completed and the parameters affecting heat transfer are reasonably well known. Ranging from $5.00 per 1000 gallons of product water for miniature stills under adverse costing conditions to $1.25 per 1000 gallons for larger units in the best circumstances, what place is there for the

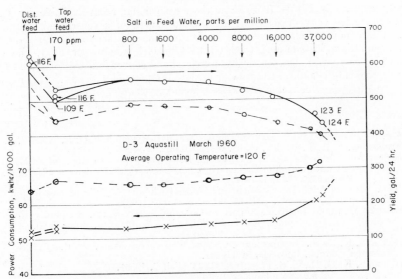

Figure 18. Operating data for Aquastill on increasing concentrations of brine

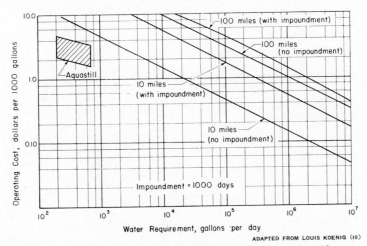

ADAPTED FROM LOUIS KOENIG (10)

Figure 19. Variation of permissible operating costs with size of installation

device in the growing armamentarium of the water conversion engineer? Is there a place for $2.00 to $5.00 water in face of the $1.00 to $2.00 water that is to be expected from the large demonstration plants recently authorized?

The answer, that there is indeed such a place, resides in the variation in the dollar standard, as applied to water supplies. Koenig (10) has brought to our notice the important rule of thumb that to compete with surface water converted water needs to be cheaper, the greater the quantities involved. On continents, at least, the largest demands are best met by channeling distant available supplies, as witness the current Feather River diversion 450 miles to San Francisco. Conversely, a demand of less than 1000 gallons per day can be met more cheaply by processing dirty water from outside the building than by leading a pipe to the village pond. One of Koenig's charts has been adapted in Figure 19 to show the ample dollar room available for a small conversion device (any device—this is no endorsement of a centrifugal compression still). When, however, larger models are in question (50,000 to 100,000 gallons per day), or multiple installations (500,000 to 1,000,000 gallons per day), the dollar standard for comparison has drastically decreased and conversion costs of $1.50 to $1.00 are attractive only if natural fresh water is more than 50 miles distant. This reasoning applies to all types of conversion processes, including those described here.

Literature Cited

(1) Am. Soc. Testing Materials, "Nonreferee Method A, 1955 Standards," Part 7, p. 1365.
(2) Armstrong, F. A. J., Boalch, G. T., *Nature* 185, 762 (1960).
(3) Badger Manufacturing Co. and Hickman, K. C. D., Report to Office of Saline Water, "Research Continuation of Badger-Hickman Centrifugal Distillation Testing on Unit No. 4," PB 616390 (March 1957).
(4) *Ibid.*, "Research and Development of Badger-Hickman Centrifugal Distillation Techniques and Equipments," PB 161387 (November 1956).
(5) Battelle Memorial Institute, Report to Office of Saline Water, "Summary Report on a Study and Development of the Hickman Sea Water Still," June 1960.
(6) Hickman, K. C. D., *Ind. Eng. Chem.* 49, 786 (1957).
(7) Hickman, K. C. D., "Symposium on Saline Water Conversion," Natl. Acad. Sci.–Natl. Research Council, Pub. 568, 51 (1958).
(8) Hickman, K. C. D., U. S. Patent 2,734,023 (Feb 7, 1956).
(9) *Ind. Eng. Chem.* 50, 28A (January 1958).
(10) Koenig, Louis, *J. Am. Water Works Assoc.* 51, 845 (July 1959).

RECEIVED for review July 7, 1960. Accepted August 1, 1960.

Sea Water Conversion by the Multistage Flash Evaporation Method

D. B. BRICE and C. R. TOWNSEND

Research Division, The Fluor Corp., Ltd., Whittier, Calif.

The cost of converting sea water into potable water is sufficiently low to make it a potentially important source of supplemental water for many parts of the world. At present, multistage flash evaporation in large-capacity plants is the most economical process. In many areas, because of the tremendous quantities of heat required, nuclear fuels are the only feasible source of energy for large-capacity sea water conversion plants. Based on today's technology, the cost of water produced by a single-purpose multistage flash evaporator using a nuclear steam generator was estimated to be in the range of 38 to 42 cents per thousand gallons. If optimistic predictions of future advances in both the evaporator plant and the nuclear steam generator are realized, an ultimate water cost of 24 to 31 cents per thousand gallons will be possible within the next decade.

For many years, fresh water has been obtained from the ocean for shipboard use by utilizing the principle of flash evaporation. More recently, modest-sized land-based multistage flash evaporation plants have been constructed and are producing potable water. Engineering evaluations of the multistage flash system have shown that it can economically supply fresh water to large population centers, although large-capacity sea water conversion plants of any kind have not yet been built. In the not too distant future, however, the installed capacity of land-based multistage flash plants will probably dwarf this year's estimated capacity of about 6,000,000 gallons a day.

Water administrators throughout the world are greatly concerned about supplementing water supplies. Many of them would like to tap the ocean as a source for future fresh water.

A. L. Miller, Director of the Office of Saline Water, summarized the problem in a recent speech. "It is hard to realize," he said, "as we stand on the threshold of space, that within a few years our number one domestic problem may be the provision of adequate supplies of plain ordinary water. The predicted increase in water use in the coming decades makes it unmistakably clear that we will need more water than can be provided from readily available natural sources of supply. The day of the water witch is over. We must turn to scientific and technological research to develop a new source of supply that can provide an ever-growing percentage of tomorrow's water."

The multistage flash evaporator process could play a vital role in making Dr. Miller's prediction of a new source of supply come true. It would convert sea water to fresh on a large scale.

Based on our evaluations, a single-purpose plant using nuclear energy to operate multistage flash evaporators would result in the most economical production of potable water from the ocean. There are, of course, special economic situations where the logical choice would be a combined power and water plant that would utilize fossil fuels, but in general, a single-purpose plant would be the most advantageous. A single-purpose multistage flash evaporator plant that uses a nuclear steam generator is shown in Figure 1.

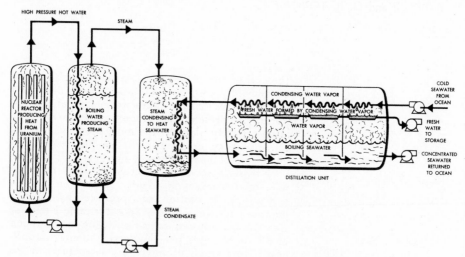

Figure 1.   Fresh water produced by multistage flash evaporation

It was established, on the basis of current technology, that the practical limit of capacity of a multistage flash evaporator plant (consisting of several vessels in series as shown in Figure 2) would be approximately 25,000,000 to 30,000,000 gallons a day. The economics of water production discussed below are based on two such units operating in parallel, nominally producing 50,000,000 gallons of potable water a day. The capacity of the plant was determined by the smallest economic size of nuclear steam generator, which would provide energy for evaporation and for driving a majority of the pumps.

Steam Generation

The steam generator selected for the optimization study (shown schematically in Figure 1) is a 370-thermal megawatt (net to the evaporator) pressurized light-water reactor. The selection of the reactor type and details of its design (3) are outside the scope of this paper. However, the steam is estimated to cost 37 cents per million B.t.u. (3), including all costs associated with the nuclear steam generator. The sea water conversion plant was optimized to consume 350 tmw in the brine heaters. The balance of the energy was required for the steam turbine pump drivers and steam jet ejectors.

A nuclear process heat reactor was selected for this application for economic reasons. Studies (1, 3) indicated that the economics of steam generation from nuclear energy are favorable where a large amount of relatively low-temperature thermal energy is required in a single-purpose plant. The source of energy used to produce the steam required is immaterial as far as the sea water evaporators are concerned.

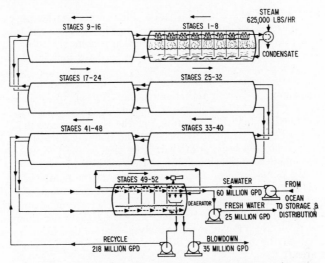

Figure 2. Typical process flow diagram for multistage flash evaporator sea water conversion plant

Capacity 25,000,000 gallons per day

Process Description

Figure 2 shows the flow of sea water, brine, and condensate through a typical multistage flash evaporator. In the specific plant shown, the sea water is pumped from the ocean through tubes in the integral deaerator and through the four lowest temperature stages of the evaporator plant before it is deaerated. Chemicals used to control scale may be added either to the sea water before it is deaerated, or to the combined recycle–make-up stream, before it is pumped through the tubes in the higher temperature stages and brine heater. The exact position of the addition of scale control chemicals depends on the method employed. The deaerated sea water serves as the make-up to the plant. It is mixed in the deaerator with the slightly concentrated brine. These two streams—now combined—are pumped through the remaining tubes of the evaporators and the brine heater before being introduced into the shell side of the highest temperature stage. The shell-side brine then cascades from stage to stage as a result of the pressure differential maintained. In each stage some of the water flashes from the brine solution. It is condensed on the tubes of the evaporator and caught in troughs positioned below the tubes. The condensate also cascades from stage to stage.

Finally, the shell-side brine and the condensate reach the lowest pressure stage. At this point, the condensate is pumped from the system as product. The brine in excess of that required for recycle is pumped from the system and discharged to the ocean as blowdown. The remainder of the brine is mixed with the make-up and recycled through the system.

An ejector system is required to remove inerts from the plant at the lowest pressure point in the system. For the plant shown in Figure 2, this point is the deaerator. Suitable instruments are required in the plant to control liquid flows, temperatures, and levels. The process and controls have been described in detail (3).

Mechanical Design

Certain mechanical designs, such as single level construction and condenser tubes that run continuously through several stages, have been incorporated in the plant because of economies that can be realized by using this type of construction. In the design shown in Figure 2, tubes run through four stages. Tube sheets are employed only at the ends, and baffles are used instead of tube sheets for the other stage-to-stage separation. The holes in the baffles are designed for a close fit to the tubes. They can also be sealed to prevent stage-to-stage steam leakage along the tubes (4).

A plant thus constructed would eliminate the need for individual water boxes for each stage and for a majority of the tube sheets, thereby effecting economy in capital costs. Also, in a large-capacity plant, the diameter of the vessels is large. For the plant shown in Figure 2 (which represents a capacity of approximately 25,000,000 gallons a day), the evaporator vessels are 30 feet in diameter. The vessels are horizontal cylinders designed to take full advantage of the shape to save metal, both in the walls and in the stiffeners required under the conditions of operation. These vessels will have to be field-erected because of their large size. However, certain components such as the tube bundles can be shop-fabricated to avoid field rolling of the tubes.

Except for the remotely located sea water pump, all the pumps in the process area (shown in Figure 2) are driven by steam turbines. Because large quantities of relatively low-pressure steam are required in the process, the use of steam-driven turbines instead of electric motors results in a savings of several cents per thousand gallons of product. Because of this, the economic analysis and optimization presented below have been based on the use of steam-driven turbine drivers for the pumps located in the process area.

Design Variables

The design variables considered in the optimization of a large-capacity plant are shown in Figure 3. The relationship between the stage terminal temperature difference (TTD), number of stages, and performance ratio (pounds of water produced per pound of steam condensed) is readily apparent upon examination of Figure 3. Unlike a

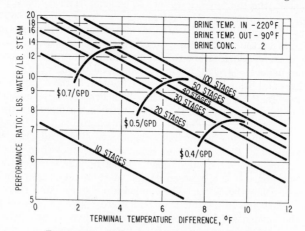

Figure 3.   Relation of design variables

multiple-effect distillation system, it is possible in the multistage flash system to select the number of stages and the performance ratio independently. There is, of course, a practical limitation to the number of stages that can be used. The number depends to a considerable extent on the over-all temperature difference between the incoming brine to the first stage and the blowdown to the ocean. Because a given stage-to-stage pressure differential is required for satisfactory regulation of shell-side brine flow, a minimum temperature difference is required from stage to stage, depending on the absolute pressure. The number of stages can be increased as improvements in methods of scale prevention permit higher brine temperatures. For the condition of 220°F. brine inlet and 90°F. blowdown (as illustrated in Figure 3), the practical limitation is probably on the order of 60 stages.

The most important design variable is the terminal temperature difference. This variable has the strongest influence on the condenser surface required in the evaporators and on the heat economy of the plant. The number of stages also has an effect, but it is considerably less than the effect of the terminal temperature difference. Also, the relationships shown in Figure 3 are for a blowdown concentration of twice that of incoming sea water. However, variation in blowdown concentration has only a minor effect on the economics.

The performance ratio or heat economy is a result of the selection of design variables previously discussed, and is not a variable as such. Lines of constant capital cost per daily gallon of capacity are also included in Figure 3. Capital costs have been based on plant capacities in a range of 25,000,000 to 60,000,000 gallons a day and a velocity in the evaporator tubes of 5 feet per second. These lines of constant capital cost per daily gallon are a result of cross plotting the results obtained in the optimization study.

Optimization

The optimization of the large-capacity multistage flash evaporator was based on the consumption of the 370 thermal megawatts of energy available from the nuclear steam generator. It was necessary to determine the capital cost for various assumed terminal temperature differences and numbers of stages. Added to the amortized capital cost were all other costs necessary for operation of a complete plant, such as steam, labor, utilities, materials, and overhead.

Results are shown graphically in Figure 4 for a brine temperature of 220°F., condenser tube velocity of 5 feet per second, blowdown temperature of 90°F., and brine concentration of twice sea water. As can be seen, a minimum water cost for these conditions is obtained with a 50-stage plant operating with a terminal temperature difference of about 4°F. Similar calculations were made for a blowdown concentration of 1.5 times sea water and for a once-through system. By cross plotting, it was then possible to determine the optimum blowdown salt concentration for the plant. It was about 1.7 times sea water. However, the curve is almost flat in the range of 1.5 to 2.0 times sea water.

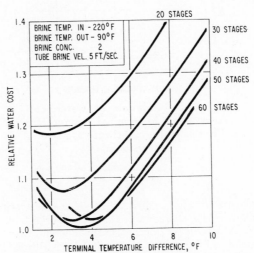

Figure 4. Relative water cost as a function of terminal temperature difference for several numbers of stages

Plant capacity 25,000,000 to 60,000,000 gallons per day

The tube brine velocity was selected after consideration of the higher pressure drop (pumping cost) and more rapid rate of erosion corrosion with higher tube brine velocity and lower heat transfer coefficients with lower velocity, consistent with sound engineering design. As a previous study (2) indicated the desirability of higher brine temperatures in terms of economic water production, the highest practical temperature (220°F.) was selected. The selection of a blowdown temperature of 90°F. was primarily based upon the vapor volume requirements at this temperature and, to a lesser extent, on the temperature of the sea water, which was in the range of 57° to 67°F.

Because a large number of calculations were required to determine material and energy balances for all the conditions required, these calculations were programmed for solution on a computer. Details of the program have been published (3). It was written so that flows, temperatures, pressures, salt concentration of the brine, and condenser surface for each stage were printed as computer output data. It was then possible to take these data, design the vessels, determine line sizes and condenser required, and estimate capital costs for plants within a capacity range of 25,000,000 to 60,000,000 gallons a day.

Figure 5 shows the relationship of the several water cost components as a function of the TTD for a 50-stage sea water conversion plant with a blowdown concentration of twice that of sea water. Because the blowdown concentration was maintained constant, the cost of chemicals for scale control remained constant.

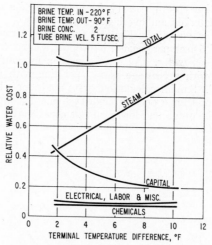

Figure 5. Relation of water cost components to terminal temperature difference for 50-stage sea water conversion plants

Plant capacity 25,000,000 to 60,000,000 gallons per day

Electrical energy costs as well as labor and miscellaneous expenses for such a plant were relatively constant. These charges were slightly higher at both low and high TTD, however. Increased costs resulted from: slightly different labor costs as the plant capacity changed, and small differences in electrical load with TTD. Over the range investigated, the only costs that largely depended upon the selection of TTD were steam cost (which increased) and capital cost (which decreased).

The sum of all these costs is shown as the total cost curve. The minimum is approximately 4°F. TTD. A cross plot of the data indicated that a concentration of 1.7 times sea water had a slight economic advantage over either 1.5 or 2.0 times sea water. All three had a considerable advantage over a once-through system (largely because of the chemical consumption for a once-through system).

Water Cost

Our studies show that a 52-stage evaporator is the optimum multistage flash sea water conversion plant that can be combined with a 370-thermal megawatt light-water nuclear steam generator that produces steam at a total cost of 37 cents per million B.t.u. This evaporator would operate with an average TTD of 4°F. and would have a performance ratio of more than 13 pounds of condensate per pound of steam. Its nominal capacity would be 50,000,000 gallons a day. The estimated capital cost of the evaporator plant, complete except for the nuclear steam generator, would be $30,700,000. The nuclear steam generator would cost $11,500,000. The estimated daily operation cost would be $20,600. A perspective of the proposed plant is shown in Figure 6.

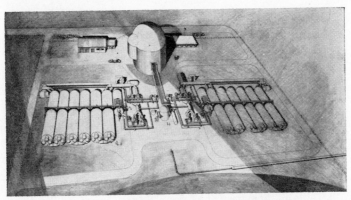

Figure 6.   Perspective of proposed plant

Table I shows a detailed breakdown of the operating cost for this plant. The cost of steam represents about half of the water cost for the optimum plant. The capital charges for the evaporator plant, which includes amortization, interest on working capital, and real estate, represent about 30%. The remaining 15 to 20% is equally divided between the cost of chemicals for scale control and all the other costs. The converted water is estimated to cost approximately 42 cents per thousand gallons. This water cost represents a realistic figure for a large-capacity multistage flash evaporator that could be built today when the energy in the form of steam costs between 35 and 40 cents per million B.t.u.

Future Improvements

More recently possible future improvements in nuclear steam generation and saline water conversion by multistage flash evaporation have been evaluated. The nuclear steam generator planned for this plant would be a heavy-water natural-uranium type. It would result in a slightly lower steam cost, both currently and in the future, than the light-water reactor used in the optimization study. The size of the water plant would be 130,000,000 gallons a day, utilizing multiple units of the flash evaporators previously described. This increase in capacity, together with lower steam cost, would reduce the estimate of present water cost from 42 to 38 cents per thousand gallons.

Based on this study (1), water costs were projected to 1972. It was concluded that the cost of water can be reduced from the present level of about 38 cents per thousand gallons (see Figure 7) to the range of 24 to 31 cents. Such a reduction would depend upon the extent of improvements that can be made in the next decade in heat transfer coefficients, in operation at higher temperatures as the result of improvements in scale control, in the possibility of using less expensive materials of construction, and in lowering the cost of steam produced in a nuclear steam generator. The possibility for such improvements was appraised as realistically as possible.

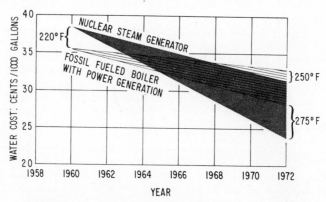

Figure 7.   Projected cost of sea water conversion

Plant capacity 130,000,000 to 150,000,000 gallons per day

For purposes of comparison, a fossil-fueled boiler producing by-product power was also included in the analysis. As shown in Figure 7, such a plant could be built today to produce fresh water at an estimated cost of about 35 cents a thousand gallons, assuming that the power plant would be base-loaded the same as the water plant. However,

Table I.   Summary of Water Cost for Optimized Plant

Capacity, million gal./day	49.3
Stages	52
Terminal temp. difference, °F.	4
Performance ratio[a], lb./lb.	13.65
Capital costs, thousands of dollars	30,700[b]

Operating Costs	Dollars/ Stream Day	Cents/ Thousand Gallons	%
Electric power	912	1.85	4.4
Steam[c]	11,090	22.49	53.9
Chemicals	1,723	3.50	8.4
Supplies and maintenance materials	246	0.50	1.2
Operating labor	314	0.64	1.5
Maintenance labor	185	0.37	0.9
Payroll extras	83	0.17	0.4
Overhead	57	0.12	0.3
Amortization[d]	5,915	12.00	28.7
Taxes and insurance	...	...	...
Interest on working capital	144	0.29	0.7
Real estate[e]	48	0.10	0.2
Tube salvage value	(129)	(0.26)	(0.6)
Total operating cost	20,588	41.77	100.0

Water cost		
Cents per 1000 gallons	42
Dollars per acre-foot	136

[a] Pounds of water produced per pound of steam condensed.
[b] Erected cost of complete evaporator plant including intake facilities, reservoir, and site development.
[c] Includes both capital and operating costs of nuclear steam generator.
[d] Evaporator plant, interest on money 4% per annum.
[e] $5000 per acre with money at 4% per annum.

less reduction in the future cost of water can be projected for a fossil-fueled boiler plant designed to produce both power and water than for a single-purpose nuclear steam generator plant to produce water alone, because of an assumption that fossil fuels will continue to increase in price (as they have over the past several years). Power generation is a necessary part of the economics of low-cost water production utilizing a fossil-fueled boiler. A single-purpose fossil-fueled boiler producing steam for the water plant would not be competitive with a single-purpose nuclear steam generator water plant. Although some plants could be built in which both the power generation and water production would be base-loaded, not all such plants can be base-loaded, because of the fluctuating demand for electrical energy and the inability to store it.

Consequently, if one is to envision a large complex of sea water conversion and power generation, only a moderate amount of the water can be produced from combination plants at a cost competitive with a single-purpose plant. This analysis, of course, is based on very large plants to serve large population areas. There are always special considerations and conditions in any given location where the combination would be the most attractive means of water production. However, many of these plants are small—too small to consider a nuclear steam generator. Therefore, a valid comparison can be made only of plants on the order of 50,000,000 gallons a day or larger as far as nuclear steam generation is concerned.

Literature Cited

(1) Brice, D. B., Dusbabek, M. R., Townsend, C. R., "Economics of Sea Water Distillation in Southern California," Metropolitan Water District of Southern California, Fluor **CRR 1056** (December 1959).
(2) Brice, D. B., Dusbabek, M. R., Townsend, C. R., Office of Saline Water Research and Development Progress Rept., **19**, Fluor **RDR 1687**, OTS No. PB 161062 (February 1958).
(3) Brice, D. B., Dusbabek, M. R., Townsend, C. R., Selleck, F. T., Office of Saline Water Research and Development Progress Rept. **34**, Fluor **CRR 1046**, OTS No. PB 161010 (August 1959).
(4) Howe, E. D., *J. Am. Water Works Assoc.* **51**, 1191 (1959).

RECEIVED for review July 7, 1960. Accepted July 15, 1960.

Design and Operating Principles in Solar Distillation Basins

GEORGE O. G. LÖF

512 Farmers Union Building, Denver 3, Colo.

Among systems for solar distillation of sea water, the horizontal evaporation basin covered by transparent condensing surfaces has most closely approached commercial use. Solar radiation absorbed on the black bottom of a basin of salt water causes evaporation into the air space. Distilled water condenses on sloping air-cooled covers of glass or plastic film and collects in troughs at the low edges of the covers; unevaporated brine overflows to waste. The interrelationship of the processes of radiant heat transmission, thermal conduction and convection, vapor diffusion and convection, and the energy and material balances is complicated. Coupled with solar and weather variability, these factors make the design of equipment and prediction of performance an involved analysis. A procedure for such an analysis has been developed and a solar distillation plant in an illustrative location has been designed. Predicted water production rates throughout a typical year, the distribution of losses, and methods for improving performance are presented.

Growing scarcity of fresh water in many places in this country and the rest of the world has stimulated the development of several potentially useful processes for saline water demineralization. Because fresh water is such a cheap commodity, these processes must demonstrate the maximum conceivable economy to compete with even the most expensive natural fresh water sources. Nearly all of these methods require considerable energy, either as heat or as electric power. Since this is a large cost item in these processes, solar distillation offers substantial operating economies, but at the expense of large investment requirement.

Minimization of construction cost has therefore been a prime objective in the development of solar distillation. Probably the most promising method for its accomplishment is the combining of all three primary elements in a distillation process—i.e., heat supply facility, evaporator, and condenser—into a single piece of very simple equipment. Such a unit is the basin-type solar distillation plant (4). But the simplicity of this equipment ceases with its general form, and over-all operation of so many functions makes the physical processes of energy and mass transfer highly complex.

This paper describes and explains the various energy- and water-transfer processes taking place in the basin-type solar distiller, shows their relative significance in affecting performance, and indicates the factors which may be altered for over-all improvement and economy.

Characteristics of Solar Radiation

In clear, summer weather, solar radiation is received on a surface normal to the sun's rays at a rate of approximately 1.3 to 1.4 cal./sq. cm., min., or about 300 B.t.u./ sq. ft., hr. On a horizontal surface in central United States, this is equivalent to about 2500 B.t.u./sq. ft., day. Cloudiness, higher or lower latitude, and seasonal changes cause average annual values to range from near 2000 in the Southwest down to about 1200 in the Northwest and Great Lakes Area (2). The low energy intensity may readily be appreciated by comparing heat transfer rates in conventional boilers, as high as 100,000 B.t.u./sq. ft., hour.

Covering a wide spectral range, solar radiation is divided roughly into two equal energy portions—the ultraviolet and visible in the 0.25- to 0.7-micron wave lengths, and the infrared out to about 2 or 2.5 microns.

Other properties of solar radiation important to its uses are its distribution between direct and diffuse, its absorption, reflection, and transmission by various opaque and transparent materials, and its chemical effects on them. As basin distillers involve no focusing of solar radiation, diffusion of solar radiation by haze and clouds is not detrimental except in the reduction of total incident energy. In these systems, the ability of common black surfaces to absorb about 95% of the solar radiation, averaged over its whole spectrum, is utilized by use of such a surface in the bottom of the basin. Glass and certain clear plastic films are almost perfectly transparent to the solar spectrum, but there are a few per cent specular reflection from these surfaces (ranging up to a large fraction at high angles of incidence, however), and some ultraviolet absorption, particularly in the impurities in glass. Some plastic films absorb ultraviolet radiation also, and if they do, there will be degradation of the film and ultimate failure due to loss of strength.

A further important property of these transparent materials is their high opacity to long wave radiation beyond, say, 5 microns. Glass in its common thicknesses is completely opaque to this thermal radiation, as emitted from a surface at temperatures below a few hundred degrees. Some plastic films have transmission bands in these ranges, but they are largely opaque. This diathermanous property or so-called "greenhouse effect" is advantageously used in solar heat systems, including solar stills, by the "trapping" of solar radiation in the transparent enclosure while greatly reducing or eliminating direct radiation loss from the heated absorbing surface.

Basin-Type Solar Distiller

Two forms of the basin-type solar distiller are shown in Figures 1 and 2. Each of these is subject to numerous minor design variations. The configuration of the glass-covered still shown is an improved form of a 1-acre brackish water distillation plant built in Chile in 1872 (3).

The basin is formed by laying asphalt or concrete on slightly sloping ground, and if not sufficiently black, some type of black paint or other coating is applied to the basin surface. Low perimeter and partition walls of concrete block, say 18 inches high, subdivide the basin into long bays several feet wide. Midway between partitions, a post and beam arrangement is provided, which, in conjunction with the tops of the partitions, supports large sheets of window glass at an angle of 10° to 15° with the horizontal. Channel-shaped neoprene extrusions serve as protective seals at the upper and lower glass edges, and pressure-sensitive tapes are applied to seal the narrow spaces between adjacent pieces of glass. A sheet metal gutter is affixed to the partition beneath the lower glass edges, with a slight slope to one end of the structure. Piping is arranged for supply of salt water to each basin section and for overflow of unevaporated brine and runoff of distillate from each section.

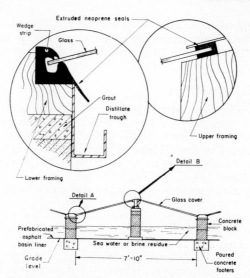

Figure 1. Typical section of glass-covered
deep-basin solar still

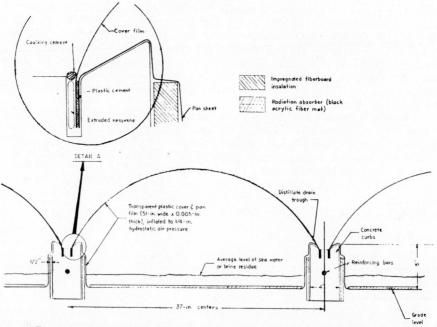

Figure 2. Cross-sectional view of basic construction of plastic stills

New designs are under development which involve simpler and cheaper construction while retaining the same general functions.

The most satisfactory form of plastic distillation unit already tested is shown schematically in Figure 2.

A tube is formed by sealing together two long strips of polyester film at their edges. [Teslar, a Du Pont polyester film in a 0.003-inch (3-mil) thickness, has been tested.]

Prior to sealing, a loosely felted mat of black acrylic fiber is laid on one of the films and secured to it at intervals with a plastic cement. This long, narrow assembly is then laid on the ground between parallel concrete curbs about 6 inches high, and the edges are anchored in grooves in the curb tops. The contour of the curb tops also forms troughs for distillate collection and flow to the lower ends of the basin. At the basin ends, the plastic film is gathered into similar slots, and inlet and outlet piping through the curbs and plastic is secured with bolted flanges. One of these pipes is connected to a small blower which inflates the plastic tube and maintains a slight positive pressure in the enclosed space. The complete assembly is then a bottom plastic film directly on the ground, a black, radiation-absorbing mat on the film, a shallow layer (1 or 2 inches) of salt water with occasional tranverse dams to maintain a completely wetted surface, an air-supported cover film, and curb sides which secure the films in place and provide channels for condensate.

This design is also being improved, primarily by widening the tube and providing simpler end arrangements.

Distillation Process

General Aspects. Superficially, solar distillation in basin-type stills is an extremely simple process. Solar radiation passes through the transparent cover and the salt water in the basin with only slight intensity reduction. It is then practically completely absorbed on the black bottom, the energy being released as heat to the black surface. The salt water is warmed by contact with the heated surface, and as its temperatures rises, so does its vapor pressure. Quiet vaporization into the air space above the water thus takes place, increasing the humidity substantially to saturation. Convection currents then carry the vapor to the vicinity of the cooler transparent surface, where condensation accordingly occurs. The air-vapor mixture, still saturated but at a lower temperature, slowly returns to the bottom of the still, where it is rehumidified. Condensate forming on the sloping cover runs down into the collecting troughs, while its latent heat of condensation is dissipated to the surrounding air by radiation and convection from the cover, actually an air-cooled condenser.

To avoid salt accumulation in the basin, brine is intermittently or continuously withdrawn, and salt water is supplied to maintain a reasonably constant level in the distiller basin. Because distillate and brine are warmer than the feed water, a heat exchanger may be used for heat conservation and higher yield.

If a comparatively shallow layer of salt water is provided, as in the plastic still described, there are large fluctuations in operating conditions and rates of water production. On a typical sunny morning, cold salt water in the still will first be slowly warmed by the rather low intensity radiation characteristics of that part of the day. As the water temperature rises, distillation commences, say at a typical 50° C. (about 120° F.). The rate rises rapidly as the salt water temperature increases up to a maximum of about 70° C. shortly after noon. It then drops off gradually in the afternoon, continuing a few hours after sundown until the salt water has cooled practically to the cover temperature.

In a so-called "deep-basin" still, there is less fluctuation because of thermal storage in about 1 foot of salt water. Solar radiation causes a daytime temperature rise of only 5° or 10° C., the basin reaching maxima of about 50° C. Distillation proceeds slowly throughout daytime hours, then increases after sundown because of lowered cover temperature due to atmospheric cooling in the evening. The stored heat causes distillation to continue throughout the night, accompanied by basin temperature decrease of several degrees. The continuous and reasonably uniform water production of the deep-basin still makes control and heat exchange comparatively simple.

Energy Considerations. As in any distillation process, the fundamental requirements for energy transfer in a solar still are supplying heat to the evaporating water and removing heat from the condensing vapor. These two heat rates are essentially equal—about 1040 B.t.u. per pound of distilled water. Incident solar radiation must provide heat for several other processes, however. These are shown schematically in

Figure 3. Except for the latent heat of condensation released at the transparent surface, they all are forms of energy loss. Of primary significance in design and in evaluation of performance is the energy balance drawn around the distiller basin. This input is seen to be the incident solar energy minus reflection from the cover and the very small absorption in the cover. The feed water might also be considered a sensible heat supply, but it would usually be cooler than the product streams, and hence at a convenient base temperature, having zero energy input.

Enthalpy leaving the basin comprises the latent heat in recovered water vapor, thermal radiation from salt water and basin bottom to the cover, sensible heat transferred from salt water surface to cover via the circulating air in the enclosure, conduction loss to the ground or other surroundings, sensible heat in effluent distillate and brine streams, and enthalpy in any vapor or liquid streams which may escape the enclosure and recovery facilities. Of these losses, the most significant are radiation from the basin to the cover and the sensible heat transferred by air. The latter is, of course, an unavoidable accompaniment of the useful transfer in the water vapor. The salt water temperature is the variable primarily affecting this loss—the higher it is, the larger is the water vapor pressure, the lower the air-water vapor ratio, and hence the lower the convective transfer loss. Thermal radiation is increased, however, as basin temperature rises, so these two principal losses are influenced by operating temperature in opposite ways.

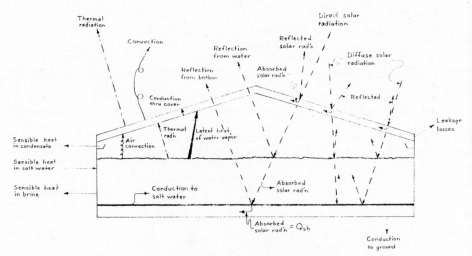

Figure 3. Energy flow in solar distiller

– – – – – Solar radiation, substantially below 2 microns
— – — Thermal radiation, substantially above 5 microns

Cover temperature is another variable which controls distillation rate and efficiency. All of the heat transferred to the underside of the cover from the basin, plus the small solar absorption in it, must be dissipated by convection to the surrounding air and by radiation to the sky. Ambient temperature, wind velocity, and atmospheric clarity all influence the temperature driving force necessary to attain the equilibrium heat transfer rate. Cover temperature, in turn, affects basin temperature, so that an over-all equality in heat flows prevails. The primary variable remains, of course, the solar energy input rate, its most important effect being the temperature level in the salt water basin.

Because sunshine is intermittent, there is always a transient effect in solar still conditions, steady state never actually being realized. Energy considerations may therefore also involve sensible heat inventory, and its change, in the salt water layer, the basin structure, and even the soil under the basin. In shallow basins, marked changes occur, hour-to-hour, and in the deeper basins, large sensible heat storage results in substantial enthalpy inventory changes from day to night and from one day to the next.

The numerous uncontrollable weather variables, the variety of heat transfer processes occurring, and the transient nature of the operation make solar distillation a much more complicated process than it first seems, particularly in so far as its design and predicted performance are concerned.

Design Procedure

Prediction of Performance. For purposes of distiller design, and particularly the determination of area requirements for a specified water production rate, or for predicting the productivity of a unit of specified design and size, simultaneous solution of several energy rate equations is required. But prior to this calculation, several decisions and assumptions must be made and some approximations relating to solar energy input need to be used. For illustration, let us assume that a glass-covered, deep-basin distiller is being considered as a means for supplying a specified annual quantity of distilled water in a particular locality where solar radiation and other meteorological data are available. The basic problem is then the determination of the annual output of a unit area of solar distiller basin operating at these conditions.

It may be further assumed that the total productivity of the distiller each month is the monthly average as determined by use of mean values of solar radiation and atmospheric temperature, and that there is sufficient thermal storage in the basin to reduce day-to-night temperature fluctuations enough for applicability of monthly mean conditions.

The heat balance on the transparent cover per unit area may be represented by the equation:

$$(h_{c,\,o} + h_{r,\,o})(t_g - t_a) = (h_{c,\,i} + h_{r,\,i})(t_b - t_g) + E\lambda \tag{1}$$

This relation neglects the very small absorption of solar energy in the transparent cover, and the small temperature drop through the cover.

An over-all energy balance on the distillation plant, above the reference temperature, t_g, is:

$$\frac{Q_{sh}}{24} = (h_{c,\,o} + h_{r,\,o})(t_g - t_a) + E(t_b - t_g) + L \tag{2}$$

It is assumed for the above equation that cover area is equal to basin area, that the brine effluent rate equals the distillate rate, that the sea water supply is preheated by exchange to distillate temperature, and that the effective sky temperature for radiation is equal to atmospheric temperature.

The evaporation rate, E, is a function of vapor pressure difference (or temperature difference) between basin and cover. It is also dependent on the rate of air convection in the enclosure and the absolute humidity difference at basin surface and cover surface. Assuming saturation at each surface,

$$E = h_{c,\,i}(t_b - t_g) \left/ \frac{w_{\mathrm{da}}}{w_{\mathrm{H_2O}}} (H_{a,\,b} - H_{a,\,g}) \right. \tag{3}$$

With E expressed in terms of t_b and t_g, this relationship can be substituted in Equations 1 and 2, which then can be solved simultaneously for these two unknown temperatures. E can then be found by use of Equation 3.

In Equation 1, $h_{c,o}$ can be evaluated at some mean wind velocity by use of the relation $h_{c,o} = a + b\,V^n$, where a, b, and n are constants. In a design study based on a California coastal location, this convection coefficient was computed at 3.1 B.t.u./ hr., sq. ft., ° F., for a wind velocity of 6 miles per hour. The radiation transfer,

$h_{r,o}(t_g - t_a)$ is equal to $0.173 \times 10^{-8}(T_g^4 - T_a^4) \times 0.937$, where the last term is the emissivity of glass. The internal convection coefficient, $h_{c,i}$ may be expressed as $h_{c,i} = 0.256(t_b - t_g)^{0.25}$ representing convection transfer between two closely spaced horizontal surfaces (6). Internal radiation transfer $h_{r,i}(t_b - t_g) = 0.173 \times 10^{-8}(T_b^4 - T_g^4) \times 0.9$, where the last term is the effective emissivity of the basin bottom and the salt water surface.

The value of E in Equations 1, 2, and 3, as obtained from Equation 3, depends on terms already described and on other factors. The ratio w_{da}/w_{H_2O} is the pounds of dry air circulating in the distiller per pound of water distilled. Assuming the air is continually saturated, alternately at basin temperature and cover temperature, this ratio depends only on vapor pressures, which depend in turn on the two temperatures. The term $(H_{a,b} - H_{a,g})$ may be replaced by $C_p(t_b - t_g)$, and

$$E = 0.256(t_b - t_g)^{0.25}(w_{H_2O}/w_{da})C_p \tag{4}$$

Although conduction losses to the ground and miscellaneous heat losses through moisture escape are functions of basin or cover temperature, they depend on other factors of indeterminate magnitude. Soil conductivity, construction tightness, and other on-site variables are difficult to predict. For these reasons, practical design can be accomplished by assuming a constant heat loss based on normally expected conditions. In the design study previously referred to, a heat loss of 50 B.t.u./sq. ft., day was assumed.

Substitution of $E = 0.256(t_b - t_g)^{0.25} w_{H_2O}/0.24 w_{da}$ into Equations 1 and 2, and replacement of other terms by their equivalents shown above, yield:

$$3.1(t_g - t_a) + 0.162 \times 10^{-8}(T_g^4 - T_a^4) = 0.256(t_b - t_g)^{1.25} + 0.156 \times 10^{-8}(T_b^4 - T_g^4) + 1.07(t_b - t_g)^{0.25}(w_{H_2O}/w_{da})\lambda \tag{5}$$

$$Q_{sh}/24 = 3.1(t_g - t_a) + 0.162 \times 10^{-8}(T_g^4 - T_a^4) + 1.07(t_b - t_g)^{1.25} \times w_{H_2O}/w_{da} + 50/24 \tag{6}$$

The term Q_{sh} is the net solar radiant energy absorption rate on the basin bottom. It is equivalent to total radiation incident on the basin cover minus reflection from the cover, the water surface, and the basin bottom, and minus loss due to structural shadowing. Its determination from Weather Bureau records of total daily radiation on a horizontal surface is complicated by many factors such as variation in angle of incidence, and resulting transmissivity of cover, hourly and seasonally, intensity change due to cloudiness, and different properties of direct and diffuse radiations. Detailed explanation of these meteorological and optical calculations is beyond the scope of this paper, but may be found in the literature (5).

After evaluation of the net solar heat input rates to the salt water, as monthly averages (or more frequently if desired), they and the atmospheric temperature averages are substituted in Equations 5 and 6. The two equations can then be solved by trial for the mean basin and cover temperatures each month. Distillation rate is then obtained by substitution of these values in Equation 4. The first and second terms on the right-hand side of Equation 5 may be separately evaluated for convection and radiation losses from basin to cover.

Figure 4 illustrates the results of this type of analysis for a deep-basin solar still in the San Diego area. Thermal radiation from basin to cover is the largest loss, followed by reflection of solar radiation from the cover and air convection inside the still. Solar utilization efficiency is the height of the lowest curve as a fraction of the height of the top curve, ranging from about 30% in January to 50% through the summer months.

From such information, the performance of a proposed solar distiller installation can be anticipated and the area requirements for a specified water production rate determined.

The equations and procedure described here apply only to steady-state operation. If there is large fluctuation in basin temperature, or if a more precise day-to-day evaluation is desired, another term must be included in the heat balances. This is the

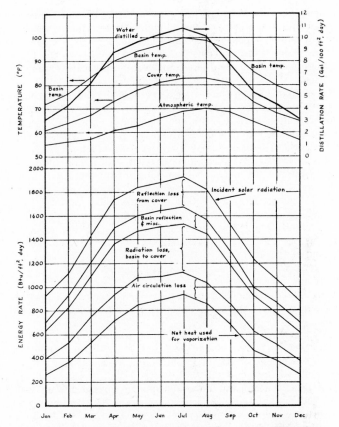

**Figure 4. Predicted average performance of deep-basin
solar distiller in San Diego area**

change in thermal energy inventory from the start to the end of the analysis period, represented by the product of the mass of salt water per square foot of basin, the temperature change from the start to the end of the period, and the heat capacity of the water. An approximation for the change in thermal storage in the basin bottom and walls ought to be made also.

In distillers carrying only a shallow water layer, distillation ceases at night because the basin cools substantially to cover temperature. Predictions of performance must therefore be based on highly varying solar and temperature conditions. The equations previously developed, including a thermal storage term, can be used in an hour-by-hour computation of temperatures and distillation rates throughout a number of typical days of low, moderate, and high solar intensities at several atmospheric temperatures, for solar positions corresponding to summer, fall, and winter (spring is equivalent to fall). The computed distillation rates can then be used in conjunction with weather data for the locality in question to estimate monthly, seasonal, and annual distilled water output per unit area.

Performance Improvement

An analysis of the solar distillation process shows that performance is remarkably insensitive to all variables except solar radiation rate. As atmospheric temperature changes, basin and cover temperatures move similarly, so that their difference remains at a value which dissipates the absorbed solar energy. Wind velocity also appears a variable of minor importance. Even the major design variable of basin depth has not yet been found of major influence on distillation rate.

Of the three major losses previously shown, reflection from the transparent cover could be most easily reduced. By the use of an interference layer somewhat less than 1 micron in thickness, the reflectivity of glass and plastics can be materially reduced. Processes for coating or etching the surface have been developed, but unless applied on large scale, they are expensive. At least one process for controlled etching of glass to produce a low-reflection surface could be extremely cheap on the scale of many thousands of square feet. Reduction of this average 20% loss to perhaps 5% would result in an increase in the basin-to-cover temperature difference, and a water distillation rate increase of about 20%. Distillers covered with plastic film rather than glass may have their performance increased even more if film reflectivity is reduced and if the film is rendered wettable, so that reflection from condensed water droplets is eliminated. Coatings of TiO_2 and other materials show promise for making permanently wettable films (1), and low reflection coatings may also be workable.

Radiation from salt water surface to the wetted cover is the largest loss, but there seems to be no assurance that it can be reduced. There is some evidence that microscopic roughening of the underside of the cover may render that surface reflective for the bulk of the long wave radiation (peaking at about 8 to 10 microns) from the water surface, without appreciably reducing its transparency for short wave solar radiation. However, even a thin film of condensate on the cover is an effective absorber for thermal radiation, so the benefit of a thermally reflective cover may not be realized in ordinary basin-type stills.

Another approach to radiation loss reduction might be the alteration of the salt water surface in some manner to lower its emissivity for thermal radiation. If a transparent thin liquid film or porous solid film of low thermal emissivity, permeable to water vapor, could be floated on the salt water, solar energy could continue to be absorbed on the basin bottom, water would vaporize, but thermal radiation loss would be reduced. Whether materials with these properties can be found and successfully utilized remains to be seen.

The third important loss is by air convection inside the distiller. This air circulation is a necessary accompaniment of water distillation. The higher the basin temperature, the higher is the water vapor pressure and the lower the ratio of air to water vapor in the atmosphere of the distillation unit. Factors tending to maximize basin temperatures will therefore reduce this heat loss because of the lower concentration of air in the atmosphere of the distiller enclosure. But as radiation loss increases with rise in basin temperature, these two losses cannot be simultaneously minimized by temperature change. Any effort toward reducing convection in the distiller would be undesirable, because this is the only significant mechanism for water distillation.

If the evaporating and condensing surfaces were very close together, perhaps an inch or less, some diffusion transfer of water vapor would occur, without physical transport by circulating air. However, limited heat transfer by conduction from basin to cover could also occur. It is possible that the net effect would be a moderate increase in the water yield and a corresponding decrease in heat loss due to air circulation. But the practicality of close positioning of salt water surface and cover is questionable.

If the relative humidity of the air in the distiller enclosure is considerably less than 100% at the salt water surface and at the cover, more convective loss is actually occurring than estimated. Increasing these air moisture contents by better contact of air and cover, or by otherwise altering circulation patterns by fan, baffles, or enclosure shape could reduce air circulation loss and increase productivity. Whether the economics of such steps might be attractive remains to be determined.

In view of the several possibilities for reducing energy losses, solar distiller yields might be substantially improved. Decrease of radiation and convection losses to half their present levels, along with the use of low-reflection cover surfaces, would result in about 50% increase in summer production and roughly double the winter performance. In sunny climates, yields of 0.2 gallon of distilled water per square foot should be possible on a sunny summer day. Average winter yields would approach 0.1 gal./sq. ft., day. Year-round performance should exceed 0.15 gal./sq. ft., day, if these improvements can be realized. The technical accomplishment of these measures as well as their economic attractiveness is, of course, not assured, but studies along such lines appear of value.

Acknowledgment

The support and cooperation of the Office of Saline Water, U. S. Department of the Interior, in a solar distillation program, a portion of which is the subject of this paper, are gratefully acknowledged.

Nomenclature

$h_{c,\,o}$ = convection heat transfer coefficient from cover to atmosphere, B.t.u./hr., sq. ft., ° F.

$h_{r,\,o}$ = radiation heat transfer coefficient from cover to atmosphere, B.t.u./hr., sq. ft., ° F.

$h_{c,\,i}$ = convection heat transfer coefficient from salt water surface to cover of still, B.t.u./hr., sq. ft., ° F.

$h_{r,\,i}$ = radiation heat transfer coefficient from salt water surface to cover of still, B.t.u./hr., sq. ft., ° F.

C_p = heat capacity of air, B.t.u./lb., °F.

t_g, T_g = temperature of transparent cover, assumed equal to distillate temperature, ° F. or ° R.

t_a, T_a = atmospheric temperature, ° F. or ° R.

t_b, T_b = temperature of salt water in basin, ° F. or ° R.

E = water evaporation (and condensation) rate, lb./hr., sq. ft.

λ = latent heat of condensation at basin temperature (plus difference in sensible heat of condensate at basin and cover temperatures), B.t.u./lb. (equals approximately 1050 B.t.u./lb.)

H = enthalpy of air, B.t.u./lb.

Q_{sh} = net solar radiation rate absorbed on basin bottom, B.t.u., sq. ft., day (equals incident radiation minus reflection from cover, salt water surface, and basin bottom)

V = wind velocity, miles/hr.

L = net miscellaneous heat loss rate, B.t.u./hr., sq. ft.

w_{da} = pounds of dry air circulating per unit time

$w_{\mathrm{H_2O}}$ = pounds of water distilled per unit time

Literature Cited

(1) Franklin Institute, "Producing Permanently Hydrophilic Surfaces on Plastic Films for Solar Stills," Office of Saline Water, U. S. Dept. of Interior, Progress Rept. 29 (1959).
(2) Hand, I. F., *Heating and Ventilating* 50 (7), 73 (July 1953).
(3) Harding, J., *Proc. Inst. Civil Engrs.* 73, 284 (1883).
(4) Löf, G. O. G., "Demineralization of Saline Water with Solar Energy," Office of Saline Water, U. S. Dept. of Interior, Progress Rept. 4 (1954).
(5) Löf, G. O. G., "Design and Evaluation of Deep-Basin, Direct Solar Heated Distiller for Demineralization of Saline Water," Rept. to office of Saline Water, U.S. Dept of Interior, 1959.
(6) Wilkes, G. B., Peterson, C. M. F., *Heating, Piping, and Air Conditioning* 9, 505 (1937).

RECEIVED for review July 20, 1960. Accepted July 22, 1960.

Field Evaluation of Solar Sea Water Stills

J. W. BLOEMER, R. A. COLLINS, and J. A. EIBLING

Battelle Memorial Institute, Columbus, Ohio

Construction methods and performance data are presented on solar sea water stills under evaluation at the Florida Solar Distillation Research Station. Three stills representing two basic designs have been constructed and operated there: a 2500-sq.-foot glass-covered deep-basin still and 2300- and 500-sq.-foot air-supported plastic stills. Other types of stills are being developed for future construction and field evaluation.

Among the methods of saline water conversion being investigated by the Department of the Interior's Office of Saline Water is direct solar distillation. One phase of the study of solar distillation includes the field evaluation of stills of promising design, which is being carried out for the Office of Saline Water by Battelle Memorial Institute.

The objectives of the research program are: to obtain realistic engineering and economic data on solar distillation plants and to develop methods of improving their initial and operating costs. Field tests are being conducted at a research station in northern Florida, where three solar stills have been constructed and others are planned to be built. The stills are extensively instrumented, so that heat losses and other performance data may be accurately determined.

Solar Distillation Research Station

The Florida research station was established in 1958 on the Ponce de Leon Lighthouse Reservation near Port Orange on land made available to the Department of the Interior by the U. S. Coast Guard. Approximately $3/4$ acre is fenced in and accessible for the construction of solar stills.

Sea water feed for the stills is pumped from the Halifax River, which at the point of feed intake has a salinity of about 35,000 p.p.m., the same as that of the ocean. Much of the research instrumentation is housed in a centrally located concrete block shelter, which was constructed underground principally to prevent its shading the nearby stills. One of the previously existing buildings on the reservation was renovated to provide an office, a conference room, and equipment storage space.

Figure 1 is a view of part of the field-evaluation site as seen from the top of the lighthouse. The two stills shown in the background are air-supported plastic units. A glass-covered deep-basin still can be seen in the foreground. The instrument house is immediately to the left of the stills. A 2000-gallon tank for storage of sea water is visible in the lower right corner of the fenced-in area.

Figure I. Solar still evaluation area as viewed from lighthouse

Deep-Basin Still

The first still constructed at the station is a glass-covered unit having a so-called deep basin that maintains the saline water at a depth of 10 to 12 inches. During operation, solar radiation, transmitted through the glass cover, heats the water in the basin beneath the cover. Some of the warm water evaporates and subsequently condenses on the underside of the cover. Condensate flows to the lower edges of the cover and is collected in suitable gutters. The thermal inertia of the large mass of water in the basin provides continuous distillation even during the night. The design calls for placement of the basin directly on the ground, with no thermal insulation, on the premise that heat losses to the dry earth will be relatively small.

Construction. The deep-basin still was conceived and designed initially by George O. G. Löf, Engineering Consultant, Denver, Colo., a consultant to the Office of Saline Water. As built at the Florida station, the still has served mainly as a research tool rather than as a demonstration of the lowest possible cost of construction. Construction was started in the summer of 1958 and completed in January 1959. The unit has been in operation about 7 months, operation having been suspended several times so that various improvements could be made.

Figure 2 is a photograph of the deep-basin still. The concrete curbing shown along the near edge of the still is part of a heat-exchanger flume in which feed water can be preheated.

Figure 3 shows a cross section of one of the bays of the deep-basin still, with enlarged views of the upper and lower glass seals. The over-all dimensions of the still are 55 × 55 feet, providing approximately 2450 sq. feet of basin area distributed among six 8-foot-wide bays. Feed water enters the basin from the heat-exchanger flume, and blowdown is removed by overflow weirs. The blowdown and the distillate effluents pass through plastic pipes immersed in the sea water contained in the heat-exchanger flume, thereby preheating the incoming feed.

The glass cover is made of 4-foot-square window-glass panels arranged in gable-roof fashion with a slope of 15 degrees. The upper edges of the glass panels are supported with timber framing members and are sealed with neoprene extrusions and aluminum cap strips. The lower edges of the glass panels are sealed by the special ex-

Figure 2.   Glass-covered deep-basin still

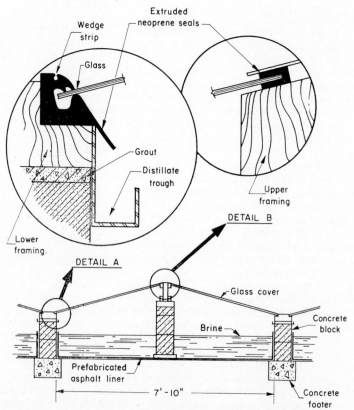

Figure 3.   Typical section of glass-covered deep-basin still

truded neoprene strips shown in Figure 3. Spaces between adjacent glass panels are sealed with pressure-sensitive tape.

The exterior walls, the basin divider partitions, and the heat-exchanger flume are constructed of concrete block on poured concrete footers. The basin was made watertight by placing prefabricated asphalt matting directly on the soil and on the inside surfaces of the walls of the still. Two-inch-thick Foamglass insulation was placed around the perimeter walls so that the edge heat losses would be comparable to those of much larger stills.

Performance. So far, the deep-basin still has been operated only under batchtype control—that is, without continuous blowdown or heat exchange to the incoming sea water. In determining the performance of the still, incident solar radiation and distillate production are measured daily. From this information, the specific production in gallons per square foot per day and the thermal efficiency can be determined. In addition to the daily collection of performance data, hourly collections are made during periodic energy- and mass-balance runs.

Figures 4 and 5 show the daily and the average monthly productivity of the deep-basin still at various solar-radiation intensities. The scatter of data points for the daily

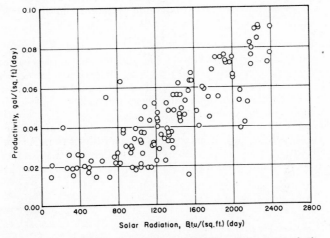

Figure 4. Variation with solar radiation of average daily distillate production of deep-basin still

pilot of productivity is wide because of the heat-storage effects on the day-to-day basis. However, it is evident from the nearly straight-line relationship of the monthly average plot in Figure 5 that the rate of distillate production is almost entirely dependent on the amount of solar radiation. During long-term operation, the effects of differences in ambient air temperature and wind velocity appear to be minor. As shown in Figure 4, the production rate of the still was never below 0.015 gallon per square foot per day, even with extremely low solar radiation. This is due to the fact that the low-radiation days are relatively few and widely spaced; consequently, the heat supplied by the warm ground beneath the still and the sensible heat stored in the brine can maintain the productivity of the still on low-radiation days. On days of low radiation which are preceded by several days of high radiation, still efficiencies as high as 158% have been calculated. On the other hand, on days of high solar radiation preceeded by several days of low radiation, efficiencies below 10% have been recorded, because heat is absorbed by the ground and the brine. The average monthly efficiencies varied between 26 and 35% but, for the above reasons, a direct relationship between thermal efficiency and radiation is not apparent.

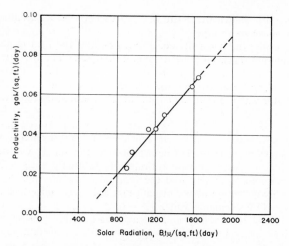

Figure 5.   Variation with solar radiation of average monthly distillate production of deep-basin still

Distribution of Energy. During a 3-day period, October 7 to 9, 1959, a continuous performance run was made on the deep-basin still for the purpose of computing an energy balance. Each item pertinent to the energy balance was measured, except convection loss to the atmosphere, which was obtained by calculations. The experimentally determined losses were then compared with the corresponding calculated losses. These showed remarkably close agreement.

Figure 6 shows the productivity, the heat flows, and some of the more significant temperatures of the still as they varied throughout the 72-hour run. As shown, the maximum distillate outputs each day occurred near 7 P.M. and 10 A.M., respectively. The total radiation curve shown in Figure 6 is the sum of the solar and atmospheric radiation.

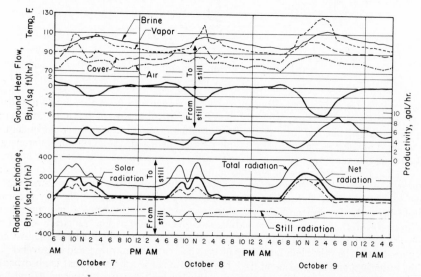

Figure 6.   Productivity, heat flows, and temperatures of deep-basin still during 72-hour period

On a 24-hour basis, the atmospheric radiation is twice as much as the solar radiation. It is doubtful that the atmospheric radiation contributes to the useful output of the still; most, if not all of it, is reradiated to the sky. However, with the methods used to measure radiation for the energy balance, it is necessary to account for radiation from all sources.

The net radiation between the still and its surroundings was measured with a radiometer. The difference between the net and the total radiation was considered to be radiation from the warm components of the still and reflection of atmospheric and solar radiation from the still. The curve of still radiation in Figure 6 is almost a mirror image of the total radiation curve, still radiation being greatest during the day when the still is the warmest and solar radiation is being reflected from the cover.

Table I gives the distribution of the energy input to the deep-basin still as determined from the results of the 3-day energy balance. As shown, 32% of the available energy was utilized for useful output of the still. The largest single loss, 25%, was heat radiation from the basin water. The remainder of the heat losses, taken separately, are relatively moderate; collectively, however, they account for about 43% of the incoming solar energy.

Table I. Approximate Distribution of Solar Radiation Reaching Deep-Basin Still

(Based on 3-day energy balance run in October 1959)

Distribution	% of Solar Radiation[a]
Evaporation	32
Brine leakage and vapor loss	0
Ground and edge heat loss	2
Solar radiation reflected by still	12
Solar radiation absorbed by cover	10
Radiation from water in basin	25
Internal convection	7
Re-evaporation of distillate and unaccounted-for losses	12
Total	100

[a] Incident solar radiation averaged 1400 B.t.u./(sq. ft.) (day) for 3-day period.

Methods of Improving Deep-Basin Still. As shown in Table I, the sum of the ground and edge losses from the deep-basin still was only 2%. This is especially noteworthy in view of the fact that the bottom of the basin is not insulated, and suggests that insulation of the basin of a large still probably could not be justified economically.

The solar radiation reflected from the surface of the basin water and the glass cover of the still amounted to 12% of the available energy. The reflection from the glass cover could be reduced by using treated glass; with present techniques, the cost may be prohibitive. Tilting the cover of the still at an angle equal to the latitude facing south would be another way of reducing the glass reflection. If this were done, the mean yearly angle of incidence between the solar radiation and the cover would be at a minimum, but more glass would be needed to cover the still. The reflection loss from the basin water could be decreased by floating an absorptive foam or mat on the water surface. The solutions for reducing reflection loss presented above would have to be examined further from an economic viewpoint to determine whether they can be recommended.

If the radiation from the basin water to the still cover could be eliminated or substantially reduced, a large gain in productivity would be effected. To accomplish this, it would be necessary to have a cover, the underside of which would reflect long-wave radiation emitted by the water surface. The ideal cover would transmit all incoming radiation, both long- and short-wave length, and reflect all radiation emanating from the basin water. Because such a cover is theoretically not attainable, the next best would be one that would transmit short-wave-length or solar radiation and reflect long-wave-length radiation. If the cover is made of glass or other material that absorbs long-wave-length radiation, it might be advantageous to treat the cover in such a way that it will reflect long-wave-length radiation from the underside only. However, water is a good absorber of long-wave-length radiation. Even a film of condensate only 0.002 inch thick on the underside of the cover would absorb almost all radiation from the basin water; consequently, the effectiveness of a specially treated cover would be nullified. To take advantage of a reflective cover, it may be necessary to use an external condenser to keep the cover free of distillate.

The internal convection loss is moderate, so that measures suggested to reduce this loss, such as replacing the air inside the still with a gas of lower specific heat or operating the still under vacuum, may not be economically feasible.

The re-evaporation of the distillate may account for a fairly large loss and should be reduced, if possible. This could be accomplished by shading the distillate collection troughs from direct sunlight. A way to measure the amount of re-evaporation accurately has not yet been devised, but calculations indicate that the loss from re-evaporation may be as large as 10%, in which case the unaccounted-for loss in Table I would be only about 2%. Drops of distillate on the relatively warm lower neoprene extrusion have been seen to evaporate before they could reach the collection trough, thus establishing visual proof of their re-evaporation. It is suspected that there is also re-evaporation in the collection troughs, particularly those on the north walls of the bays which are heated by direct sunlight.

Experience gained during construction pointed to several ways in which the still could be substantially improved from the standpoints of sounder construction and lower cost. For example, considerable labor and materials could be saved by eliminating the footers beneath the perimeter walls and supporting the walls directly on the waterproof basin liner. The weight of the superstructure of the still is much less than the bearing capacity of most types of soil, including sand.

Another design change that would reduce construction costs would be elimination of the partitions between the bays. The bottom of the basin, instead of being composed of several separate mats bordered by dividing walls, could consist of one continuous watertight mat. All supports for the glass cover, both upper and lower sections, would then be on concrete-block pedestals resting directly on the basin bottom. This arrangement would be similar to that used to support the center ridge of the existing deep-basin still. The bottom of the still could be constructed of waterproof blacktop on crushed rock rather than of prefabricated asphaltic mat. This material could be laid quickly and economically in large areas with standard equipment.

Preliminary cost estimates indicate that in addition to making these suggested improvements, it is highly desirable to work toward the design of a still that might have a life of 50 years with low maintenance. In designing for a life of 50 years, no wood should be considered for the structure; the center ridge support could be constructed of aluminum or of preformed concrete beams. These materials may be more expensive than wood, but when the maintenance and replacement of wooden components for a 50-year period are considered, it is apparent that concrete or aluminum components would be more economical.

Air-Supported Plastic Stills

The two air-supported plastic stills were constructed during the winter of 1958–1959. Some additional and some modified bays were installed in the large plastic still after that time. Both stills have been in continuous operation since January 1959, and, as a result, considerable performance data have been collected. Inasmuch as the performance of the two plastic stills is similar, for brevity the discussion in this paper deals mainly with the larger unit.

Construction of Du Pont Stills. The air-supported plastic stills were built with the cooperation and assistance of E. I. du Pont de Nemours & Co., which also furnished the plastic films used in the construction. Frank E. Edlin of Du Pont designed the air-supported stills and assisted in their construction at the research station.

Figure 7 is a photograph of the 2300-sq.-foot air-supported plastic still. This still consists of rows of separate channels, each provided with a waterproof plastic basin and an air-supported transparent plastic cover. The design incorporates a relatively shallow basin, containing only a few inches of water, so that there is much less thermal inertia than in the deep-basin still.

Figure 8 shows the construction features of the air-supported plastic stills. A plastic pan sheet contains the feed water in the basin. A transparent plastic cover transmits the solar radiation and provides a condensing surface for the vapor. The cover film on the 500-sq.-foot still is 3-mil Teslar, while the cover film on the 2300-sq.-foot still is 5-mil Weatherable Mylar, except for three of the bays which have been replaced recently with Teslar bays. In each still, the cover film is supported by air pressure supplied by a small blower. Concrete curbs constitute the side walls of the basin and also provide an anchor for the plastic films. The pan sheet and cover films are secured by inserting their edges, together with an extruded neoprene strip, into a groove in the curbing. The basins walls and bottom are insulated to reduce heat losses. Other plastic films serve as a ground sheet and as an envelope to protect the thermal insulation from ground moisture. A black Orlon mat in the basin facilitates trapping of the solar radiation. The distillate collected in the troughs formed by the curbs flows to the low end of the bay. Still operation is a batch process, with make-up and brine flushing scheduled concurrently at intervals of approximately 1 week.

During the construction of the air-supported stills, two cost items were identified which can be reduced substantially: curbs and labor for assembling the plastic materials. One suggestion is to use extruded plastic curbing material with sand, water, or concrete for ballast. An extruded plastic cap with built-in grooves could be impressed in the concrete curb while the concrete is fresh.

The cost of labor for assembling the plastic materials in the field was high at first, because each of the plastic films comprising each bay had to be tucked into the grooves of the curbing. Later a prefabricated design was developed by Du Pont, utilizing Teslar envelopes. Each envelope consisted of a 4-mil Teslar pan sheet with an Orlon mat attached to it by means of a randomly applied spot adhesive and a 4-mil Testar cover film. The pan and cover film were sealed along the edges into a continuous envelope. No ground sheet was used. Three such prefabricated bays were installed in the large Du Pont still on the existing concrete curbs. The labor required for the installation of the prefabricated units was only one fourth of that required for the original bays.

Performance of Large Air-Supported Still. The large air-supported still has been in continuous operation since January 1959. One of the prefabricated bays (No. 14), which was installed in the large still, has no distillate leaks, whereas the other bays of the still have leaked distillate in varying amounts along the grooves in the curbing. These leaks represented a serious loss in productivity. Inasmuch as the loss can be prevented in future stills, the productivity of bay 14, rather than that of the entire still, is the better measure of the performance.

Figure 9 shows the variation with solar radiation of the average monthly production of the large Du Pont still for the first 12 months of operation. Similar data are given for the nonleaking bay, No. 14, during its 5 months of operation. As was the case with the glass-covered still, there is little deviation from a straight-line relationship between solar radiation intensity and productivity, indicating that the production of the still is primarily a function of solar radiation, not affected greatly by weather conditions. The difference between the two curves in Figure 9 attests to importance of obtaining completely leakproof seals at the seams. For example, at a solar radiation intensity of 2000 B.t.u./(sq. ft.) (day), bay 14 produced at a rate of 0.080 gal./(sq. ft.) (day), whereas the average for the entire still was 0.056 gal./(sq. ft.) (day). Inasmuch as all of the bays operated under approximately the same conditions, except for leakage, the average loss of distillate through leakage can be assumed to be 0.024 gal./(sq. ft.) (day) or 30%.

Figure 7.   Air-supported plastic still

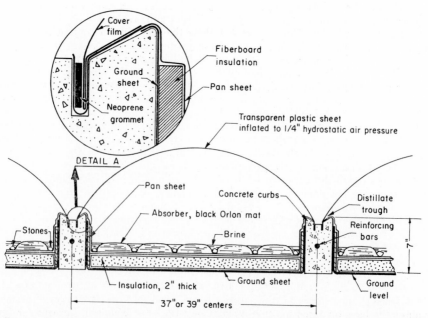

Figure 8.   Cross-sectional elevation showing construction of air-supported plastic stills

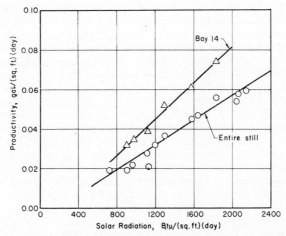

Figure 9. Variation with solar radiation of average monthly distillate production of large Du Pont still and bay 14

Figure 10 shows the performance of the large Du Pont still for the full year 1959. The production curve follows the solar radiation curve closely. The efficiency, although erratic, tends to increase with increased solar radiation. The production curve for bay 14 is also shown in Figure 10 and includes estimated values for the earlier months of the year, based on leakage rates derived from Figure 9.

The productivity of the large Du Pont still reaches a peak each day around 1 P.M. and drops off gradually during the night to almost zero by 6 A.M. Thus, the maximum

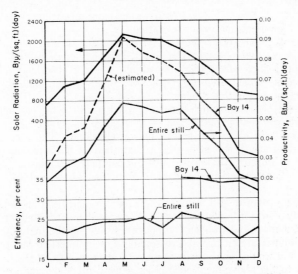

Figure 10. Performance of large Du Pont still by months in 1959

productivity lags only about 1 hour behind the peak solar radiation. There is about a 6-hour lag with the deep-basin still.

Energy-balance runs made with the large plastic still have shown that the heat loss to the ground through the insulated basin is negligible. The heat loss resulting from brine and vapor leakage appears to be about 2%, but this loss would be reduced to an even less significant amount in a fully developed still.

A comment should be made concerning the reflux of condensate in the air-supported plastic stills. Plastic films, unless specially treated, cause condensation in droplets which grow to considerable size before they run down the cover. Near the crown, the droplets frequently become so large that they fall into the brine. The reflux has been observed to be particularly severe when the cover is agitated by gusts of wind. One of the Mylar-covered bays of the large still was treated for wettability prior to installation, which appeared to reduce the reflux and gave evidence of increasing the output of the bay. Distillate leaks precluded the exact determination of the increase in productivity. The trial run, however, shows the desirability of developing methods of producing permanently hydrophylic surfaces on plastic covers. The Franklin Institute, under Office of Saline Water sponsorship, has treated both Mylar and Teslar films, and it is planned to place these on some of the bays of the large still.

Plans for Evaluation of Other Concepts of Solar Stills

The glass-covered deep-basin still and the air-supported plastic stills described in this paper represent only two of several designs that have been proposed for solar stills. Construction of additional solar stills at the Florida station is planned. These include: (1) an air-supported plastic still of improved design being developed by Du Pont, (2) a Telkes tilted single-effect still to be fabricated by the Curtiss-Wright Corp., (3) a plastic envelope-type still developed by the Bjorksten Laboratories, and (4) a glass-covered still designed for minimum cost and long life.

The new air-supported still will be of prefabricated construction. Teslar films will be used and the still will feature bays about 8 feet wide as compared with the 3-foot bays of the present still. Thus, the amount of curbing needed will be reduced considerably. Also, the piping will be greatly simplified, further reducing the cost of construction. Extruded plastic caps are being considered for the concrete curbs to simplify curb construction. Three 100-foot-long bays, providing a total of 2400 sq. feet, are planned for construction at the station.

Five modules of the Telkes tilted single-effect still, totaling 500 sq. feet, will be constructed by the Curtiss-Wright Corp. and shipped, unassembled, to the Florida station. The tilted single-effect still is essentially a black absorbent fabric supported at an angle by an impermeable sheet of plastic or metal and surrounded by a transparent cover above and an opaque cover below.

The Bjorksten plastic envelope-type still will be built of several modules totaling 600 sq. feet. It will consist of an almost vertical, black-fabric absorber-evaporator surrounded on all sides by a transparent plastic envelope. The concept of this still is similar to that of the Telkes still, except that there is no impermeable film on the underside of the absorber; the entire cover is composed of plastic film. Bjorksten Laboratories will construct the modules and ship them, unassembled, to the Florida station.

The new glass-covered still being considered for construction would follow the design previously described, wherein the still would be supported on a continuous watertight asphalt mat. All wooden components would be eliminated. A 50-year life expectancy, with low maintenance and reasonably low first cost, is the prime objective. The size of the still would be approximately 2500 sq. feet.

In addition to the above-mentioned stills, several other designs are being investigated at Battelle's laboratory in Columbus. Two of these are single-tube and double-tube stills. The single-tube still is merely a transparent plastic air-supported tube which lies in a shallow basin scooped out of the ground. The water in the basin serves to anchor the still, thereby eliminating the need for curbs. The distillate trough is heat-sealed to the transparent tube.

The double-tube still consists of an outer tube of air-supported transparent plastic film and an inner tube, in which the brine is contained, made of porous black plastic material. The porous inner tube transmits water vapor but not liquid water. Water evaporated inside the porous tube is transmitted through the porous material and condenses on the inside surface of the outer tube. The condensate collects in the trough which exists between the two tubes.

With respect to future activity in the field of solar distillation, three basic categories of solar stills can be visualized: permanent, semipermanent, and expendable. It is not possible to single out any one type as the best, because each has advantages in particular applications which may range from small remote domestic installations to plants covering many acres and serving municipalities, industry, and agriculture.

The glass-covered deep-basin still is an example of a permanent-type still. The initial cost of such a still might be relatively high and yet fresh water would be produced at a reasonable operating cost. Some of the plastic stills might be considered as being of the semipermanent class. These may be lower in initial cost than the permanent stills, but they are constructed of materials which have a shorter life. The single- and double-tube stills might be considered in the expendable category. If they can be manufactured at an extremely low cost, they could be replaced completely when any component failed. Little field preparation would be required for their construction, and they could be shipped compactly folded.

Conclusions

The experience in constructing and evaluating the solar stills at the research station has led to several important observations:

A productivity attainment of 0.10 gal./(sq. ft.)(day) at solar radiation intensities of 2000 B.t.u./(sq. ft.)(day) is possible. If careful attention is given to heat losses and to the use of selective radiation surfaces, productivity may be pushed appreciably above this. However, the economics of incorporating the means of improvement which have been presented must be determined on the basis of the results of further research and development.

The net heat loss to the ground in large basin-type stills is so small that the use of thermal insulation probably cannot be justified.

Because of the low output per unit of area of solar stills, even small distillate and brine leaks cannot be tolerated. Some of the sealing techniques used successfully in laboratory investigations have been found inadequate in field installations.

Evaporation of brine in a basin-type still can be carried to high concentrations without precipitation.

Algae growth did not occur in the stills when sea water feed was used, but developed on several occasions when brackish well water was supplied to the deep-basin still.

The use of "weed killer" or other means of preventing growth of vegetation under plastic basins is desirable to prevent punctures of the plastic films.

In addition to desirable transmissivity and reasonably long life, plastic films should be capable of being sealed readily at seams, of withstanding temperatures of up to 250°F. without melting, and of inducing film condensation when used as covers.

A pressure-sensitive tape having an extremely long life under sunlight exposure is needed for use in sealing gaps between glass panels.

Acknowledgment

The authors acknowledge the support and cooperation of the staff of the Office of Saline Water, under whose guidance the research program is being conducted. Many other persons have contributed to the research program, especially George O. G. Löf, engineering consultant, Frank E. Edlin of Du Pont, J. E. Rogers, Battelle technician at the research station, and D. W. Locklin of Battelle, who was formerly associated closely with the project.

RECEIVED for review July 7, 1960   Accepted July 15, 1960

Sea Water Demineralization by Ammonium Salts Ion Exchange

PAUL B. STEWART

Department of Mechanical Engineering and Sea Water Conversion
Laboratories, University of California, Berkeley, Calif.

Experimental data on mixed-bed ion exchange show
that ammonium bicarbonate—sea water salts ion
exchange is a possible route to saline water demineralization. Material balances for two processing
schemes are presented: a four-stage ion exchange
demineralizing plant using a regenerant solution of
ammonium bicarbonate in fresh water, and a seven-
stage plant, the first five stages of which use a
regenerant solution made by dissolving ammonium
bicarbonate in filtered sea water followed by two
stages of sodium chloride—free regenerant. The
distillation requirements for removing the ammonium salts between ion exchange stages and from
all effluent streams are examined, and compared to
the distillation load on multiple effect and multistage flash plants. On the basis of distillation
requirements alone, the ammonium salts ion exchange method is not competitive with direct
distillation.

Ion exchange, starting with natural zeolites used for water softening for approximately a half-century, has developed through the years to many other fields of application, including boiler feed water treatment, metals recovery from aqueous solution, the removal of ionized materials from sugar solutions, and the production of high purity water for special uses. This expansion of the uses of ion exchange technology has in large measure been made possible by improved ion exchange media: synthetic zeolites, the so-called carbonaceous zeolites, and most recently the various classes of synthetic resin ion exchange materials.

Since the advent of the resins capable of being regenerated with acids and alkalies, respectively, exchanging cations for the hydrogen ions and anions for the hydroxyl ion, it has been realized that ion exchange processing is a possible route to water demineralization. The cost of the regenerant chemical, acid and base, has prevented the use of the process except in certain "clean-up" applications where the quantity of ionic materials to be removed is extremely small.

Gilliland (6) suggested the possibility of an ion exchange process using regenerant chemicals that could be recovered by distillation. His patent on this subject (7) appeared in 1957.

Basically, the relative volatility of the components in sea water or saline waters is reversed by this type of ion exchange. Thus, the 3.5% of ordinarily nonvolatile salts present in sea water are made volatile by substituting for them a volatile salt such as one of the ammonium carbonates. This substitution puts distillation in an entirely different light: The minor component is now to be distilled away from the major component, water, which should reduce the amount of distillation to be done per unit quantity of water produced by manyfold compared to distillation (or evaporation) processes in which all of the recovered water must be distilled.

Prior Work

In the course of this work, particularly in its initial stages, extensive use was made of the pertinent technical literature.

United States Patents. Gilliland's patent (7) covers mixed-bed ion exchange of nonvolatile salts for "thermolytic salts"—those which decompose on heating or reduction of pressure into gaseous compounds, or into gases and insoluble solids—followed by recovery of the thermolytic salt and its re-use for regeneration of the ion exchange bed. Ammonium bicarbonate is specifically claimed as one of the possible thermolytic salts.

The example cited in the patent used a mixed bed of Amberlite IRA 400 and Dowex 50 resins, and on an ammonium carbonate–sodium chloride exchange cycle reported a reduction of the sodium chloride content of the brine from $0.6N$ to $0.2N$ in one stage ($0.6N$ is approximately the value of total dissolved salts in sea water).

Ion Exchange Literature. The technical literature on ion exchange is rather voluminous, but not much of it is pertinent to the subject at hand. As might be expected, far more information is available on the laboratory use of ion exchange than on its processing applications. Two of the best books, general references, are by Kunin (17) and Nachod and Schubert (19). The annual reviews published by *Industrial and Engineering Chemistry* are excellent summaries of the literature appearing in the preceding year.

Among the few quantitative data on ion exchange performance in the technical literature are those reported by Myers (18) of the Rohm and Haas Co. He reports experimental results using Amberlite IR-1 in the hydrogen cycle with a sodium chloride feed solution, giving both feed and effluent concentrations.

More typical of most of the journal articles are those by Bonner, Argersinger, and Davidson (2), Gregor, Belle, and Marcus (8), and Bonner and Payne (3). In the first of these papers the authors report on studies in dilute solutions of ion exchange reactions of the type

$$A^+ + B \text{ Res} = A \text{ Res} + B^+$$

An equilibrium constant formulated as

$$K_m = \frac{m_{B+}}{m_{A+}} \times \frac{N_{A \text{ Res}}}{N_{B \text{ Res}}}$$

where $m =$ molality in solution and $N =$ mole fraction on resin, gives good correlation of the experimental results.

There is an extensive literature on applications of ion exchange in analytical chemistry.

Trade literature published by the manufacturers of ion exchange resins is a valuable source of information. These manufacturers include the Chemical Process Co., Redwood City, Calif.; Dow Chemical Co., Midland, Mich.; and Rohm and Haas, Philadelphia, Pa.

Equilibrium Data. Liquid and Solid Phases, NH_3–CO_2–H_2O System. Equilibrium in condensed systems in the 20° to 40° C. temperature range and from 1- to 4.5-atm. absolute pressure are reported by Neumann and Domke (21). Similar data are reported by Terres and Weiser (26) and Guyer and Piechowicz (9) but over a wider temperature range and for less complex systems. The latter authors also report that ammonium bicarbonate in water solution evolves carbon dioxide, but make no mention of ammonia in the carbon dioxide.

Gas and Liquid Phases. Equilibrium data (*P-V-T*) and thermodynamic properties for the single-component systems water (steam) and ammonia are complete and apparently of the best accuracy because of the extensive use of these substances in cyclic systems (*14, 20*).

Similar data for the two-component system water–ammonia are also available and complete, because of the use of this system in absorption refrigeration. The data of Scatchard and coworkers are the most recent (*24*), and are unique among such compilations in that the availability function is tabulated as well as the usual enthalpy, entropy, and Gibbs free energy. These data have been converted to graphical form (charts) by Kohloss and Scott (*16*) and Bulkley and Swartz (*4*). Older data, but more complete in the low concentration range, are those of Jennings and Shannon (*11*).

Data for the three-component system ammonia–water–carbon dioxide are in a less satisfactory state. Pexton and Badger (*22*) report data at 20°, 30°, and 40° C. Badger and Wilson (*1*) extend the data to the higher temperature range of 90° to 100° C., but this was done with solutions not at the boil. Egalon, Vanhille, and Willemyns (*5*) measured the partial pressures of ammonia and carbon dioxide over solutions of ammonium carbonates in the 20° to 50° C. range.

Ion Exchange Experimental Work

The experimental work can be divided into two general classes: (1) exploratory experiments to find ion exchange resins suitable for the proposed application, and (2) obtaining quantitative data on one resin pair selected.

Ion Exchange Resins. Ion exchange resins, regular commercial products, were obtained from the Chemical Process Co., Redwood City, Calif.

Duolite C–20 is a polystyrene cation resin with sulfonic acid functional groups. It has a rated capacity of 0.8 equivalent per liter for cation exchange, except in the hydrogen cycle, for which its capacity is 1.5 equivalents per liter. Sulfonic acid groups are characterized as strong acid groups.

Duolite A–102, an anion exchange resin, has strong quaternary ammonium functional groups, with a capacity of 0.8 equivalent per liter.

Quantitative Data. A series of 18 experimental runs was made to determine quantitatively the performance of a mixed-bed ion exchange column using Chemical Process Co. resins C–20 and A–102. Laboratory data are summarized in Table I.

The columns used were fabricated from acrylic plastic (Plexiglas) tubing, 6 inches in outside diameter, $5^3/_4$ inches in inside diameter, and 48 inches long. Flanges were cemented to the tubing both top and bottom, and cover plates with nozzles were bolted to the flanges. The capacity of these columns was calculated to be 0.721 cubic foot (5.4 U. S. gallons). A solution feed tank of 40-U. S. gallon capacity was mounted on a wall bracket and above the top of the ion exchange columns to provide gravity feed. Connections (piping) were of glass tubing $^{17}/_{32}$ inch in outside diameter with joints made with rubber tubing. Laboratory screw clamps were used as flow control devices.

An ion exchange resin bed 32 inches deep made up of equal volumes of C–20 and A-102 resins was used in each of the two columns. The bed was supported by several inches of gravel covered with 2 to 3 inches of coarse sand. In one run (No. 7–1) the two columns were used in series to approximate a deeper bed (64 inches).

The "sea water" used in these experiments was San Francisco Bay water collected at the laboratory's salt water supply intake on the pier at the Richmond Field Station. Because of the diluting and polluting effect of the Sacramento River as well as other effluents dumped into the bay, the salinity of bay water at Richmond varies widely during the tide cycle. In order to obtain water of maximum salinity, the intake pump is controlled by float switches and permits the pump to operate only at or near high tide for approximately 3 hours in 24. Even with this limited pumping schedule the

Table I. Summary of Ion Exchange Laboratory Data

Run	NaCl, % Regenerant	NaCl, % Feed	Regenerant Vol., liters	Regenerant Vol./vol. prod.	Regenerant Av. % NH₄HCO₃	Regenerant Av. % NaCl	Rinse Vol., liters	Rinse Vol./vol. prod.	Rinse Av. % NH₄HCO₃	Rinse Av. % NaCl	Regenerant + Rinse Vol., liters	Regenerant + Rinse Vol./vol. prod.	Regenerant + Rinse Av. % NH₄HCO₃	Regenerant + Rinse Av. % NaCl	Product Vol., liters	Product Av. % NH₄HCO₃	Product Av. % NaCl
1		2.87	15	0.625	2.39	3.54	6	0.25	10.25	2.52	21	0.875	4.68	3.24	24	4.59	0.804
2	0	0.91	18	0.360	2.62	3.83	9	0.180	9.93	1.91	27	0.540	5.08	3.14	50	1.47	0.190
3	0	0.21	18	0.083	4.24	2.24	12	0.055	5.39	0.863	30	0.139	4.71	1.69	216	0.334	0.0442
4	0	0.05	15	0.0815	2.82	1.485	6	0.033	10.17	1.99	21	0.114	4.98	1.63	384	0.111	0.0454
2-1	2.56	2.87	15	0.715	3.74	3.53	6	0.285	10.75	2.92	21	1.00	5.70	3.30	21	2.87	1.93
2-1A	2.56	2.87	30	1.333	7.53	3.23	6	0.333	9.60	2.54	36	1.67	7.89	3.11	18	2.71	1.80
2-2	2.56	1.83	21	0.700	4.75	3.60	9	0.300	9.20	2.54	30	1.00	6.09	3.28	30	1.48	1.14
2-3	2.52	1.14	21	0.584	5.59	2.26	9	0.250	10.35	2.45	30	0.833	7.03	2.32	36	1.22	0.511
2-3A	2.61	0.94	21	0.467	5.71	3.28	12	0.267	8.68	2.09	33	0.733	6.79	2.54	45	0.960	0.506
2-4	2.82	0.61	21	0.318	6.25	2.99	9	0.136	9.27	2.27	30	0.455	7.15	2.78	66	0.703	0.312
2-5	2.42	0.29	21	0.167	5.52	2.65	15	0.119	6.01	1.556	36	0.286	5.72	2.17	126	0.305	0.144
3-1	0.92	0.29	21	0.140	4.70	1.97	15	0.100	6.44	0.892	36	0.240	5.32	1.52	150	0.362	0.0867
3-2	0.98	1.00	21	0.412	5.76	2.16	6	0.118	8.90	1.20	27	0.530	6.73	1.83	51	1.29	0.356
4-1	0.31	0.33	21	0.140	5.17	2.26	12	0.080	7.06	0.823	33	0.220	5.85	1.74	150	0.447	0.0650
4-2	0.31	1.00	21	0.368	4.36	1.95	9	1.58	10.46	1.05	30	0.527	6.22	1.66	57	1.46	0.222
5-1	1.75	2.00	21	0.700	5.58	2.47	6	0.200	10.0	2.20	27	0.900	6.58	2.41	30	2.10	1.091
6-1	2.45	2.87	42	0.933	6.56	3.10	9	0.200	12.21	2.51	51	1.133	7.57	2.99	45	2.61	1.90

Runs 1 through 6-1 made at av. flow rate of 1 gal./min./sq. ft. Mixed bed of C-20 and A-102 resins (Chemical Process Co.) 32 inches in depth Run 6-1 up flow. All others down flow.

dilution by mixing with less saline water is apparent. Table II gives some analyses of bay water made at various times, and shows that, judged on the chloride ion content, the bay water at Richmond is approximately half sea water and approximately half water of low chloride content. The ratios of calcium ion to chloride ion, and of sulfate ion to chloride ion are both higher in bay water than in normal sea water.

Table II. Analysis of San Francisco Bay Water at Richmond

Date	Hardness as $CaCO_3$, P.P.M.	Ca^{+2}, P.P.M.	Mg^{+2}, P.P.M.	Cl^-, P.P.M.	SO_4^{-2}, P.P.M.	Alkalinity as $CaCO_3$, P.P.M.	Na^+	Rain in Preceding 2 Days, Inches
12–13–57	4560	440	840	14,400	2000	...		0
12–17–57	3440	297	656	8,570	1830	840		1.37
1–27–58	3050	186	627	8,930	1420	290		1.01
1–28–58	3100	226	618	9,840	1960	190	7500	0.01
1–29–58	3300	232	660	9,760	1610	120		0.01
1–30–58	3340	232	671	10,000	2000	135		0.42
1–31–58	3280	220	660	9,660	...	140		0.43
2–1–58	3260	220	670	9,530	1570	120		0.02
Av.	3416	257	675	10,080	1770	262	7500	...
Av. sea water	6464	420	1318	19,324	2696	124	10,722	...
				Ratio to Chloride				
Av. bay water	0.339	0.0255	0.0670	1	0.1755	0.026	0.745	...
Av. sea water	0.335	0.0217	0.0680	1	0.1395	0.006	0.554	...

To obtain the more concentrated "sea water" used in these experiments, the concentrated effluent from solar stills was used. This was settled, decanted, and filtered to obtain a clear product, and then adjusted to the desired chlorinity by dilution with tap water.

The ammonium bicarbonate used was a technical grade product manufactured in the United Kingdom by the Imperial Chemical Industries, Ltd. Titration of this product for ammonia with sulfuric acid to the methyl orange end point indicated a purity of approximately 100%.

The experimental procedure was kept as simple as possible. First the regenerant solution was fed to the ion exchange column, followed by the "sea water" or diluted "sea water." Although the flow rate varied somewhat, it was held as close to 1 gallon per minute per square foot of bed cross section as conditions permitted. The effluent from the column was collected in 3-liter portions, a sample from which was reserved in a glass-stoppered bottle for chemical analysis. Thus the analyses are those for 3-liter portions of effluent, the composition of which was changing constantly, and represent (in heat transfer terminology) a mixed-mean average analysis. The chemical analyses used were Mohr titration for chloride ion, and acid titration for ammonia, the results of which were calculated to sodium chloride and ammonium bicarbonate.

In the course of this work two phenomena were noted for which no explanation was sought. When ammonium bicarbonate was added to sea water to prepare a regenerant solution, a white precipitate was formed which was settled out and discarded with no attempt made at chemical analysis. Toward the end of some of the regeneration cycles and at the start of some of the feed cycles, gas was evolved in the ion exchange columns, which eventually disappeared. This gas, which was not identified, caused serious flow impedance.

In working up the data presented in Table I, the total effluent from the ion exchange column(s) is divided into three portions: the regenerant, the rinse, and the product. For a complete cycle, the first portion, equal in volume to the regenerant solution intro-

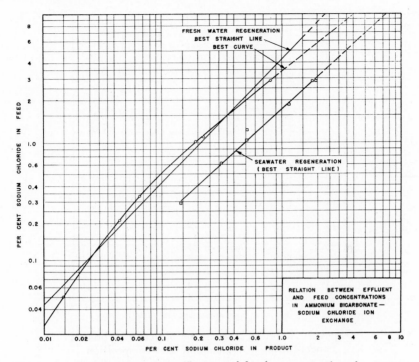

Figure 1.   Relation between effluent and feed concentrations in ammonium bicarbonate–sodium chloride ion exchange

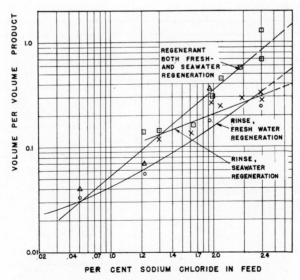

Figure 2.   Effluent volumes (based on stage product volumes) as a function of feed composition ion exchange

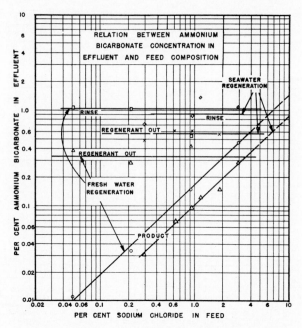

Figure 3.   Relation between ammonium bicarbonate
concentration in effluent and feed composition

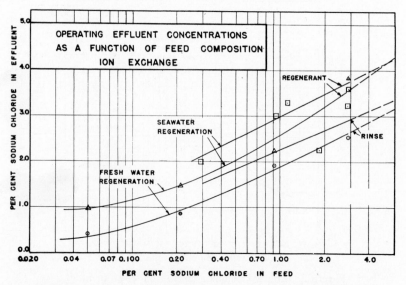

Figure 4.   Operating effluent concentrations as a function of feed
composition ion exchange

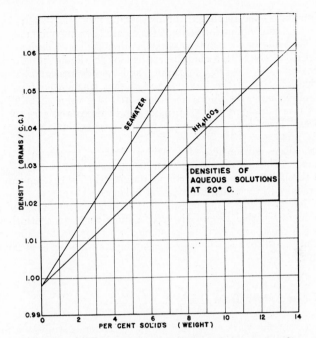

Figure 5. Densities of sea water and aqueous solutions of ammonium bicarbonate at 20° C.

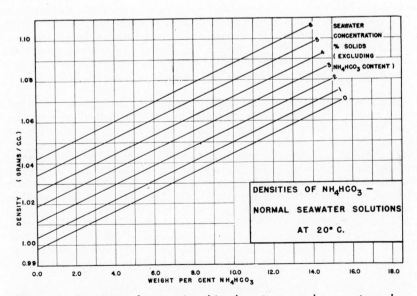

Figure 6. Densities of ammonium bicarbonate—normal sea water solutions at 20° C.

duced, is designated as the regenerant or regenerant product. Characteristically, this fraction increases in ammonium ion content (calculated as ammonium bicarbonate) with throughput. The chloride ion content (calculated as sodium chloride) starts out at a value determined largely by the chloride content of the liquid initially in the column from the preceding cycle, rises to a maximum, and then decreases.

The product portion of the total effluent is that fraction containing less chloride than the feed. In general, the chloride content starts at a value slightly less than in the feed, decreases to a minimum, and then more slowly rises to the feed value as the ion exchange process slows down. The ammonium concentration decreases with volume through in this fraction.

The intermediate portion, called the rinse, shows a maximum in ammonium ion concentration and a steadily decreasing chloride ion concentration.

Figures 1 through 4 are plots of certain data given in Table I, prepared to facilitate interpolation required in working up material balances.

The densities of sea water, normal, diluted, and concentrated, and of aqueous solutions of ammonium bicarbonate are given as a function of concentration in Figure 5. Figure 6 gives the densities of solutions of ammonium bicarbonate made up in sea water of varying salinity. All of these density measurements were made at 20° C. by means of a pycnometer.

Discussion of Laboratory Data

The first part of this work comprised an initial economic study of a process such as that proposed by Gilliland. On using the few data available, extrapolations, estimates, and even pure guesses, the results of this initial work indicated that further work was in order. Two questions were left very much unanswered: Would the ion exchange process work, and if so, how well; and what about recovery of chemicals? These data provide some answers to the first question, and only to that question.

Because the first stage in any economic evaluation of a proposed process involves a tentative flow sheet for the process, followed by materials and energy balances, the data for such calculations were considered to be of paramount importance. These aspects had to be encouraging, because they could make or break the entire concept.

The data herein presented were gathered with that purpose in mind, and answer the objective, at least in part. The influent and effluent stream volumes, specific gravities, and concentrations enable the preparation of materials balances around the ion exchange units. However, such material balances are no better than the data on which they are based. Therefore, it is advisable to consider the assets and liabilities of the data.

Among the assets is that of fairly large size operation; the columns were 6 inches in diameter instead of smaller units frequently used. The method of operation was designed to simulate as far as possible the visualized operation of a production unit—as simple and foolproof as possible.

The chemical analyses used were kept to a minimum, and as simple as possible. More data could have been gained by complicating this factor; and in retrospect, it would be comforting to have such data. The aliquots from 3-liter samples certainly masked out completely any short-term transients. Also, the fate of the ions other than chloride and ammonium is not known.

The approximate 1 foot of clear liquid above the resin bed is another troublesome factor. Mixing must occur in this volume when the composition of the influent solution is changed. As there was no visual evidence of gross turbulence in this volume, this effect was not investigated. On this basis these data are conservative; perhaps too much so.

This list of what was not done could continue for some length. Suffice it to say that the description of what was done and how is thought to be sufficiently complete so that this is not necessary.

Material Balances for Sea Water Processing

By using the laboratory data described and presented above, particularly the graphical correlations, and making some engineering assumptions, material balances for a sea water conversion plant using the ammonium bicarbonate ion exchange process were then developed.

As there is practically no difference in the laboratory data with bed depths of 32 inches and 64 inches, and ion exchange operations are reversible, it appears necessary to strip the product from one ion exchange stage of its ammonium bicarbonate before sending it on to the next stage.

Also, the limited solubility of ammonium bicarbonate in water, approximately 13% at room temperature, indicates that if one were to attempt to produce a distillate of greater concentration there would be danger of deposition of solids with attendant possible plugging in parts of the rectification or stripping units. On this basis, it was decided to fix arbitrarily, at least as a first approximation, the distillate composition from the stills at 13% ammonium bicarbonate.

This decision then led to another: The saturated ammonium bicarbonate solution obtained from the various stills is a regenerating solution for the ion exchange units—the so-called fresh water regenerant of the laboratory work.

No distillation calculations of any kind were carried out, other than the simple material balance type. It was assumed that all of the ammonium bicarbonate fed to a still would go to the distillate product, plus sufficient water to form a 13% ammonium bicarbonate solution, and that all of the sodium chloride plus the remaining water would be the still bottoms product.

Distillation of Ammonium Bicarbonate Solutions. Vapor-liquid equilibrium data for ammonium bicarbonate solutions at the boil are apparently not available in the literature. The data in the literature, however, do indicate that when the temperature of such a solution is increased, or the pressure on it decreased, the gas that is evolved is predominantly carbon dioxide. Thus, it appears that such a distillation would be two consecutive processes: first, a steam stripping of the carbon dioxide in the solution, followed by a distillation of ammonia from an ammonia-water mixture containing perhaps some carbon dioxide. Possibly the ammonia, carbon dioxide, and water in the distillate product would recombine completely in the condenser to form an ammonium bicarbonate solution. Perhaps an absorption tower would be necessary to effect the recombination.

Even though many questions concerning the distillation, or stripping, of the ammonium bicarbonate solutions remain unanswered, there seems to be no reason to assume that this operation cannot be carried out, and this assumption is made in this work.

The first system for which a material balance was computed was made up of four units in series, each consisting of an ion exchange stage and a distillation assembly to remove the ammonium bicarbonate from the ion exchange product effluent (Figure 7 and Table III).

Table III. Summary of Main Process Streams

(13% NH_4HCO_3 solution distillates)

Stream No.	Designation	Volume, Gal.	% NaCl	ΔV, Gal.	% Loss	Lb. NaCl/ 100 Gal. Feed	Δ Lb. NaCl	Total % NaCl Removed	% Entering NaCl Removed
1	X-1 feed	100	3.21			27.4			
4	X-1 prod.	73.2	0.94	26.8	26.8	5.87	21.57	78.6	78.6
7	X-2 feed	46.7	1.525	26.5	36.2	6.01	+0.14[a]	+0.51[a]	
10	X-2 prod.	37.5	0.36	9.2	10.7	1.145	4.865	17.8	81.0
11	X-3 feed	31.6	0.434	5.9	15.7	1.145	0	0	
14	X-3 prod.	28.9	0.084	2.7	8.5	0.202	0.943	3.44	82.2
15	X-4 feed	27.2	0.0887	2.7	9.3	0.202	0	0	
18	X-4 prod.	26.0	0.0220	1.2	4.4	0.475	0.155	0.566	76.9
19	Fresh water	25.7	0.0222	0.3	1.2	0.475	0	0	

[a] Increase because of recycle from X-4.

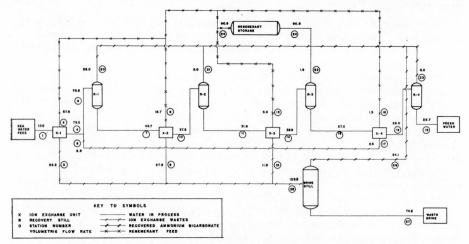

Figure 7. Flow diagram of sea water demineralization by ammonium bicarbonate ion exchange

Another possibility in the ammonium bicarbonate distillation is to assume that a distillate of anhydrous ammonium bicarbonate can be recovered from all of the stripping units or rectification assemblies. This assumption would seem to be the lower limit on the quantity of material to be distilled.

On this assumption, and the further one that the anhydrous ammonium salt is dissolved in filtered sea water to form the regenerant solution, another material balance was made. Seven ion exchange stages are required; the first five use sea water regenerant, and the last two, fresh water regenerant. (If the product water from such a plant and the anhydrous ammonium bicarbonate distillate are used to make up all fresh water regenerant, insufficient water is produced for the in-plant requirements of regeneration make-up.) Table IV is a summary of the material balance thus developed.

Table IV. Summary of Ion Exchange Stream
(Anhydrous NH_4HCO_3 distillates)

Stage	Feed Weights Total	NaCl	NH_4HCO_3	H_2O	% NaCl	Product Weights Total	NaCl	NH_4HCO_3	H_2O	% NaCl
1	11,570	371	0	11,199	3.21	8550	179	256	8115	2.09
2	8,855	190	0	8,665	2.14	6908	93	145	6670	1.34
3	7,202	99	0	7,103	1.37	5809	48	81	5680	0.825
4	5,960	50	0	5,910	0.84	4995	23	37	4935	0.46
5	5,059	23	0	5,036	0.455	4402	10.4	22	4370	0.236
6	4,380	10.4	0	4,370	0.238	4120	2	18[a]	4100	0.048
7	4,089	2	0	4,087	0.049	3965	0.57	4[a]	3960	0.0144
								563		

Stage	Nonrecycled Effluent Streams	NaCl	NH_4HCO_3	H_2O	Stage	Recycled Effluent Streams	NaCl	NH_4HCO_3	H_2O
1	7,578	302	476	6,800	5	733	13.3	53.7	666
	3,502	98	318	3,086	6	439	6	15.2	418
2	4,497	166	276	4,055		301	2.4	29.0	270
	2,246	55	201	1,990	7	119	1.1	9.5	109
3	2,661	89	162	2,410		130	0.4	2.9	127
	1,608	36	133	1,440				109.3	
4	1,514	47	87	1,380					
	1,092	27	89	975					
5	823	23	41	759					
			1783						

[a] Recovered as 13% solutions.

Discussion and Conclusions

The objective of any sea water conversion process is twofold: to produce a demineralized water whose quality is adequate for the proposed use, and to produce this water at as low a cost as possible. In considering any new conversion process, after the establishing of the scientific and technologic soundness of the method, the question to be answered is the probable relative economics of the proposed process as compared to other processes, either actual (preferable) or proposed. One method of making this comparison is to prepare cost estimates. However, in some cases, such as this one, other indexes can be used.

Multiple-effect evaporation, or multistage flash evaporation of sea water, is as simple a distillation process as can be visualized, because it involves only the separation of a solvent from a nonvolatile solute. Rectification is not involved in this operation. These distillation processes are those most advanced technologically at the present time, and therefore are a logical standard for comparison. In addition to these reasons, the ammonium bicarbonate ion exchange process employs rectification, not merely simple distillation, to effect the ion exchange regenerant recovery. Therefore, a comparison of the distillation requirements of the two processes could be interesting. The distillation requirements, on the basis used in making the first material balance, for the ammonium bicarbonate ion exchange process are summarized in Table V.

Table V.   Summary of Distillation Requirements

(Ammonium bicarbonate ion exchange process, 13% NH_4HCO_3 solution distillate)

No. of Stages	No. of Stills	Feed, % NaCl	$\dfrac{\text{Lb. H}_2\text{O Distilled}}{\text{Lb. Product}}$	$\dfrac{\text{Total Lb. Distilled}}{\text{Lb. Product}}$
1	2	0.0887	0.0459	0.0527
2	3	0.434	0.227	0.274
3	4	1.525	0.90	1.035
4	5	3.21	3.29	3.78

In any plant distilling sea water directly to obtain a demineralized water, the ratios of pounds of water distilled per pound of product, and pounds of total material distilled per pound of product, are identical and are equal to unity. Therefore, if a competing process has a distillation ratio greater than unity, it is clearly uneconomical when compared to direct distillation. Table V shows either a three-stage or four-stage plant to fall in this category; the ion exchange process, as visualized, involves more distillation than does direct distillation.

Another factor increasing the cost of distillation in ion exchange regenerant recovery is the need for supplying reflux to the rectifying columns. The boil-up for the reboilers is the distillate product plus the reflux, where in direct distillation the reboiler has to vaporize only the product.

If ion exchange regenerant recovery as a 13% ammonium bicarbonate solution involves too much distillation for the process to be attractive, might not some other distillation conditions appear more favorable? To answer this question the second material balance was made which assumed a still overhead product of a 1:1:1 mole ratio of $NH_3:CO_2:H_2O$, the same ratio in which these compounds unite to form anhydrous ammonium bicarbonate. This is the composition of the distillate which gives a minimum amount of distillate product, and still a process which might be feasible.

Summing up the ammonium bicarbonate to be distilled, in Table IV, gives a total of 2455 pounds to produce 3965 pounds of water. On mentally adding on the extra reboiler load to produce the reflux, probably several times the distillation product as a minimum, the comparison of this process to multiple-effect evaporation does not appear promising.

Another question comes to mind at this stage: If the ion exchange process using ammonium bicarbonate does not appear to be promising, might not some other salt perform more satisfactorily?

Criteria for Choice of Salt. Gilliland has chosen to call these chemical compounds "thermolytic salts." He defines them as materials which, upon increase in temperature, reduction in pressure, or both, decompose into gases, or into gases and insoluble solids. The idea behind this is to have an ion exchange material that can be recovered without having to boil away all of the solvent, water. Also implicit in this idea is the wish that the ion exchange material, after its decomposition, be easily separable from water. It is on this last factor that ammonium bicarbonate does not meet the desiderata.

In a water desalting operation, there appears to be no means of avoiding dealing with water. However, at first glance it seems possible to substitute some other base-forming gas for ammonia. The only such gases known to the writer are the substituted ammonias, or the amines. And all of the amines considered seem to be less desirable than the parent compound, ammonia, for reasons such as boiling point, cost, chemical stability, and even odor. Other nonmetal hydrides similar to ammonia that might be considered, such as phosphine and arsine, can be ruled out because of toxicity, without considering any other properties.

Another substitution that can be considered is that of using some acidic gas other than carbon dioxide. The hydrogen halides do not appear to fill this need, because the chloride ion, derived from one of them, is the principal anion present in sea water. Hydrogen cyanide and hydrogen sulfide can both be eliminated from consideration because of toxicity, and so on down the list until we come to sulfur dioxide.

Sulfur dioxide, forming two series of salts, the sulfites and the bisulfites, seems to merit a second look. The solubility of the ammonium sulfites in water—32 to 60 grams of anhydrous salt for the normal sulfite per 100 grams of saturated solution in the temperature range of 0° to 100° C., and 71 to 86 grams of salt for the bisulfite, per 100 grams of saturated solution in the 0° to 60° C. range, as reported by Seidell (25)—is several times that of ammonium bicarbonate. The vapor-liquid, or gas-liquid, equilibria appear to be less favorable than for ammonium bicarbonate. The system NH_3–H_2O–SO_2 has been studied moderately extensively as a possible means of recovering or removing sulfur dioxide from stack gases (12, 13, 15, 23). This system is also of interest to the sulfite pulp industry, as a means of both increasing quality of product and decreasing water pollution problems, as is attested by a series of publications (10, 27). Apparently the ammonium sulfites are more stable chemically than the bicarbonate, and more difficult to recover from aqueous solution. Certainly these solutions are more corrosive to metals. Therefore, the ammonium sulfites appear to be less well suited to this ion exchange cycle than the bicarbonate.

Summary

Of the possible thermolytic ammonium salt ion exchange processes for sea water demineralization, the ammonium bicarbonate process appears to be the best. But it appears inferior to multiple-effect evaporation processes on the sole basis of the amount of distillation required for the regenerant recovery.

Acknowledgment

James Weldy, assistant research chemist, carried out the ion exchange resin evaluation. Mr. Weldy, and Enneth Frohman, Myron Dunn, and Bruce Whipperman, engineering aides, performed the quantitative ion exchange experiments. Calculations work was, in part, carried out by engineering aides Eugene Barrington, Bruce Whipperman, and Gerd Behrsing.

Literature Cited

(1) Badger, E. J. M., Wilson, D. S., *J. Soc. Chem. Ind.* **66**, 84–6 (March 1947).
(2) Bonner, O. D., Argersinger, W. J., Jr., Davidson, A. W., *J. Am. Chem. Soc.* **74**, 1044–7 (1952).
(3) Bonner, O. D., Payne, W. H., *J. Phys. Chem.* **58**, 183–5 (1954).
(4) Bulkley, W. L., Swartz, R., *Refrig. Eng.* **59**, 660–2 (1951).

(5) Egalon, R., Vanhille, R., Willemyns, M., *Ind. chim.* **1954**, 293–8.
(6) Gilliland, E. R., *Ind. Eng. Chem.* **47**, 2410 (1955).
(7) Gilliland, E. R. (to Ionics, Inc.), U. S. Patent 2,776,258 (Jan. 1, 1957).
(8) Gregor, H. P., Belle, Jack, Marcus, R. A., *J. Am. Chem. Soc.* **76**, 1984–7 (1954).
(9) Guyer, A., Piechowicz, T., *Helv. Chim. Acta* **27**, 858–67 (1944).
(10) Hayden, D. T., "Vapor-Liquid Equilibria in the System Ammonia–Sulfur Dioxide–Water," Ph.D. thesis, University of Washington, 1955; *Dissertation Abstracts* **15,** 1935 (1955).
(11) Jennings, B. H., Shannon, F. P., *Refrig. Eng.* **35**, 333 (May 1938).
(12) Johnstone, H. F., *Ind. Eng. Chem.* **27**, 587 (1935).
(13) Johnstone, H. F., Keyes, D. B., *Ibid.*, **27**, 659 (1935).
(14) Keenan, J. H., Keyes, F. G., "Thermodynamic Properties of Steam," Wiley, New York, 1936.
(15) Kelley, K. K., Anderson, C. T., U. S. Bur. Mines, Bull. **384**, 30 (1935).
(16) Kohloss, F. H., Jr., Scott, E. L., *Refrig. Eng.* **58**, 970 (1950).
(17) Kunin, R., "Ion Exchange Resins," 2nd ed., Wiley, New York, 1958.
(18) Myers, R. J., *Ind. Eng. Chem.* **35**, 859 (1943).
(19) Nachod, F. C., Schubert, J., eds., "Ion Exchange Technology," Academic Press, New York, 1956.
(20) Natl. Bur. Standards, "Tables of Thermodynamic Properties of Ammonia," Circ. **142** (1923).
(21) Neumann, Bernhard, Domke, Richard, *Z. Elektrochem.* **34**, 136 (1938).
(22) Pexton, S., Badger, E. H. M., *J. Soc. Chem. Ind.* **57**, 106–13 (1938).
(23) St. Clair, H. W., U. S. Bur. Mines, Rept. Invest. **3339** (1937).
(24) Scatchard, George, Epstein, L. F., Warburton, James, Jr., Cody, P. J., *Refrig. Eng.* **53**, 413 (May 1947).
(25) Seidell, Atherton, ed., "Solubilities of Inorganic and Metal Organic Compounds," 3rd ed., Vol. 1, p. 1120, Van Nostrand, New York, 1940; Suppl. to 3rd ed., p. 405, 1952.
(26) Terres, Ernst, Weiser, Hans, *Z. Elektrochem.* **27**, 177 (1921).
(27) Thode, E. F., Lee, V. H., *Tappi* **33**, 257–60 (1950).

RECEIVED for review November 23, 1959. Accepted June 24, 1960.

Osmosis through a Vapor Gap Supported by Capillarity

GERALD L. HASSLER and J. W. McCUTCHAN

Department of Engineering, University of California, Los Angeles, Calif.

The semipermeable membrane proposed for the demineralization of sea water is based on H. L. Callendar's theory that osmosis takes place through the membrane as vapor, condensing at the opposite membrane surface. The actual membrane being used consists of two sheets of untreated cellophane separated by a water-repellent powder, such as a silicone-coated pumice powder. The vapor gap is maintained by an air pressure in excess of the pressure on the sea water and the cellophane sheets support the capillary surfaces, which will withstand pressures up to 1500 p.s.i. A number of successful experiments are reported with over 95% desalinization. The present effort is directed toward obtaining reproducible experimental results and better methods of fabricating the vapor gap.

The term "osmosis" is used to describe spontaneous flow of water into a solution, or from a more dilute to a more concentrated solution, separated from each other by a suitable membrane. To obtain fresh water from sea water, the flow must be reversed, from the solution into a fresh water stream. Hence the term used to describe this process is "reverse osmosis."

Certain experiments (*16*) associated with the theoretical ideas of Callendar (*2*) show that, in some instances at least, osmosis takes place through evaporation of the water at one membrane surface, passage through the membrane as vapor, and condensation again at the opposite membrane surface. The experiments reported here have been based entirely on this type of osmosis. It seems probable that in other instances, when certain types of membranes are used, osmosis takes place without a change of phase. For example, the fresh water ions may pass through channels in the membranes too small to permit passage of the solute ions, or again, the water may dissolve in the membrane (and possibly part of the membrane also dissolves in water), while the solute does not so dissolve and does not pass. This distinction is developed by McBain (*10*) and Glasstone (*4*).

The osmotic pressure of a solution is defined by Glasstone (*4*) as the excess pressure which must be applied to a solution to prevent the passage into it of solvent when they are separated by a perfectly semipermeable membrane. Actually no membrane is perfect in this respect, but copper ferrocyanide, $Cu_2Fe(CN)_6$, has been found to be most selective.

Data collected with membranes of this type played an important part in the formulation of present-day solution theory—so much so that the authors have used this theory without hesitation to compute osmotic pressures of solutions whose osmotic pressures have never been precisely measured. Such a solution is sea water. The copper ferrocyanide membrane is "leaky" to solutions of strong electrolytes. Some data have been obtained on weak solutions of strong electrolytes by the Townend method (16), but no one has made precise measurements on the osmotic pressure of sea water.

Recent work by Reid (13), Breton (1), and Loeb (9) shows promise that cellulose acetate may be used for such osmotic measurements. However, their objective was to study the desalinization process and not the equilibrium measurement of osmotic pressure.

The osmotic pressure (OP) of solutions expressed in atmospheres is usually calculated from the freezing-point depression, ΔT, in degrees Centigrade, in accordance with the relation

$$OP = 12.06\Delta T - 0.021(\Delta T)^2$$

where ΔT is obtained from the International Critical Tables (8). By taking average concentrations of the various salts in sea water, the osmotic pressure is calculated to be approximately 25 atm. (370 p.s.i.).

Proposed Osmotic Membrane for Sea Water

The semipermeable membrane proposed at UCLA in 1950 (7) is based on Callendar's theory that osmosis takes place through evaporation of the water at one membrane surface, passage through the membrane as vapor, and condensation at the opposite membrane surface:

The scheme is

Capillary membrane $\longrightarrow$	Fresh water channel	P_1
Capillary membrane $\longrightarrow$	Diffusion gap	P_2
	Salt water channel	P_3

$$P_2 > P_3 \gg P_1$$

P_2 must be $> P_3$, in order that water containing salt will not flow through the membrane but, rather, pure water will evaporate from the top of the capillary surfaces.

If $P_3 - P_1 = $ osmotic pressure of the salt solution, no flow by diffusion will occur across the gap. For pressure differences less than this, $\Delta P < (P_3 - P_1)$, normal osmotic flow would occur from the fresh water stream into the salt water. Thus, if we are to reverse this process, ΔP must be greater than $(P_3 - P_1)$, in order that water will distill from the salt water side to the fresh water side.

Before equipment can be designed, a decision must be made concerning pressures P_1, P_2, and P_3. Three pressure arrangements have been considered based on the assumption that the osmotic pressure of sea water is 25 atm. (Table I).

Table I. Pressure Data

Condition	Pressure, Atmospheres		
	A	B	C
Fresh water	−25	−24	1
Gap	0.01+	1+	25+
Sea water	0.01	1	25

Thus any pressure differential in excess of the 25-atm. osmotic pressure should produce some yield of fresh water. The question then becomes one of rate of production. An analysis made as follows shows that the limiting factor, so far as rate is concerned in a well designed system, will be the diffusion of the water vapor across the gap. Walker *et al.* (*17*) present Stefan's equation for the diffusion of vapor through a gas film. When there is no diffusion of air, the equation becomes:

$$\frac{dN_A}{dA} = \frac{-D_m dP_A}{P_B dZ}$$

This equation shows us that the practical problem is to design a narrow gap, thus making Z small, or to decrease the air pressure in the gap, P_B (Townend's approach), which necessitates a partial vacuum in the gap and pulling tension on the fresh water column in the equipment.

Theoretically this is possible, and -150-atm. tension has been demonstrated experimentally on water in Berthelot (*3*) tubes. However, negative pressures in Townend's experiments with dilute solution were less than 1 atm. and it is felt that more basic research on liquid tensions is necessary before schemes A and B of Table I can be considered for solutions as concentrated as sea water. Townend measured only equilibrium and had no need for rapid vapor transfer.

This leaves arrangement C, Table I, in which the narrow air gap functions as a semipermeable membrane, as the most promising. The choice of material with capillaries small enough to support the pressure necessary for reverse osmosis of sea water is a research project in itself.

The desirable properties for the authors' equipment are air entry pressures greater than 750 p.s.i., stability (many plastic films deteriorate with time), low air permeability of the wetted film, availability, and low cost. Cellophane seems to come closest to satisfying these requirements.

The decision to use cellophane was based on the work of Richards (*15*), whose classic studies on high values of vapor pressure and low saturations in soils led him to test many plastic sheets before deciding to use Visking casing in his high pressure equipment.

Prediction Equation

The process of pressure distillation through a homogeneous membrane is based first on the common fact that the vapor pressure of any liquid can be increased by compressing it or decreased by placing it under suction, and second on the equally common fact that only pure water vapor escapes from water into vapor or air, leaving nonvolatile salts behind the phase boundary. In operating the processes of vaporization—heat transfer and diffusion across an extremely thin gap—no new phenomena or new properties of materials are required. However, the novel combination of capillary surfaces, pressure, and extremely short paths for heat and diffusion offers an opportunity for improvements in film properties and methods of construction not known before.

The following calculation as made for the Saline Water Project (*6*) shows the relation between pressure applied and production rate. The dominant factors are: (1) the salt solution whose osmotic pressure must be overcome, (2) the pressure, as an energy source, (3) the diffusion of heat and (4) vapor as resistance factors, and (5) viscous losses within the cellophane capillaries.

The vapor density, like the vapor pressure, can be used as a thermodynamic potential whose total change around a closed path is zero. According to this argument, the effect of the above five factors on vapor density can be mathematically expressed and summed to zero. Beginning at the product water outlet, move to salt water by adding M, compress the salt water to pressure p, and subject it to the thermal loss of latent heat transfer, the diffusion loss of mass transfer, and the viscous loss of pressure in cellophane and manifold passages. This returns the path to fresh water and a closed circuit.

Salt. The departure from standard vapor density, $\Delta\rho_v$, will be given by $-\Delta\rho_v = 0.61 \times 10^{-6} M$ gram per cc.

Pressure. The effect of pressure is (by a straight-line approximation of the Kelvin equation)

$$+\Delta\rho_v = 1.31 \times 10^{-8}\, p \text{ grams per cc.}$$

Diffusion of Heat. In dynamic equilibrium, a transfer of vapor from liquid through a vapor phase to a second liquid (the two liquids being thermally connected only across the thin gap) will require reverse transfer of the heat of vaporization. This will accompany a temperature difference determined by the ratio of heat flow to the thermal conductance of the two heat paths. These two are the diffusion vapor gap and the series of salt water and plastic films. For the diffusion gap the c.g.s. air value 5.7×10^{-5} is chosen for the thermal conductivity (neglecting the separating powder), while for the series polyethylene (50×10^{-4} cm. thick), wet cellophane (50×10^{-4} cm. thick), and water (200×10^{-4} cm. thick) the respective thermal conductivities are 3.5×10^{-4}, 4×10^{-4}, and 14×10^{-4}.

$$\Delta\theta = \frac{\lambda_w}{\left(\dfrac{k}{z}\right)_{\text{gap}} + \left(\dfrac{k}{l}\right)_{\text{disk}}}$$

$$\Delta\theta = \frac{585w}{\dfrac{5.7 \times 10^{-5}}{z} + \dfrac{1}{\dfrac{50 \times 10^{-4}}{3.5 \times 10^{-4}} + \dfrac{50 \times 10^{-4}}{4 \times 10^{-4}} + \dfrac{200 \times 10^{-4}}{14 \times 10^{-4}}}}$$

$$\Delta\theta = \frac{585w}{0.57 + 0.0244} = \frac{585w}{\dfrac{5.7 \times 10^{-5}}{z} + 0.0244}$$

Such a temperature difference will cause a further departure from standard vapor density given by

$$-\Delta\rho_v = -1.02 \times 10^{-6}\,\Delta\theta = -\frac{6.0 \times 10^{-4}\, w}{\dfrac{5.7 \times 10^{-5}}{z} + 0.0244}\text{gram per cc.}$$

Diffusion of Vapor. The difference in vapor density needed to cause diffusion across the gap is

$$-\Delta\rho_v = \frac{w}{D} \times z$$

where the diffusion coefficient, D, for water vapor through air is a function of pressure.

$$D = \frac{0.208}{p} \text{ sq. cm. per second}$$

[See the Gilliland equation (12).]

Viscous Pressure Loss. The viscous pressure loss as described by the measured permeability of cellophane (15) is

$$\Delta P = \frac{W}{13.8 \times 10^{-6}} \text{ (one sheet of cellophane)}$$

This pressure drop will be reflected in the density of vapor in equilibrium with water. Substituting the above and including two sheets of cellophane:

$$-\Delta\rho_v = 1.31 \times 10^{-8}\, p = \frac{1.31 \times 10^{-8}\, W}{6.9 \times 10^{-5}} = 1.9 \times 10^{-3}\, W$$

Now setting the sum of these five terms equal to zero:

$$\Delta\rho_{\text{salt}} + \Delta\rho_{\text{pressure}} + \Delta\rho_{\text{thermal loss}} + \Delta\rho_{\text{diffusion}} + \Delta\rho_{\text{viscous flow}} = 0$$

$$-0.61 \times 10^{-6}\, M + 1.31 \times 10^{-8}\, p - \frac{6.0 \times 10^{-4}\, W}{\dfrac{5.7 \times 10^{-4}}{z} + 0.025} - \frac{p \times z}{0.208}\, W - 1.9 \times 10^{-3}\, W = 0$$

Figure 1 shows a plot of this equation. Flow rates were plotted against pressure for several values of air gap thickness, z, for sea water (3.5% salt, $M = 0.537$).

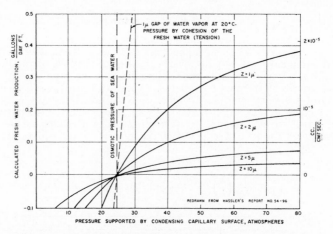

Figure I. Calculated fresh water flow rate as a function of pressure for several thicknesses of the compressed air diffusion cap

If a scheme could be devised to apply liquid tension as noted in Table I, A, the diffusion loss would approach zero. This curve is shown in Figure 1 and is labeled liquid tension curve.

Townend's Experiments on Osmosis

In 1928 Townend (16) described a procedure for determining osmotic pressure, tried out at Johns Hopkins University. Figure 2 presents the idea where the basic problem is to maintain the tension on the fresh water column.

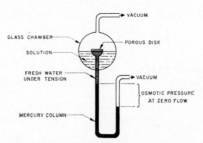

Figure 2. Idea sketch of Townend system

In the glass vacuum bulb is a thistle tube reaching above the solution's surface. In the tube is sealed a porous disk made from a mixture of special clay and powdered glass; the capillaries are large enough to permit the passage of liquid through them, but so small that the maximum capillary rise is greater than the osmotic pressure to be measured.

Later developments on this method were reported by Martin and Schultz (11), who obtained the following data on potassium chloride solutions, repeated here because they are most similar to the author's problem with sea water.

Mole KCl/1000 Grams Water	Tension for Zero Rate of Distillation (Osmotic Pressure), Mm. Hg
0.00504	187
0.00298	112.4
0.00298	111.5
0.00298	136.5
0.0020	96.5

Early Experiments at University of California

In 1954, Hassler had a project then known as "A Demonstration of Distillation by Pressure Alone" (5), which was sponsored initially by the State of California under authority of Everett Howe. It was then sponsored for a time by the Office of Saline Water, U. S. Department of the Interior.

Three demonstration models were made for the Office of Saline Water. Figures 3, 4, and 5 give the basic elements of these models. The most obvious design change was the use of cellophane sheets for the capillary surface instead of the porous ceramic plates. The use of cellophane with its high entry pressure permitted tests on sea water as well as dilute sodium chloride solutions. Other evolutionary changes had to do with better techniques of gap fabrication and pressure control.

Present Reverse Osmosis Equipment

It became apparent that to proceed further the mechanical components would have to be made more reliable. After reviewing the past models, it was believed that

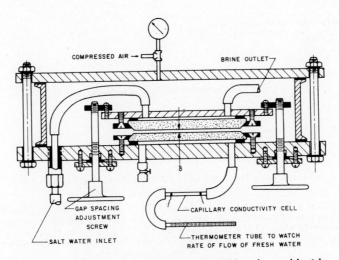

Figure 3. Porous plate model for 0.01N sodium chloride solution

Redrawn from (6)

Gap spacings 3, 10, and 25 microns were maintained between two standard porous clay plates, ground flat. The largest measured yield was 5.23 cc. per hour, per square foot.

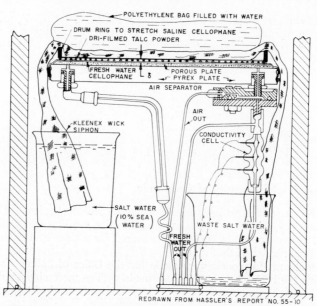

Figure 4. Cellophane capillary condensing model

A wick siphon was used to provide flow of salt water over the cellophane and to avoid the need for tubes through the pressure tank wall.
The rates of distillate production showed a sharp cutoff at the osmotic
pressure and dependence on gap thickness.

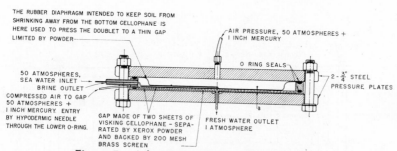

Figure 5. Adaptation of Richards equipment

Pressure membrane extractor, Catalog No. 1000, Soilmoisture Equipment Co., Santa
Barbara, Calf.

By inserting a hypodermic needle through the O-ring seal, this equipment was
adapted to reverse osmosis experiments by using a cellophane doublet separated by a
powder gap in place of the single cellophane used by Richards (14). After some
difficulty with the reliability of the pressure system, fresh water was produced at the
rate of 0.06 gallon per square foot per day.

a trouble-free design would contain a reliable compressed air system, pressure vessel,
salt water circulating system, "evaporator" plate assembly, "condenser" plate assembly,
and gas spacing and gap pressurization.

Figure 6 shows the existing pilot plant.

The compressed air system consists of a Sprague gas booster pump, receiver tanks, Grove pressure regulators, and a Barton differential gage. The booster pump operates on the 80-p.s.i. plant air line and boosts the pressure to 1500 p.s.i. The pressure regulators control the operating pressures within the range 200 to 1000 p.s.i. at any preset level to ±10 p.s.i., and the differential gage reads the difference in pressure across the sea water capillary membrane.

Figure 6. Reverse osmosis sea water demineralization pilot plant

The pressure vessel was made by the Los Angeles Boiler Works. It is a 997-p.s.i. A.S.M.E.-approved vessel 18.75 inches in diameter and 20 inches in working depth. The depth was specified because the authors plan to assemble a stack of membranes. So far all tests have been made on a single osmotic gap assembly.

The salt water circulating system proved to be one of the most troublesome problems, because of rust build-up in the recirculating system. However, this was solved by pumping the sea water through only once. The sea water is pumped from a 5-gallon glass bottle by a Milton Roy stainless steel positive-displacement, variable-volume pump which has a maximum capacity of 1.1 gallons per hour at 950 p.s.i. The sea water is collected in a pressure tank with a controlled air pressure dome.

The evaporator plate and condenser plate assemblies are practically identical and are best described by Figure 7. They are stainless steel and differ only in that the sea water plate has in and out connections, while the condenser plate has only the outflow connection.

Finally, gap spacing and pressurization are truly the heart of the problem. The desirable conditions are fineness of the spacer material, its water repellency, and the degree to which it maintains the air pressure excess over the entire membrane surface. Drifilmed talc powder, Xerox powder, and silicone-coated pumice powder have all been used with success with relatively low pressure differentials across the sea water capillary membrane.

The most recent development has been to increase the gap pressure differential from 5 to 50 p.s.i. It was discovered that at this higher pressure, water repellency did not seem to be such an important variable. A more reproducible gap has been obtained by using the air gap excess pressures to hold the wetted sheets against flat backing screens instead of pressing them together against powder. In this arrangement the nylon hair nets, partially pressed into the cellophane, determine the average thickness of the air gap as well as assure complete access of the air to every part of the gap through flow channels next to the nylon monofilaments.

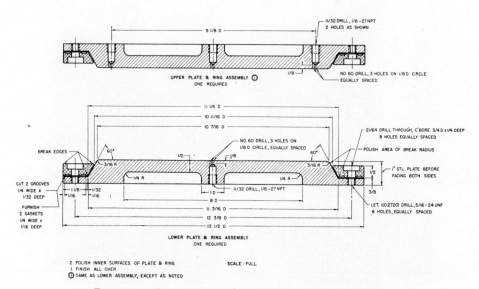

Figure 7. Evaporator and condenser plate assemblies

Figure 8 shows the assembly that gave the data reported here.

Recent Experimental Results

By the summer of 1959, it was believed that the problems of mechanical reliability had been solved; so the following experiments were planned in the hope of demonstrating that the experimental results would now be reproducible.

Preliminary tests were run for 100 hours with little or no difficulty. Silicone-coated pumice powder was still used as the gap spacing material. Three runs were made; then these conditions were repeated. The results and the controlled pressure setting are shown in Figure 9.

Upon completion of these experiments it became apparent that the differential pressure in the gap was a more important variable than the water repellency of the powder. Hence a 3×3 orthogonal set of experiments was planned, using nylon hair nets as the spacer instead of silicone-coated pumice. It was believed that this design would be more reproducible.

Nylon hair nets had been tried in the past with gap pressure differential of 5 p.s.i., and without the water-repellent powder in the gap there was no marked desalinization.

Table II shows the plan of the experiments.

P, air pressure in the gap, represents the total pressure across the condensing capillaries. The pressure differential, Δp, is across the sea water membrane, so that the total pressure on the sea water is $(P - \Delta p)$. The number of nylon hair nets used to maintain the gap between the two sheets of cellophane is n.

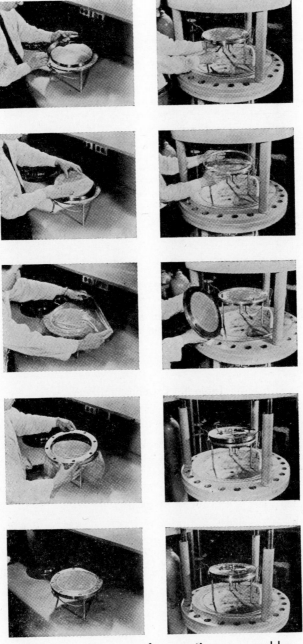

Figure 8. Vapor transfer osmotic gap assembly

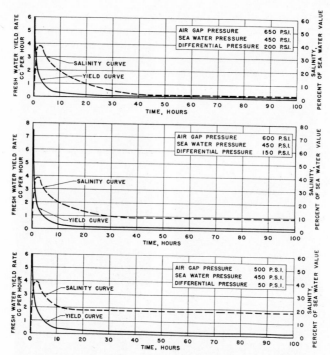

Figure 9. Composite yield and salinity curves for 100-hour run

Table II. Experimental Plan

$P = 1000$ p.s.i.	$P = 1000$ p.s.i.	$P = 1000$ p.s.i.
$\Delta p = 150$ p.s.i.	$\Delta p = 100$ p.s.i.	$\Delta p = 50$ p.s.i.
$n = 1$	$n = 2$	$n = 3$
$P = 750$ p.s.i.	$P = 750$ p.s.i.	$P = 750$ p.s.i.
$\Delta p = 150$ p.s.i.	$\Delta p = 100$ p.s.i.	$\Delta p = 50$ p.s.i.
$n = 3$	$n = 1$	$n = 2$
$P = 500$ p.s.i.	$P = 500$ p.s.i.	$P = 500$ p.s.i.
$\Delta p = 150$ p.s.i.	$\Delta p = 100$ p.s.i.	$\Delta p = 50$ p.s.i.
$n = 2$	$n = 3$	$n = 1$

The transient data shown in preliminary experiments were typical of the yield in this series. Because of time considerations, the yield for the second day is reported as the so-called steady-state figure. As the salinity (in all cases but one) started low and continued low, the salinity reported is typical of the entire run.

The data are tabulated in Tables III, IV, and V. The empirical equations for yield and salinity are helpful summaries of these tables, but it should always be kept in mind that the basically derived yield equation gives more clues for improving the process.

$$\text{Yield (ml. per hour)} = 0.095 + 0.00026P - 0.0555n$$
$$\text{Salinity (\% of sea water value)} = 5.47 - 0.0028P - 0.009\Delta p - 0.8n$$

Table III.   Steady-State Data Arranged According to Pressure Level

(December 9, 1959, to January 15, 1960)

Pressure, P.S.I.	Differential Pressure, P.S.I.	No. of Hair Nets		Yield Rate, Ml./Hr.	Salinity, P.P.M.	Salinity, % Sea Water Value
1000	150	1		0.2938	150	0.5
	100	2		0.2495	100	0.3
	50	3		0.1400	75	0.2
			Mean	0.2411	108	0.3
750	150	3		0.1333	200	0.7
	100	1		0.2138	200	0.7
	50	2		0.2033	100	0.3
			Mean	0.1835	167	0.6
500	150	2		0.0934	75	0.2
	100	3		0.0711	75	0.2
	50	1		0.1698	1400	4.7
			Mean	0.1114	517	1.7

Table IV.   Steady-State Data Arranged According to Gap Pressure Differential

(December 9, 1959, to January 15, 1960)

Differential Pressure, P.S.I.	Pressure, P.S.I.	No. of Hair Nets		Yield Rate, Ml./Hr.	Salinity, P.P.M.	Salinity, % Sea Water Value
150	1000	1		0.2938	150	0.5
	750	3		0.1333	200	0.7
	500	2		0.0934	75	0.2
			Mean	0.1735	142	0.5
100	1000	2		0.2495	100	0.3
	750	1		0.2138	200	0.7
	500	3		0.0711	75	0.2
			Mean	0.1781	125	0.4
50	1000	3		0.1400	75	0.2
	750	2		0.2033	100	0.3
	500	1		0.1698	1400	4.7
			Mean	0.1710	525	1.4

Nomenclature

D = gaseous diffusion coefficient of water through air, 0.208 sq. cm. per second
D_m = diffusivity of water vapor in air
$\dfrac{dN_A}{dA}$ = rate of mass transfer of water vapor per unit area
k = thermal conductivity of air, 0.0000568 cal./sec./° C./cm.

λ = heat of vaporization of water, 584 cal. per gram
M = formal concentration of (sea) salt, as formula weights per liter, 0.537 for 3.5%
     sea water
p = pressure exerted on liquid, atm.
p_o = osmotic pressure, atm.
P_A = partial pressure of water vapor
P_B = partial pressure of air
ρ_v = density of water vapor in equilibrium with liquid, 1.73×10^{-5} gram per cc.
     at 293.18° K.
θ = temperature, ° K.
w = flow rate, grams/second/sq. cm.
z = thickness of diffusion air gap, cm.
Z = gap thickness, cm.

Table V. Steady-State Data Arranged According to Number of Nylon Hair Nets Used as Gap Spacers

(December 9, 1959, to January 15, 1960)

No. of Hair Nets	Pressure, P.S.I.	Differential Pressure, P.S.I.	Yield Rate, Ml./Hr.	Salinity, P.P.M.	Salinity, % Sea Water Value
3	1000	50	0.1400	75	0.2
	750	150	0.1333	200	0.7
	500	100	0.0711	75	0.2
			Mean 0.1148	117	0.4
2	1000	100	0.2495	100	0.3
	750	50	0.2033	100	0.3
	500	150	0.0934	75	0.2
			Mean 0.1822	92	0.3
1	1000	150	0.2938	150	0.5
	750	100	0.2138	200	0.7
	500	50	0.1698	1400	4.7
			Mean 0.2258	583	2.0

Conclusion

The promise of the theory, summarized by the curves of Figure 1, is that a process has been found for securing thermodynamic efficiencies of the order of 50%, flow rates of the order of 10^{-5} cm. per second (0.2 gallon per day per square foot) by using relatively coarse, cheap material (cellophane) to support, by capillarity, a semi-permeable-micron air film which will not dissolve away because it is continually replaced.

The results were obtained in two classes of experiments. First, in work for the Office of Saline Water gap spacings of the order of 25 to 75 microns (0.001 to 0.003 inch) produced the expected osmotic flow behavior (zero flow when the pressures are below the osmotic pressure) with the effective surface permeabilities of 0.7×10^{-6} cm. per second for each atmosphere pressure in excess of the osmotic value as measured over a 2-hour transient experiment. There was also an energy loss to air diffusion, in which 0.06×10^{-6} cm. per second of standard air escapes (through one 0.0013-inch sheet of PT 450 and 0.004-inch sheet of Visking sausage casing together) for each atmosphere of total pressure. Apparently pure water was produced, but because the experiments were of limited duration and certainty, one could not be sure. In the second class of experiments designed for absolute reliability, reproducibility, and certainty of operation, fresh water of unquestioned purity was produced from sea water on a continuous basis at the rate of 0.005×10^{-6} cm. per second for each atmosphere of pressure in excess of osmotic. This lower flow rate apparently is obtained indefinitely. Very high rates are obtained during the first few hours and these rates are clearly osmotic water production, not leaks or other types of error.

The reduction in yield apparently has to do with a reforming of the structure of the gel under prolonged application of pressure. The change in the nature of the condensing cellophane can be felt by the hand as a hardening and densification, as well as by the change in its permeability.

By this process of reverse osmosis salts can be removed at very high values of osmotic pressure by exposing the solution to a thin vapor gap supported by capillarity. The process needs for its economical operation a gel which will remain permeable, while supporting the high air gap pressure.

Acknowledgment

The authors acknowledge past support of the Office of Saline Water, U. S. Department of Interior, and present support from the California State Legislature. This work is being done under the executive responsibility of Everett D. Howe and L. M. K. Boelter, Department of Engineering, University of California.

Literature Cited

(1) Breton, E. J., Jr., Office of Saline Water, U. S. Dept. Interior, R & D Rept. 16 (1957).
(2) Callendar, H. C., *Proc. Roy. Soc.* **80**, 466 (1908).
(3) Dorsey, N. E., "Properties of Ordinary Water Substance," Reinhold, New York, 1940.
(4) Glasstone, Samuel, "Textbook on Physical Chemistry," 2nd ed., p. 657, Van Nostrand, New York, 1946.
(5) Hassler, G. C., Dept. Eng., Univ. California, Los Angeles, Rept. **54-11** (1954).
(6) *Ibid.*, **54-96** (1954).
(7) *Ibid.*, **1376** (1950).
(8) International Critical Tables, Vol. 4, p. 254, McGraw-Hill, New York, 1928.
(9) Loeb, S., M.S. thesis, University of California, Los Angeles, 1959.
(10) McBain, J. W., "Colloid Science," p. 123, Heath, Boston, 1950.
(11) Martin, F. T., Schultz, L. H., *J. Phys. Chem.* **35**, 638 (1931).
(12) Perry, J. H., "Chemical Engineer's Handbook," 2nd ed., Sec. 10, p. 1168, McGraw-Hill, New York, 1941.
(13) Reid, C. E., Natl. Acad. Sci.–Natl. Research Council, Pub. **568**, 238 (1958).
(14) Richards, L. A., *Agr. Eng.* **28**, 451 (1947).
(15) Richards, L. A., *Soil Sci.* **51**, 377 (1941).
(16) Townend, R. V., *J. Am. Chem. Soc.* **50**, 2958 (1927).
(17) Walker, W. H., Lewis, W. K., McAdams, W. H., Gilliland, E. R., "Principles of Chemical Engineering," 3rd ed., McGraw-Hill, New York, 1937.

RECEIVED for review July 7, 1960. Accepted September 8, 1960.

Electrochemical Demineralization of Water with Porous Electrodes of Large Surface Area

JOHN W. BLAIR and GEORGE W. MURPHY

Department of Chemistry, University of Oklahoma, Norman, Okla.

Research began as an investigation of electrically induced ionic adsorption on porous "inert" electrodes. Electrode pairs based on carbon have been developed which will demineralize saline water at low voltage, and can be regenerated upon reversal of polarity. Various carbon electrodes have been conveniently classified into cation- and anion-responsive types. As received carbons are normally cation-responsive, but anion-responsive types have been made by chemical treatment. Laboratory demineralization cells based on this principle have been constructed and operated. Owing primarily to the low cost of basic construction materials, the process shows great promise for the economical conversion of saline waters.

The basic elements of a new electrochemical approach to saline water demineralization under study at the University of Oklahoma for the past three years are two porous electrodes, one of which is responsive to cations and the other to anions. When an appropriate voltage is applied to such an electrode pair immersed in saline water, cations are removed by the former and anions by the latter. In the regeneration phase, reversal of voltage gives up these ions to a reject solution.

The key to the successful development of this method lies in the development of inexpensive electrodes possessing high electrical conductivity, chemical and physical stability, large selective ion removal capacity, and reasonable electrochemical efficiency. Graphite and carbon-based materials are considered to be the most promising.

Research accomplishments reported herein include the development of demineralization cells, power supply, fluid control equipment, a means of monitoring the salt concentrations in the flow streams, and demineralization studies.

Principles

The proposed electrochemical method of saline water demineralization is similar to electrodialysis, in that ions are removed from a solution by electrical transference. If the electrodes are porous, oppositely charged ions will be attracted to them and thus be removed from the solution. This might be referred to as a condenser effect. To produce substantial salt removal, one must go beyond the simple condenser effect, and relate ion removal by a definite half-cell reaction in accordance with Faraday's laws. This rules out the practical use of inert electrodes, but necessitates stable and preferably thermodynamically reversible ones. The term "ion-responsive" is used here to indicate reversibility to one ion—cation or anion—whether complete or not. Efforts in electrode development have been directed toward two selective electrodes, cation-responsive and anion-responsive, each of which possesses high ion-combining capacity.

The demineralization process, as applied to a sodium chloride solution, would consist of two steps. In the first, the sodium and chloride ions are removed by electrodes A and C in accordance with the following schematic half-cell reactions

$$A + Cl^- = A^+Cl^- + e$$

$$C + Na^+ + e = C^-Na^+$$

followed by a second step where the polarity is reversed and the ions are given up to a reject solution. A becomes an anion exchanger upon oxidation, while C becomes a cation exchanger upon reduction.

Electrodes A and C will, it is hoped, be fabricated from large graphite-type carbon molecules. Some electrochemically active functional groups which may be present in various carbons have been discussed by Garten and Weiss (3–6), Hallum and Drushel (8), and Studebaker (12). Other possibilities, including functions imparted by chemical treatment, are discussed below. Oxidation of edge carbon atoms could possibly yield a quinone-type structure that could undergo a quinone-hydroquinone type of electrochemical cation-responsive reaction. The experimental data given below show that the graphites and other carbons tested are cation-responsive. Under chemical and electrical oxidizing conditions the cation capacity of graphite electrodes has been successfully increased. These results can be satisfactorily interpreted by the quinone-hydroquinone type theory.

Other responsive groups might be built into the graphite-type polymer. Functional groups common to synthetic ion exchange polymers, such as carboxylic groups, sulfonic acid groups, and quaternary ammonium groups on the edge of the graphite lattice, could produce selective responsive electrodes. In addition to the alteration of edge functions there also exists the possibility of pseudo-clathrate structure where functional groups, like bisulfate, could prove responsive when built into the interstitial laminar graphite structure. X-ray data (10) are reported to prove the existence of this type of structure for graphite bisulfate. Graphites, as well as carbons, are known as pigment-type molecule adsorbents where especially large aromatic-type adsorbed molecules are retained with noticeable tenacity. The possibility of occlusion of responsive groups by adsorption should be considered. Consider the adsorption of oxidation-reduction prototypes A and B:

Because the molecule upon oxidation acquires a double positive charge, it will take up two anions. On the other hand, a typical triphenylmethane dye might undergo the reaction taking up an anion, but giving up a cation in the process. Prototype A should

yield an electrode responsive to the anion, while B should yield one responsive to both ions. It has been reported (*11*) that prototype A molecule tetramethylphenylenedi-amine (TMPD) is indeed anion-responsive, while the dye neocyanine is responsive to both ions in accordance with prediction for prototype B molecules.

In many experiments a noncarbon-base anion-responsive electrode, silver-silver chloride, was employed. This electrode was selected for pairing with cation-responsive carbon-based electrodes because of its known properties and ease of preparation.

Additional treatments that could conceivably be useful in the development of carbon electrodes would include temperature, pressure, reactions involving inorganic substances, and select dispersing agents on any of numerous carbon materials.

Electrodes

The most effective method of porous electrode preparation has been the deposition of aqueous dispersions of colloidal graphites and carbons on fibrous backing materials.

Possible backing materials, including glass cloth, filter paper (Whatman No. 17), and seven nonwoven synthetic fiber fabrics received from the manufacturer (Troy Blanket Mills, New York, N. Y.), have been evaluated for thermal stability, graphite uptake, resistance, and subsequent water permeability. Small samples of these materials were soaked in a 1 to 1 dilution of Aquadag, air-dried, and heated to 200° C. for 5 hours. The weight increase and resistance were recorded. The resistance was determined using the simple block of Lucite that binds a 1.75-inch sample strip between brass plates separated 1.25 inches. The water permeability of the samples was tested in the apparatus of Figure 1, where the flow path was lengthwise through the graphited fabric as it was in demineralization cell DC-2. The nongasketed area provided a flow path 4 cm. long by 1.5 cm. wide. The resulting permeation rates are intended to be comparative only. In addition, the ungraphited fabric was subjected to 200° C. for 2 hours, and effects of this heat treatment were noted. The results of the tests are shown in Table I.

Table I. Percolation and Resistance Tests on Backing Materials Impregnated with Graphite

Material Tested	Weight of Backing, G.	Weight of, Graphite on Backing, G.	Results of 200° C. on Material	Resistance of Impregnated Sample after Heating, Ohms	Percolation Results, Ml./Min.
Troytuf Dacron, 1-ounce 1-9	1.3484	1.4966	No apparent effect	2.2	14.3
Troytuf Orlon, 2–2.25 C	0.3263	0.3209	Yellowed	8.8	0.15
Troytuf Dacron 1–2.25 C	0.3887	0.3702	No apparent effect	8.4	0.40
Troytuf Orlon 1-ounce 2–9	1.1250	0.9562	Yellowed	3.2	0.24
Troytuf felt of Dacron	2.5388	0.4621	No apparent effect	13.5	2.32
Troytuf Dacron 1–2.5 to Em10 (cloth backed) $^1/_2$-ounce 1–4.5	0.7759	0.5792	No apparent effect	6.6	0.51
Troytuf Dacron, $^1/_2$-ounce 1–4.5	0.7259	1.0217	No apparent effect	3.5	0.41
Whatman paper No. 17	1.8131	0.3321	No apparent effect	10.1	0.07

Dacron felt was considered the most promising of the materials tested. The effect of drying conditions on Aquadag-impregnated Dacron patches (1.5 × 1.75 inch) was tested (Table II). These patches were air-dried for 24 hours, weighed, heat-treated, and soaked in 50 ml. of distilled water, after which they were again air-dried, heated at 100° C. for 30 minutes to ensure dryness, and then reweighed. From these results, electrodes which were stable on water immersion, indicative of complete coagulation of the colloid, were obtained by air-drying followed by heating for 1 hour at 100° C.

Among the manufactured predispersed graphites previously considered, Aquadag (Acheson Colloids Corp.) was found to be best in terms of low resistance and high surface area. Inasmuch as it contains an unknown dispersant and the graphite cannot be chemically manipulated prior to deposition without coagulating the colloid, the techniques of dispersing various carbon and graphite molecules were investigated. A colloid mill (Eppenbach, Inc.) was used to reduce the particle size to near colloidal dimensions, after which treatment with a chemical dispersant produced satisfactory dispersions. The following method proved effective (1,13).

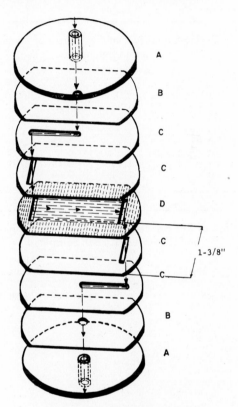

Figure I. Exploded view of cell (less end clamps) for determining permeability of graphited fabrics

Arrows indicate flow path

A. 1/4-inch Lucite disks
B. 1/16-inch polyethylene spacers
C. 1/50-inch polyethylene spacers
D. Sample gasketed surface

To each 100 grams of finely milled carbon were added 30 ml. of a water solution containing 5 grams of tannic acid (TA). The resulting mixture was thoroughly mulled to a uniform thick paste—additional water added if necessary to produce a paste—and then set aside to digest. The mixture was stirred frequently for at least 2 days because with many carbons the paste does not remain homogeneous but separates to a hardpan covered by the fluid. After digestion, the resulting product was diluted with 50 ml. of 15N ammonium hydroxide. Further water dilution is possible without breaking dispersion.

A number of carbon samples were dispersed with tannic acid by the above technique and applied to Dacron felt patches suitable for use in demineralization cell DC-1. The resistances of these patches, as determined on the Lucite resistance block, were much less than patches made from undispersed material (Table III). Demineralization studies on a few of these patches are presented elsewhere in this report.

Treatment of Graphite with Nitric-Sulfuric Acid Mixture. The following experiment was carried out in an effort to prepare a more highly oxidized graphite than the Aquadag preparation previously studied.

Table II. Effect of Drying Conditions on Resistance of Aquadag-Impregnated Dacron Patches

Patch No.	Temp., ° C.	Time, Min.	After air-drying	After soaking	Change	Initial	Final	Change
			Weight, Grams			Resistance, Ohms		
1	. . .	. .	1.2543	1.2450	0.0093	7.4	10.4	3.0
2	100	30	1.2172	1.2130	0.0042	7.2	9.7	2.5
3	100	60	1.2635	1.2600	0.0035	6.7	8.9	2.2
4	100	90	1.2201	1.2142	0.0059	7.0	9.7	2.7
5	150	30	1.2628	1.2580	0.0048	7.3	9.2	1.9
6	150	60	1.2572	1.2524	0.0048	7.6	9.1	1.5
7	150	90	1.2494	1.2444	0.0050	7.6	9.8	2.2

Table III. Comparison of Resistances of Dacron Patches Impregnated with Milled and Dispersed Carbon Samples

Carbon Material	Milled, Ohms	Dispersed, Ohms
Air-spun graphite (Dixon)		
Type 200-10	3,200	28
Type 200-39	860	24
Vulcan XC-72R (Cabot)	960	34
Spectrographic carbon (National)	12,200	42
Statex (Binney and Smith)	. . .	24
Kosmos 20 (United Carbon Co.)	850	46
Carbon decolorizing Norit No. P1731 (Eastman)		(Not coherent)
Graphite bisulfate prepared from commercial graphite	. . .	46
Attempted sulfonation product of commercial graphite	. . .	21
Mixed acid–treated Aquadag graphite (Acheson)	. . .	28
Kosmos C (United Carbon Co.)	. . .	2800

Twenty grams of stock Aquadag (containing about 4.4 grams of solid material) were added to 20 ml. of a 1 to 3 mixture of concentrated nitric and sulfuric acids. The resultant product was allowed to settle for about 30 minutes, after which it was filtered through a fritted-glass filter. The retained solid was transferred to a flask and again treated with 20 ml. of the same mixed acids. After 6 hours of undisturbed reaction, the solid was again separated by vacuum filtration through a fritted-glass filter and transferred to a beaker. Repeated washing with distilled water, largely by decantation, eventually gave a filtrate test on the basic side of methyl orange. The solid residue was air-dried for a few minutes by continued aspiration of the residue on the filter. Without further drying, the product was dispersed by the tannic acid technique and applied to Dacron patches.

The mixed-acid treatment was also made on commercial graphite, National Carbon Co. spectrograph carbon (Catalog No. L4309), and Dixon's Air-spun, Type 200–10. The resulting Air-Spun product was tested for sulfur by opening a sample using sodium carbonate fusion and then testing a solution of the resultant material for sulfate and for sulfide.   No sulfur was found.   An electrode was formed from the dispersed, mixed acid–treated Aquadag graphite.   Resistance measurements made on this electrode are shown in Table III.

Treatment of Graphite with Oleum.   Commercial graphite and two high purity graphite samples—National Carbon Co. spectrograph carbon (Catalog No. L4309) and Air-Spun 200–10—were sulfonated by prolonged treatment with oleum. The resulting products were washed until no sulfate could be detected in the filtrate as tested with a barium chloride solution.   Subsequent sodium fusion as well as sodium carbonate fusion of the resulting Air-Spun graphite gave negative tests for sulfur as sulfate and as sulfide.

Mixture of Graphite and Ion Exchange Resin.   A heterogeneous mixture of ion exchange resin–Aquadag (1 to 4 on dry basis weight) was used to prepare electrodes with the hope of electrically inducing desorption from the resin.   These mixtures were prepared with 400-mesh Dowex 1 (anion exchanger) and Dowex 50 (cation exchanger) resins slurried in a 1 to 1 dilution of stock Aquadag.

Treatment of Graphite to Increase Iron.   Iron in some form is known to be present in Aquadag and in many other sources of graphite.   A graphite of low iron content, Air-Spun Type 200–10, was treated to increase its iron content by intimate mixing with electrolytic iron dust.   The mixture was heated overnight in a 400° C. furnace, and then treated with mixed acid.   An electrode prepared from this product, dispersed with tannic acid, was compared with an electrode made from mixed acid–treated, tannic acid–dispersed stock Air-Spun.

Dispersant Reagents.   The role of the dispersant in electrode responsiveness was tested by performance comparison of electrodes that differed only in the dispersant used in the graphite preparation.   The following dispersants were performance compared with Aquadag (dispersant unknown):   Mallinckrodt's analytical reagent tannic acid (TA), Monsanto's Lustrex X-710 polystyrene sulfonic acid (PSA), and Badische Anilin und Soda Fabrik A.G. poly-N-vinylimidazol which was quaternized   in this laboratory according to the procedure of Gregor and Gold (7), to give the iodide form of the polymer (PVI).   Electrodes were prepared from Air-Spun graphite Type 200–10 dispersed with tannic acid, polystyrene sulfonic acid and PVI by a procedure similar to those detailed above.   These electrodes were then performance-compared with Aquadag.

Tannic acid-dispersed Air-Spun Type 200–10 was treated with mixed acid in another comparative study and then redispersed with tannic acid.   The performance of an electrode prepared with this product was compared with electrodes prepared from mixed acid–treated Aquadag TA redispersed.

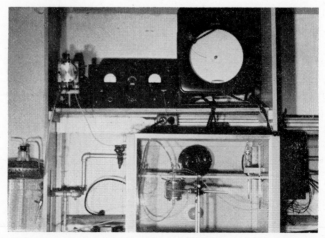

Figure 2.   Demineralization apparatus assembly

Apparatus

The basic elements needed for demineralization experiments are a demineralization cell, solution reservoir and pump, constant voltage power supply, conductivity cell (with temperature regulation) and bridge and voltage and current meters. A typical demineralization assembly is shown in Figure 2.

Three demineralization cells designated DC-1, DC-2, and DC-3 (Figure 3) were used.

Figure 3.   Demineralization cell DC-3

Left. Assembled
Right. Components

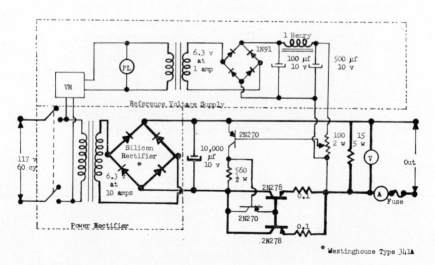

Figure 4.   Low voltage power supply

Pump. Solution is pumped at low flow rate through the cell by means of a Lapp Pulsafeeder pump Model LS-10. Difficulty in maintaining constant flow at slow flow rates was traced to small air pockets in the diaphragm pump head that would not spontaneously pass the exit check valve. This difficulty was remedied by the aspiration of the feed solution to remove dissolved gases. To minimize the hazard of implosion of the feed reservoir, a cage was made from $1/4$-inch hardware cloth to fit the 20-liter reservoir.

Power Supply. The constant voltage power supply is a transistor-regulated device that maintains a constant output to 0.01 volt over a wide load range. The maximum current output is about 10 amperes over a range of 0.25 to 6 volts. The regulator circuit, molded after a basic one supplied by Avco Manufacturing Co., Lawrence, Mass., is shown in Figure 4. The apparatus has proved reliable above 0.25 volt, but has no regulatory control at lower voltages because of the threshold control characteristics of the 2N278 transistors. The Raytheon AC voltage regulator Type VR6111 virtually eliminates any dependence of output voltage on line fluctuations.

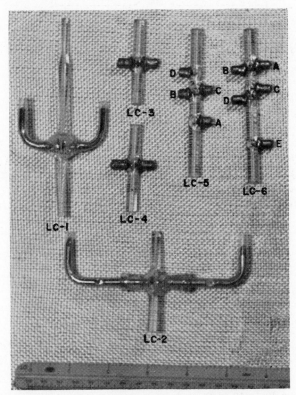

Figure 5.   Six conductance cells with wide range of cell constants

Conductance Cells. A conductance cell with large electrodes closely spaced can be used for dilute or poorly conducting solutions, while small electrodes widely spaced are desirable for more concentrated electrolyte solutions.

Six conductance cells, LC-1 through LC-7, each constructed of borosilicate glass with platinized platinum electrodes, are shown in Figure 5 (LC-7 is similar to LC-5 and

LC-6). Cells LC-1 and LC-2 have holdup volumes of 2.0 and 0.7 ml., respectively. In the case of LC-2 the platinum electrodes and mercury well side arms are part of a standard-taper joint assembly. Cells LC-3 and LC-4 have holdup volumes of 0.16 ml. and external copper electrode caps. Cells LC-3 and LC-4 were stacked so as to be able to shift scales during the demineralization and regeneration half cycles, but a more convenient design was achieved in the compound cells, LC-5 and LC-6, with effective holdup volumes between 0.25 and 0.55 ml. Figure 6 is a drawing of LC-4 and LC-5. By using several inputs into the recorder, a continuous record can be obtained over a wide concentration range.

Air Bath. Temperature regulation necessary for meaningful conductance data was achieved by an air bath.

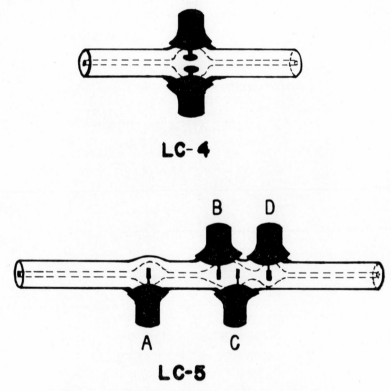

Figure 6.   Details of conductance cells (actual size)

The air bath (Figure 2), which holds both the demineralization cell and the conductance cell, is a 19 × 19 × 26 inch box constructed from $^3/_8$-inch plywood with a vertically sliding front glass window. Air circulation is furnished by a small squirrel-cage blower with outside mounted motor. Temperature control is provided by a 50-watt light bulb heater actuated by a mercury thermoregulator and an electronic relay. If the ambient temperature is higher than the bath temperature, refrigerated cooling water can be circulated through radiator coils within the box.

Conductance Recorder. The instrument used for monitoring salt concentrations is a six-record Foxboro Dynalog electronic conductivity recorder, range 0 to 1000 micromhos.

Meters. The above power supply eliminates the need of a voltmeter except to establish the desired operating voltage. Current data for a demineralization run are recorded on a Sargent strip chart recorder, Catalog No. S-72150. The current curve for each half cycle resembles a capacitor-charging current decay because of the electrochemical reverse potential of the cell, as well as electrode loading. Both of the conductance and the current changes in a cycle may later be used as a basis for automatic switching devices for a self-operating system.

Demineralization Studies

Cell DC-1. This Lucite cell (Figure 7) had a center section which holds the electrodes vertically (electrode dimensions are 1.7 by 1.1 inches) with a separation gap of $1/_8$ inch. Small Lucite inlet and outlet tubes are provided at the top and bottom of the center section. Platinum wires make intimate contact along the perimeter of each electrode, and then pass through the side walls to external lugs. This cell is normally operated with only the solution gap between the electrodes.

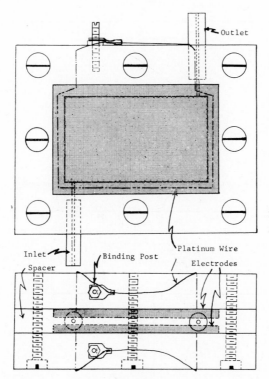

Figure 7. Demineralization cell DC-1 (actual size)

In studies on electrodes prepared from the Aquadag and ion exchange mixtures, one electrode contained the anion exchanger and the other the cation exchanger. After the cell had been washed thoroughly with 0.003N sodium chloride solution, the flow rate was adjusted to 6 ml. per hour and 0.8 volt was applied in such a direction that desorption of ions from the exchange resins would be aided. The anticipated concentration increase in the effluent did not appear; instead, there was a slight, probably not significant, decrease. Similar results were obtained when the current was reversed. Thus electrically induced desorption from the resins was not found under these experimental conditions. Higher voltages, leading to electrolysis of the water, have not been tried.

A number of demineralization investigations were made employing a silver–silver chloride electrode, known to be reversible to the chloride ion, *vs.* graphite-impregnated Dacron felt in cell DC-1. A silver electrode fabricated from 20-mesh gauze was anodized at 2 volts in concentrated sodium chloride solution until a thick silver chloride coating was achieved. This electrode was mounted in cell DC-1 along with a Dacron-backed carbon electrode prepared as described above. After several current reversals, carried out to condition the electrodes properly, performance of the carbon electrode was evaluated. When the Aquadag graphite was cathode (Figure 8), a graphical integration indicated that 8.51×10^{-5} equivalent of sodium chloride was removed by 0.0267 equivalent of carbon in the active graphite area. These experiments were the first to prove conclusively that demineralization with a pair of electrodes, one reversible to the cation and the other to the anion, is a feasible operation.

Similar data were obtained with an electrode fabricated from tannic acid–dispersed Air-Spun graphite 200–10 *vs.* a silver–silver chloride electrode in cell DC-1 (Figure 9).

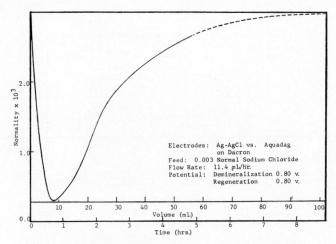

Figure 8. Demineralization curve for run IAG1-5

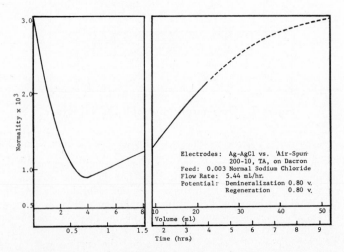

Figure 9. Demineralization curve for run IAG1-6

It was estimated by a graphical integration that these electrodes removed 5.00×10^{-5} equivalent of sodium chloride.

Several of the tannic acid-dispersed carbon electrodes listed in Table III, having favorable electrical conductances, were tested for cation responsiveness in cell DC-1. The anion-responsive electrode was the silver–silver chloride electrode. This experiment series was carried out with a feed solution of $0.003N$ sodium chloride, demineralization potential of 0.80 volt on each half cycle, and flow rates similar to the above. Carbon electrodes made from Air-Spun graphite 200–39, oleum-treated commercial graphite, United Carbon Co. Kosmos C, and National Spectrographic Carbon (Catalog No. L4309) electrodes were found to give up graphite to the effluent and were not evaluated here. The results of the Aquadag, Air-Spun 200–10, and mixed acid–treated Aquadag tannic acid–dispersed are presented as part of Table IV.

Table IV. Summary of Electrode Capacity Determinations from Selected Experiments

Code Designation	E.M.F. Appl., Volt		Flow Rate, Ml./Hr.	Max. Demin. Factor	Est. Demin. Cap., Equiv./ Sq. Inch $\times 10,000$	Comments[a]
	Regen.	Demin.				
1AG1–5	0.80	0.80	11.4	7.9	0.45	
1AG1–6	0.80	0.80	5.4	3.3	0.27	Air-Spun 200-10, TA
1AG1–7	0.80	0.80	5.7	12.3	1.01	MA[b]Aquadag TA
2GG1–8	0.80	0.80	33.1	3.6	0.344	Anion-permeable membrane, Dacron-backed electrodes
3AG5–3	0.40	0.40	13.2	4.1	0.113	Glass cloth separators, internal shorting
3AG9–4	0.40	0.40	11.6	7.0	0.045	Glass cloth separators, internal shorting
3AG9–6	0.80	0.80	13.2	8.0	0.138	Glass cloth separators, internal shorting
3AG9–12	0.40	0.40	16.4	30	0.157	Filter paper separators, internal shorting
3AG9–22	0.40	0.40	18.7	20.	0.267	Dacron felt separators
3AG9–27	0.80	0.25	24.4	9.0	0.170	Dacron felt separators
3AG9–28	0.80	0.25	36.7	20.	0.363	Dacron felt separators
3AG9–34	0.80	0.25	8.1	1.8	0.370	Dacron felt separators

[a] Unless otherwise noted, all electrodes are Aquadag deposited on Dacron felt vs. silver–silver chloride.

[b] Mixed-acid treatment prior to dispersion.

The demineralization results obtained from the mixed acid–treated tannic acid–dispersed Aquadag graphite are shown in Figure 10. This study employed a demineralization potential of 0.80 volt and afforded a notable increase in the resultant cell capacity of 1.88×10^{-4} equivalent. As it was known from previous experiences with silver–silver chloride electrodes that lower potentials are desirable, another study with a similar graphite electrode was carried out at 0.30 volt. For these experiments a freshly prepared graphite electrode was used. After electrical conditioning a demineralization capacity of 1.58×10^{-4} equivalent was obtained. This capacity was 84% of the capacity obtained at the higher 0.80-volt potential. The new electrode possibly contained less graphite and tannic acid than the previous one.

In another series of experiments electrodes fabricated from several carbon materials were tannic acid–dispersed and performance-tested in DC-1 against silver–silver chloride. Generally it was necessary to soak the electrode (after drying) in a concentrated sodium chloride solution to coagulate the carbon more completely before mounting in the cell. In this series, a feed solution of $0.03N$ sodium chloride, identical applied voltages (0.30

volt during the demineralization half cycle and 0.80 volt during the regeneration half cycle), and similar flow rates were employed. The resulting demineralization capacities were roughly estimated (Table V).

Table V. Performance Results of Several Electrodes in Which Carbon Prior to Deposition Was Dispersed with Tannic Acid

Potentials.   0.30-volt demineralization and 0.80-volt regeneration
Feed solution.   0.030N sodium chloride

Code Designation	Flow Rate, Ml./Hr.	Est. Demin. Cap.,[a] Equiv.[b]/ Sq. Inch × 10,000	Type of Carbon and Comments
1AG1–14	5.28	0.91	MA[c]-Aquadag
1AG1–17	4.13	0.48	Vulcan XC-72R
1AG1–19	9.15	0.80	Statex
1AG1–26	5.30	Small	Oleum-spectrographic carbon
1AG1–27	5.43	0.32	MA[c]-Air-Spun 200–10
1AG1–28	5.80	0.27	MA[c]-Air-Spun 200-10 and iron
1AG1–30	11.90	0.91	Aquadag and TA-loaded Norite

[a] Area of electrode for DC-1, 1.87 sq. inches.
[b] All dispersions deposited on Dacron felt.   Silver–silver chloride was anion-responsive electrode.
[c] Mixed-acid treatment prior to dispersion.

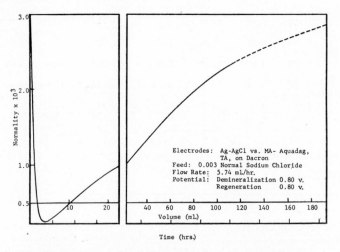

Figure 10.   Demineralization curve for run 1AG1-7

This experiment series, the results of which are summarized in Table V, includes the special cases of iron (1AG1-28) and Norite (1AG1-30) loaded Air-Spun.

Except for the oleum-spectrographic carbon 1AG1-26, which may be suspect because of poor electrode coherence, the TA-dispersed materials have capacities of the same order of magnitude. A comparison of 1AG1-27 and 1AG1-28 reveals little if any significance of added iron. The capacities of mixed acid-treated Aquadag, Statex, and Norite-loaded Aquadag are nearly the same and considerably higher than the others. It is not clear from the results of this experiment series what effect the tannic acid itself has on capacity.

A comparison of results with different dispersants (Table VI) is more revealing.

A TA-dispersed (1AG1-6) Dixon Air-Spun Type 200-10 electrode has four times the cation capacity of one dispersed with PVI (1AG1-22). This difference in electrochemical properties imparted by TA and PVI to electrodes is even more strikingly demonstrated when the Air-Spun receives a prior treatment with mixed acid (IAG1-27 and 1AG1-32). In this case, a cation capacity in the PVI-dispersed case was virtually undetectable. A comparison of the TA (1AG1-27) and the poorly coherent PSA (1AG1-29) dispersed electrodes revealed no significant difference in capacity; however, the results of experiments 1AG1-5 and 1AG1-31 on Aquadag with and without PSA indicate that the latter adds nothing to the cation capacity. This series of experiments does not demonstrate a specific cation-responsive capacity of either TA or PSA, but it seems clear that PVI has the effect of *reducing* the cation capacity of an electrode.

Table VI.   Dispersant Effect on Resulting Cell Capacity

Potentials.   0.30-volt demineralization, 0.80-volt regeneration
Feed solution.   0.030N sodium chloride

Code Designation	Flow Rate, Ml./Hr.	Est. Demin. Cap.,[a] Equiv./ Sq. Inch $\times$ 10,000	Carbon	Dispersant[b]
1AG1-6[c]	5.40	0.27	Air-Spun 200-10.	TA
1AG-22	4.08	0.064	Air-Spun 200-10.	PVI
1AG1-27	5.43	0.32	MA[d]-Air-Spun 200-10	TA
1AG1-32	5.73	Small	MA-Air-Spun 200-10	PVI
1AG1-29	2.00	0.30	MA-Air-Spun 200-10	PSA
1AG1-5[c]	11.40	0.45	Aquadag	None
1AG1-31	5.94	0.37	Aquadag	PSA added
1GG1-24	7.60	0.21	⎰MA-Aquadag ⎱Air-Spun 200-10	TA ⎱ PVI⎰

[a] Area of electrode for DC-1, 1.87 square inches.
[b] All dispersions deposited on Dacron felt.   Silver–silver chloride anion-responsive electrode used on all experiments except 1GG1–24.
[c] Feed solution 0.0030–NaCl; demineralization and regeneration potentials 0.80 volt.
[d] Mixed-acid treatment prior to dispersion.

The anion-responsive properties of PVI-dispersed Dixon Air-Spun 200-10 were then tested against mixed acid-treated Aquadag. The result was positive, the anion capacity being comparable to the cation capacity of similar material dispersed with TA. The oxidizable iodide ion originally present in the electrode, if incompletely exchanged by chloride in the demineralization cell, would doubtless contribute something to anion responsiveness.

Cell DC-2.   Earlier demineralization studies by Lyon (*9*) employed cell DC-2. This was a sandwich-type cell with Lucite side plates bolted together with two epoxy resin–gasketed graphite electrodes separated by an anion-permeable membrane. The membrane was necessary because a suitable anion-responsive electrode was not then known. The principle of operation is that in the cathode compartment, after several current reversal conditioning cycles, sodium ions are removed by the cathode while chloride ions migrate from the cathode through the membrane to the anion chamber. In the anode chamber, sodium ions, from the previous half cycles, are rejected from the anode. The net result was salt depletion in the cathode chamber and a similar concentration increase in the anode chamber.

Glass cloth–backed Aquadag graphite electrodes were found to have a capacity of 2.9×10^{-6} equivalent per square inch of area with a current efficiency of 62.5% during the first 90 minutes of a run. In the present study these electrodes were replaced with Aquadag-impregnated Dacron felt. Such electrodes contain considerably more graphite and are not subject to the questionable role of the ion-exchanging glass fibers previous studies. The Dacron felt electrodes had a capacity of 3.4×10^{-5} equivalent per square inch. On several runs the pH of samples from each compartment were determined using a Model H-2 Beckman pH meter. No significant pH changes were found.

After the feasibility of demineralization with coupled cation- and anion-responsive electrodes had been established, it became possible to dispense with the membrane; no further experiments were planned with DC-2.

Cell DC-3. After the preliminary investigations employing silver–silver chloride and Aquadag graphite electrodes in DC-1 had been carried out as described, a multiple-effect or cascade-type cell, DC-3, could be studied. The cell consists of a stack of alternating graphite and silver–silver chloride disks with $1\frac{1}{2}$-inch circular active area separated by spacers and compressed between Lucite ends backed by rigid brass plates. The tie bolts were four $3/_{16}$-inch stove bolts sheathed with Tygon tubing to prevent solution contacting and electrical shorting. The cell and its components are shown in Figure 3.

Solution flows in a direction perpendicular to the disks. Each disk must have an external ring-gasketed area which will conduct electricity but be impervious to the solution. These gasketing criteria were achieved in the case of the graphited felt by impregnation of the electrode's gasketed area with epoxy resin, as with previous electrodes for cell DC-2; and in the case of the silver–silver chloride electrodes by fusing under pressure and heat 0.02-inch polyethylene sheets with 20-mesh silver gauze between.

From the previous studies with Aquadag and silver–silver chloride electrodes the performance of cell DC-3 with similar electrodes was readily predicted. The maximum extent of demineralization and the capacity of DC-3 did not immediately provide the anticipated results; the performance was considerably poorer. However, after many experiments, causes of malfunctioning were found and remedied.

Two external contacting problems with cell DC-3 were overcome. The first was due to adjacent electrode contacting and was easily remedied by careful reassembly of the cell with adequate insulation. The second was that of achieving low resistance contacts between the similar alternate electrodes. Here brass contacting bolts were supplemented by compressible graphited felt washers and later replaced by copper rivets in the polyethylene spacer gasketing ring, aided by the application of silver print to the electrode contact region.

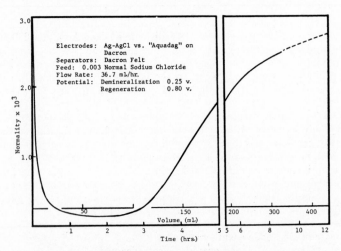

Figure 11.   Demineralization curve for run 3AG9-28

Two internal shorting problems that resulted in poor demineralization capacity were also remedied. The spacers used to separate adjacent electrodes were too thin to prevent internal shorting due to electrically induced precipitation of silver chloride. Thicker spacers provided a partial remedy for this persistent problem. Further, it was realized that the silver chloride difficulty developed only during the demineralization half-cycle and could be greatly reduced by decreasing the demineralization potential.

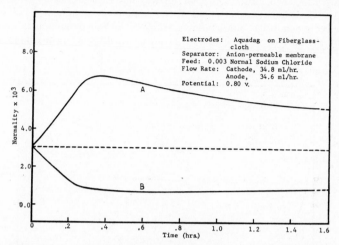

Figure 12.   Concentration of enriched (A) and depleted (B) streams in run 2GG1-4

The spacers initially used to separate the electrodes were epoxy resin–gasketed glass cloth about 2 mils thick. The spacers were successively replaced by filter paper disks fitted to polyethylene rings 0.02 inch thick and then by Dacron felt $1/16$ inch thick. With the latter spacers, the gasketing material enclosing the periphery of the $1^1/_4$-inch-diameter Dacron separator was polyethylene rings 0.10 inch thick.

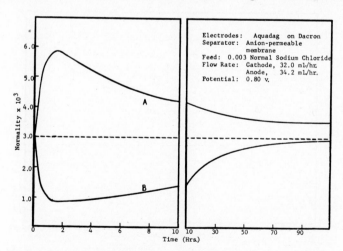

Figure 13.   Concentrations of enriched (A) and depleted (B) streams in run 2GG1-8

Results of Demineralization Experiments. In Table IV are presented the results of selected studies with the three demineralization cells, showing the conditions, results, and comments on each particular experiment. Table V gives capacity data of various carbon tannic acid–dispersed electrodes in DC-1. In Table VI the dispersant capacity effects are tabulated.

The data for significant runs were treated by plotting concentration *vs.* cumulative volume of effluent (Figures 8 to 14). Demineralization capacities were obtained by graphical integration. In most cases the run was not carried to the point where the concentration of the effluent equaled that of the influent. Consequently, the demineralization capacity is somewhat uncertain. Estimates of the demineralization capacity represented by the uncompleted portion of the curve are always on the conservative side.

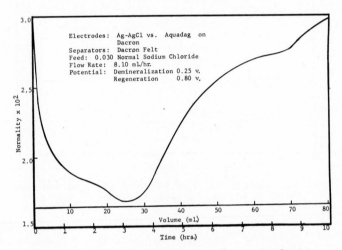

Figure 14.   Demineralization curve for run 3AG9-34

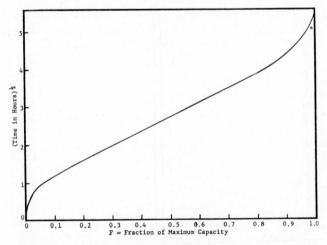

Figure 15.   Demineralization rate curve for run 1AG1-7

Rate Considerations. Consideration of the decrease of demineralization rate with time led to the conclusion that the above studies were controlled by the rate of diffusion of solution through the graphite material on the electrode. This type of rate-controlling step is analogous to particle diffusion (2) processes known in ion exchange chromatography. The conclusion that the above studies were particle diffusion rate-controlled was drawn from the data conformity to the particle diffusion equations. Figure 15 shows a plot of the fractional attainment of maximum capacity, F, vs. the square root of time. It is apparent from this plot that a reasonably linear curve is obtained over the range of $0.1 < F < 0.9$. The induction period is attributed to holdup volume of saline solution prior to the application of a potential to the electrode, and the curvature above $F = 0.9$ is attributed to the exhaustion of available reaction sites in the electrode. Future cell and electrode design with the above considerations should facilitate greater percolation rates and reduce the cost of an eventual demineralization plant.

Conclusions

Demineralization of saline water by a pair of electrodes—one responsive to cations and one to anions—has been found to be a feasible operation. Several facts revealed in the course of these studies lend encouragement to continued work aimed at a low-cost process for the demineralization of saline water.

A program of chemical characterization of factors has begun, aimed at improvement of the demineralization capacity. Ion-responsive functional groups have been built into carbon electrodes. Further improvement of electrodes will determine whether an eventual application of this method will be economically important.

Equipment, techniques, and understandings have evolved to a point where semi-automatic data obtaining facilities are available, numerous promising carbon materials and molecular additives can be treated, and deeper insight into what is required of an electrode in order to possess desired properties is now known. From here on, accelerated progress toward the ultimate goal should be expected.

Literature Cited

(1) Acheson, E. G., J. Alexander's "Colloid Chemistry," Vol. III, pp. 547–54, Chemical Catalog Co., New York, 1931.
(2) Boyd, G. E., Adamson, A. W., Myers, L. S., *J. Am. Chem. Soc.* **69**, 2836 (1947).
(3) Garten, V. A., Weiss, D. E., *Australian J. Chem.* **8**, 68–95 (1957).
(4) *Ibid.*, pp. 309–28.
(5) Garten, V. A., Weiss, D. E., *Revs. Pure Appl. Chem.* **7**, 69–122 (1957).
(6) Garten, V. A., Weiss, D. E., Willis, J. B., *Australian J. Chem.* **10**, 295–308 (1957).
(7) Gregor, H. P., Gold, D. H., *J. Phys. Chem.* **61**, 1347–52 (1957).
(8) Hallum, J. V., Drushel, H. V., *Ibid.*, **62**, 110–17, 1502–4 (1958).
(9) Lyon, R. J., "Electrical Demineralization of Water with Graphite Electrodes of Large Surface Area," master's thesis, University of Oklahoma, 1958.
(10) Moeller, T., "Inorganic Chemistry," pp. 661–9, Wiley, New York, 1952.
(11) Murphy, G. W., Arnold, B. B., "Studies on the Electrochemistry of Carbon and Chemically Modified Surfaces," *J. Phys. Chem.*, in press.
(12) Studebaker, M. L., *Rubber Chem. Technol.* **30**, 1401–64 (1957).
(13) Weiser, H. B., "The Colloidal Elements," p. 266, Wiley, New York, 1933.

RECEIVED for review July 7, 1960. Accepted July 15, 1960. Research supported by the U. S. Department of the Interior, Office of Saline Water, under Contract 14-01-001-160 with the University of Oklahoma Research Institute.

Interaction of Technical and Economic Demands in the Design of Large Scale Electrodialysis Demineralizers

DONALD A. COWAN

Physics Department, University of Dallas, Dallas, Tex., and Texas Electric Service Co., Fort Worth, Tex.

In an electrodialysis demineralizing system, performance is restricted by changes in the thin unstirred layer next to the membrane. When the layer is so thick that diffusion will not supply the current, polarization, charge concentration, and pH change result. Thickness of the layer and limiting current density are functions of fluid velocity through the cell. Fluid velocity controls current density, which in turn controls the ratio between membrane costs and electrical costs. This ratio sets the lowest cost under given circumstances. The lowest cost of demineralization may be expressed as a function of input and output concentration, membrane cost and resistance, and stream thickness. Large scale experiments in municipal-sized demineralizers show that optimum conditions can be very nearly achieved.

In the design of an electrodialysis plant, economic and technical aspects are powerful determinants. In general, economic factors control the quantity of membranes required, and technical considerations govern their arrangement.

The following cost equation shows the economic elements divided into three groups, each affected differently by current density.

$$MF \int_{N}^{N_o} dN/j + EF \int_{N}^{N_o} (jr + V)dN + C$$

$$12.4 \text{ cents/kilogallon } M \int_{N}^{N_o} dN/j + 0.101 \text{ cent/kilogallon } E \int_{N}^{N_o} (jr + V)dN + C$$

where M = cents/sq. foot/year
j = ma./sq. cm.
r = ohm/sq. cm./cell pair
C = cents/kilogallon

E = cents/kw.-hr.
N = equivalents/liter

224

Because salt is carried by current, less membrane area per volume of water produced is required as current density increases; consequently, in the first group, all costs associated with area vary inversely with current density. The second group—I^2R electric cost—increases with current density. The electrode and concentration potentials, V, which also appear in this group, may be handled as a perturbation of resistance and hence, in the interest of simplicity, omitted from further consideration. A third group is unaffected by current density.

If the derivative of the cost expression is set equal to zero and solved for current density, a value is obtained which will desalt the water at smallest cost. This smallest cost, the required "optimum" current, and the resulting membrane area are:

$$2.24 \text{ cents/kilogallon } \sqrt{ME} \int_{N}^{N_o} \sqrt{r}\, dN + C$$

Current condition $\qquad j = 11.1 \sqrt{M/Er} \text{ ma./sq. cm.}$

$$\text{Membrane area } 2 \times 0.408 \sqrt{E/M} \int_{N}^{N_o} \sqrt{r}\, dN \text{ sq. feet/gallon/day}$$

$$\text{Electric energy } \qquad 1.12 \sqrt{M/E} \int_{N}^{N_o} \sqrt{r}\, dN \text{ kw.-hr./kilogallon}$$

No limitations are placed on the arrangement by this smallest cost requirement. Many short parallel stacks or a few long stacks satisfy the requirement; only the total area is specified.

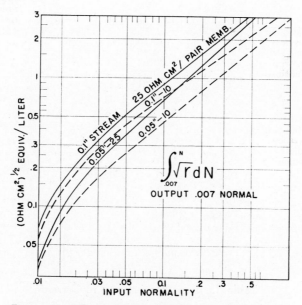

Figure 1. Effect of steam thickness and membrane resistance on cost with optimum current density

For cost, multiply by 2.24 cents/kilogallon $\sqrt{ME}$ and add C. For membrane area, multiply by 2 X 0.408 $\sqrt{E/M}$ sq. ft./gal./day. For electric energy, multiply by 1.12 $\sqrt{M/E}$ kw.-hr./kilogallon (M in cents/sq. ft./yr.; E in cents/kw.-hr.)

The value of the parameters can be determined with only a cursory consideration of design. The area resistance, r, is composed of the membrane resistance and the stream resistance, its square root appearing in the smallest cost expression. The membrane resistance quoted by manufacturers is a static value, measured while the membrane still has its minority carriers and consequently is not yet markedly permselective. In operation the membrane has a resistance nearly twice the values quoted. A value of 25 ohms per sq. cm. per pair, measured for some thin membranes, is used in the following calculations. Because the resistance of the concentrate stream can be made arbitrarily small by an increase of concentration, a value $5/4$ of dilute stream resistance has been used for the fluid resistance in the preparation of Figure 1.

The effect of stream thickness is clearly evident in this figure. Only a minor saving could be effected with thinner spacing—about 2-cent difference per kilogallon for brackish water between 100 and 50 mils in thickness. Furthermore, this saving is not available unless one is operating near optimum current. Until 12- instead of 30-cent water is being considered, this 2-cent margin does not warrant interest. The problem of getting water in and out of the cell, and of keeping it flowing, is much more easily solved in wide passages than in thin ones. Admittedly, in order to accomplish the same dilution, a cell must be twice as long if it is twice as thick; but twice as much water is produced when the size is doubled. The only penalty is that shown in Figure 1. For sea water, the penalty for 100 mils instead of 50 mils amounts to about 7 cents; but of far more importance is the membrane resistance, where greater saving could be effected. Until one considers 50-cent water from the sea instead of that costing $1.00 or more, the thin passages are an unnecessary complication.

Table I. Costs Proportional to Area

	Dollars/Sq. Foot	Amortization, Interest, and Insurance
20-year life		
Press	0.50	
Side strips	0.40	
Instrumentation	0.03	
Contingencies	0.19	
Engineering	0.21	
	1.33	0.122
3-year life		
Membranes	1.10	
Spacers	0.50	
Inlets and outlets	0.01	
Assembly	0.42	
	2.03	0.769
1-year life		
Electrodes		0.030
Labor, administration, and overhead		0.007
Interest on working capital		0.001
		M = 0.929

$$M = 92.9 \text{ cents/sq. foot/year}$$

Table II. Costs Proportional to Current

	Dollars/Kw.-Hr.
Demineralizing current	0.007
Add 10%, efficiency, and 10%, pumping	0.0014
Instrumentation	0.0002
Rectifiers	0.0001
Labor, administration, and overhead	0.0007
	E = $0.0094

$$E = 0.94 \text{ cent/kw.-hr.}$$

The parameter, M, representing the cost per square foot of membrane area per year (Table I), covers most of the cost items listed in the standard cost procedure (2). Some of the items are projected future costs. For example, a membrane cost of 50 cents per square foot is used. Membrane costs have been about $2.00 per square foot, but the present cost is likely to be about half this figure for a large order, and manufacturers give assurance that the 50-cent figure is in sight. The total cost per square foot-year is 92 cents, 77 cents of which is for 3-year-life items—membranes, spacers, inlets and outlets, and assembly cost. Should the stack prove to have a 10-year life, the total cost would drop to 41 cents per square foot-year, and one might accept this figure as the optimistic limit.

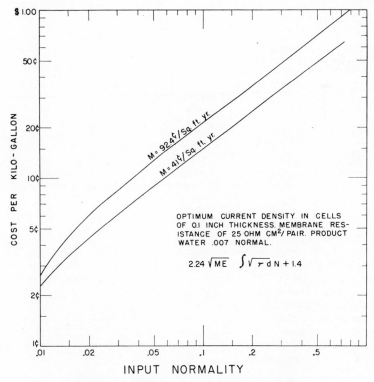

Figure 2. Potential cost of desalinization

M. Cost of entire plant per square foot of active membrane area

The electric cost (Table II) is the cost at the suggested 7 mils per kilowatt-hour of the energy previously calculated, increased by 10% to account for pumps, lighting, and rectifier efficiency and by another 10% for current efficiency.

The cost group unaffected by current density (Table III) includes operating costs and certain portions of the amortization. Wages have been distributed among the three categories.

With these figures, one can specify the cost of 500-p.p.m. water produced by a plant of optimum design now—that is, the 92 cents per square foot per year cost—and the cost at the optimistic limit (Figure 2).

Two additional elements of cost apply primarily to inland waters: the cost of clear, raw water and the cost of salt disposal. Surface water must, in all probability, be treated before desalinization. This cost may be about 4 cents per 1000 gallons. Salt disposal problems have not yet been solved; it seems likely that this requirement will add 20 to 50% to the cost of water.

Table III. Costs Proportional to Volume Only

	Dollars/Kilogallon/Day Capacity	Dollars/Kilogallon
Building and site	8.00	
Raw water supply, 20% blowdown	6.00	
Product water storage	10.00	
Pumps and pipes	2.00	
Construction	7.14	
Contingencies	3.14	
Engineering	3.40	
	$39.68	0.010
Taxes and insurance		0.003
Fuel, chemicals, supplies		0.003
Labor, administration, and overhead		0.008
		$0.024

$$C = 2.4 \text{ cents/kilogallon}$$

Summing up the economics, one can say that brackish water of 2100 p.p.m. can be made into good water of 500 p.p.m. at a cost of about 18 cents per 1000 gallons, including salt disposal, with a possibility of producing it at about 14 cents. Similarly, sea water can be made usable at 72 cents per kilogallon, with an optimistic limit of 48 cents. The problem that remains, then, is how nearly can these optimum conditions be realized?

Realization of Optimum Conditions

Arrangement of membranes into long or short cells has no bearing upon cost. The economic requirement on design is only that it ensure the optimum current density at every point in the cell. A technical requirement, however, imposes a further restriction upon design: that the current density be maintained in the neighborhood of the "diffusion limiting current."

The phenomenon of limiting current is marked by a nonohmic increase of voltage as the current is increased. A rather simple study of the ratio of current to voltage will reveal this increase. The voltage is the sum of the electrode voltage, V_e, whatever polarization voltages are present, V_p, and the IR drop:

$$V = V_e + V_p + IR$$

The data can be sharpened by a change in the variables:

$$V/I = R + (V_e + V_p)/I$$

Now the plot of V/I vs. I^{-1} has R for the intercept and V_e for the slope until polarization sets in as a sharp change of slope. A plot of experimental data shows this slope change at a critical current density (Figure 3). At this same current value, the pH begins to change. This diffusion limiting current point moves to higher current density values as stream velocity and concentration increase.

In experimental work at the Texas Electric laboratory this relationship has been established (1). The work reported applied to fluids in turbulent flow and hence to relatively high velocities. Since that time the studies have been extended to lower velocities. To support thin membranes, a pierced, corrugated material was placed in the streams with the corrugations in the direction of flow, in a manner to cause the smallest pressure drop; this obstruction induced strong mixing and simulated turbu-

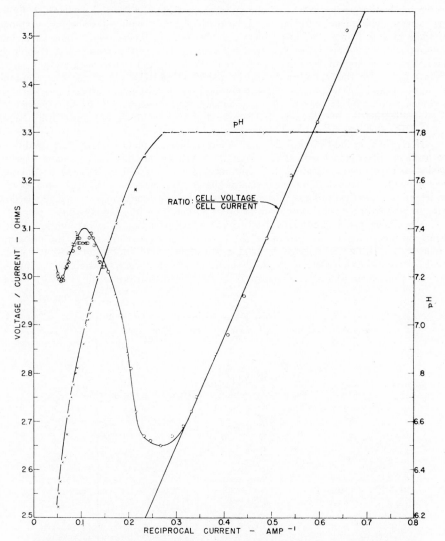

Figure 3. Value of current density at change of slope is fixed by rate of diffusion of salt through thin laminar layer of fluid next to membrane on dilute side

lence at rather low Reynolds numbers. On the basis of these studies, an empirical expression has been constructed for the limiting current density over the entire range of velocities:

$$j = 0.04 \, N/w \, U^{1/2} \, (U + 1.9)^{1/3}$$

where U is the flow rate of the diluting stream in gallons per minute per inch of width, w is stream thickness in inches, and N is normality in equivalents per liter. The expression is based on studies with sodium sulfate; other salts should have only slightly different limiting current densities.

A number of effects set in at current densities above this limiting value. The voltage increases above ohmic values; the pH changes, dropping in the dilute stream and increasing in the concentrate; and the membranes themselves become polarized, forming electrets which persist for hours. It seems likely that scaling is associated with one of these effects; hence scaling problems can be avoided if the cell is operated below limiting current. The Texas Electric experiments thus far indicate that trouble is associated with current densities in excess of the limit, and it has been accepted as a dictate of nature that membranes not be polarized and the pH of the water not be changed—that is, that limiting current not be exceeded. On the other hand, there is a reason to operate as near to the limiting current as possible. Current efficiency of demineralization is low when the cell is operating at current densities markedly below the limiting current.

Here, then, is the technical demand in electrodialysis plant design: that conditions be fixed so that operation is always near the limiting current. This demand was revealed in experimental studies; it is not merely a theoretical nicety, but a practical requirement. Fortunately, on each side of the critical conditions there is some leeway which allows practical designs at small penalties, but it is necessary to change the flow rate from stage to stage downstream in order to maintain limiting current.

The design problem resolves itself, thus, to the satisfying of two conditions, optimum current and limiting current. The current density can be set at the optimum value by adjusting the voltage from stage to stage. This optimum current can be made the limiting current by an adjustment of the flow rate through paralleling of stream from stage to stage. Thus the two conditions can be satisfied. Figure 4 shows

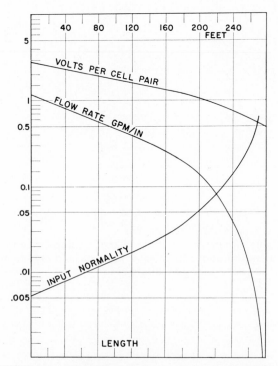

Figure 4. Voltage and flow rate per cell which
establish optimum current and limiting current
simultaneously, as functions of position
along path length

0.1-inch stream thickness and 25 ohm/sq. cm. per pair
resistance assumed

these required conditions. Because the stream velocity is high at the output end, it may prove expedient to accept a small penalty and drop below the optimum velocity in the last stage or two. The resulting design will inevitably call for a large plant; the single unit should approach 2,000,000 gallons per day as now envisioned, a size quite acceptable for community supplies. A stage length of 40 feet appears to be practical for cells with stream thicknesses of 0.1 inch. The Texas Electric Service Co. is now operating a 40-foot stage at Forth Worth as part of a developmental study. A brackish water plant might use three such stages, whereas a sea water plant would require nine in series, with many parallel stacks at the input so that the entering water would flow slowly.

Conclusions

To produce low-cost water, a plant must meet two main conditions: a moderate cost per square foot of active area and a relative freedom from expensive supervision and frequent overhaul. These conditions can be met by large cells. In fact, large scale, community-sized electrodialysis plants can allow the freedom of design needed to make desalinization economically feasible.

Literature Cited

(1) Cowan, D. A., Brown, J. H., *Ind. Eng. Chem.* **51,** 1445 (1959).
(2) Office of Saline Water, Washington, D. C., PB **161,375** (1955).

RECEIVED for review July 20, 1960. Accepted August 31, 1960.

Some Practical 1959 Advances in Electric Membrane Demineralization

WILLIAM E. KATZ

Ionics, Inc., Cambridge 42, Mass.

During 1959 several important advances have increased the efficiency and lowered the costs of electric membrane demineralization: development of an improved permselective membrane which has a lower electrical resistance than those formerly used but retains the structural, mechanical, and chemical stability characteristics for successful demineralization under the high rate of flow necessary for economic operation; a practical membrane stack with available membrane area over three times that of stacks formerly used; and a continuous-flow, two-stage, single-stack brackish water demineralizer to provide 65 to over 90% demineralization on flows of 1 to 20 gallons per minute. Formerly batch recirculating–type units were standard for this range of operation. The new units are simpler in construction and more efficient in the use of membrane area.

The electric membrane or "electrodialysis" process for removing excess dissolved salts and minerals from water is rapidly increasing in use, both in the United States and abroad. In the United States for example, as of January 1, 1958, there were only two production—i.e., nonexperimental—electric membrane plants in operation. By April 1, 1960, only 2 1/4 years later, 11 plants with a combined capacity of 350,000 gallons per day were serving almost 10,000 people in Montana, Texas, Alaska, New York State, California, Utah, South Dakota, Arizona, and Illinois.

In the Persian Gulf and North African areas (where oil activity is combined with a notable lack of fresh water), the first significant electric membrane installations were erected about five years ago, and as of April 1, 1960, more than 25 plants with an aggregate capacity of some 200,000 gallons per day were in operation or under construction to serve over 250,000 people with fresh drinking and culinary water in Saudi Arabia, Bahrain, Kuwait, Qatar, Egypt, Libya, Tunisia, and Algeria.

This compilation does not include a number of experimental units in operation or under construction in this country and abroad, including a large experimental plant which has been under construction and alteration in South Africa for several years and which was designed to produce about 3,000,000 gallons per day.

World capacity of commercial electric membrane equipment, as detailed above, currently stands at a little under 600,000 gallons per day. New orders received or in prospect lead to the prediction that world capacity of commercial electric membrane plants will be at least doubled by early 1961, reaching 1,000,000 to 1,500,000 gallons per day or more.

Electric Membrane Process

The electric membrane process has been described in detail (4, 5, 7). Briefly, the process operates by the action of a direct current electrical field on charged ions in solution (Figure 1). Typical natural saline waters contain varying amounts of sodium, calcium, and magnesium as cations (positively charged) and chloride, sulfate, bicarbonate, or nitrate as anions (negatively charged). When a saline water is exposed to a direct current, all the cations move in one direction and all the anions in the opposite direction. Advantage can be taken of this ion movement to deionize or demineralize the water, if suitable means are available to control the ion movement and prevent the removed ions from re-entering purified water.

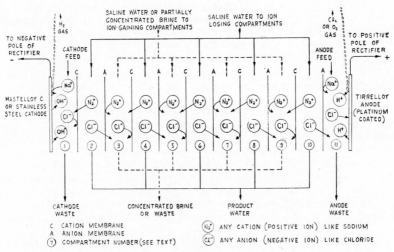

Figure I. Basic ion and water flow in electric membrane stack

The ion movement can be controlled by ion exchange or ion transfer membranes, thin sheets of cross-linked organic polymers with ion exchange properties—for example, sulfonated polystyrene-divinylbenzene polymers. Both cation-permeable and anion-permeable membranes are available and have been described (3, 9). To achieve demineralization, these membranes are spaced alternately between a cathode and an anode which introduce direct current. The compartment between each pair of membranes is filled with a saline water. The resulting ion motion is controlled by the membranes, so that one set of compartments—for example, the even-numbered compartments—lose ions and the odd-numbered compartments gain ions. The product from the ion-losing cells is collected and comprises electrically demineralized water.

For electrical demineralization, the amount of electric current, the membrane area required, and the costs of the process depend on the amount of salt removed. The electric membrane process is currently most attractive for treatment of so-called brackish waters containing from 1000 to 10,000 p.p.m. of total dissolved solids.

Brackish waters in this concentration range are widely available from wells or streams in many arid and semiarid parts of the world, including the southwestern and north central United States, most coastal areas, the Middle East, North and West Africa, Australia, South Africa, parts of South and Central America, and most islands.

There are a number of critical variables in the design of successful electric membrane equipment. Among these are the properties and cost of the membranes, the design and cost of the spacers, the size, cost, and construction of the alternating membrane-spacer-assembly—called the membrane stack—and the current density at which the unit is operated.

This paper describes three important practical advances made in electric membrane demineralization during 1959. These advances, which affect one or more of the critical areas mentioned above, have markedly increased the efficiency and decreased the cost of electric membrane demineralization of brackish waters.

Development of a pair of improved, commercially available cation and anion membranes having a lower electrical resistance than those formerly used but retaining the structural, mechanical, and chemical stability characteristics necessary for successful demineralization at high current densities and rates of throughput.

Development of a continuous-flow, two-stage, single-stack brackish water demineralizer. This equipment, operating at higher current densities than formerly, provides greater simplicity of construction and better use of membrane area than the batch-type equipment which has been standard for similar service. It provides up to 93% demineralization of a brackish water without recirculation.

Development of a new larger membrane stack with over three times the available area of any previously available commercially proved stack.

Ion Exchange Membrane Advance

Ion exchange or ion transfer membranes have two important types of function in practical operating electric membrane systems: an electrochemical function, and a structural function.

The electrochemical function of an ion transfer membrane is to allow the passage of ions of one kind with the least possible electrical resistance while barring as completely as possible the passage of ions of the opposite sign and the electro-endosmotic flow of water. Electrochemical properties of ion exchange membranes are readily measured on small samples in the laboratory and are routinely reported by investigators in the field (2, 6, 9). The most frequently reported properties include electrical resistance or resistivity, permselectivity, ion exchange capacity, water content, and electro-endosmotic water transfer. The specific electrical resistivity or conductivity of a membrane and the other properties listed above are determined by the chemical composition and the method of preparation of the membranes. However, the electrical "through" resistance of 1 sq. cm.—a practical operating variable—is determined by the specific resistivity and the thickness. From an electrochemical point of view, the ideal membrane would be only a few molecules thick, in order to minimize the electrical through resistance. However, from a structural point of view, such a membrane would be difficult if not impossible to utilize in a practical operating system.

Thus in at least one important respect the optimum electrochemical properties of a membrane do not coincide with its optimum structural properties. The designer must make compromises between the ideal in theoretical efficiency and the practical requirements of structural strength.

The structural properties of ion exchange membranes and their importance in practical electric membrane equipment design have been to a large extent ignored in the published literature to date. The thickness of ion exchange membranes is usually reported and this is the one structural property which is generally recognized as being significant. In some instances the Mullen burst strength in pounds per square inch has also been reported. A number of other structural properties of ion exchange membranes are also important and routine tests should be devised for determining and reporting them. Among the additional structural properties not listed above which could be of importance are: the tendency to plastic flow under pressure, the deflection under pressures applied normal to the face of the membrane over a given unsupported span, the brittleness or ability to withstand shock, fatigue under repeated shocks or vibrations, and the ability to withstand bending and creasing.

Among the many complications of structural testing of membranes is the variety of approaches to membrane stack design proposed by different groups working in the field (1, 8). The necessary service conditions of a membrane are determined not only by the membrane itself but also by the type of spacer employed with it, the flow rate and pressure drop across the face of the membrane, pressure differences which can exist either permanently or temporarily from one side of a membrane to the other, the ease and frequency of disassembly and assembly of the stack, and the way in which it is supported.

The Nepton membranes described in this paper are operated under the most severe mechanical conditions and with the severest mechanical requirements known to exist in the field. They are capable of operation in units where influent pressure can equal 60 or more pounds per square inch and where flow velocities can go up to 2 feet per second. At such high rates of demineralization relative to the polarization point, very slight changes in flow path dimensions due to bowing could result in a sufficient change in the polarization point to cause polarization and the consequent effects of precipitation of insoluble salts.

In the absence of further work on specifying the additional important mechanical properties of membranes referred to above, we have followed the usual practice in reporting the thickness, the Mullen burst strength, and the presence of a "backing" or reinforcing material of given weight. However, the mechanical properties of these membranes are sufficient so that operation up to two years on natural brackish waters containing potentially insoluble substances such as magnesium hydroxide, calcium carbonate, and calcium sulfate (see Table II) at pressures up to 60 p.s.i. and flow velocities up to 2 feet per second is smooth and trouble-free without the formation of scale. This field operation is an empirical test which indicates that when more detailed mechanical and structural tests are done on these membranes, the values reported can be related to successful operation under the conditions noted above.

Until early 1959, the two standard commercial membranes proved in field operation of electric membrane equipment were Nepton CR-61 on 9-ounce glass cloth backing with a thickness of 30 mils and Nepton AR-111A on 9-ounce dynel, also with a thickness of 30 mils. The Mullen burst strengths of these two membranes were well over 200 p.s.i. These membranes were generally operating in Ionics Mark I electric membrane stacks having maximum influent pressures in the neighborhood of 30 p.s.i. Under these conditions of operation, these membranes, separated by Mark I tortuous path spacers (8) (generally 0.040 inch thick), gave sufficient mechanical strength to hold up for several years under frequent stack disassembly, wiping, scrubbing, or even steel wooling of the surface. Their structural rigidity under pressures normal to the face was sufficient so that the dimensions of the flow path were essentially constant under full load operation. No polarization-induced precipitation or scaling was noted even after operation in hard waters with substantial bicarbonate and sulfate anions as well as chloride, assuming that Langelier indices of -1.0 to -2.0 were maintained in the concentrated stream.

The evidence as to the structural suitability of these membranes collected over a period of five years suggested that some reduction in thickness and Mullen burst strength could be tolerated for operation in Mark I equipment and even for projected operation in Mark II equipment with pressures up to 60 p.s.i. instead of 30 p.s.i. Accordingly, two new membranes were synthesized and, after field testing, put into production. These membranes differ from the previous standard materials only in their thickness and the weight of the backing material. Simultaneously, it was decided to change from glass cloth backing for the cation membranes to dynel cloth backing. The glass backing of the cation membranes had been shown in field tests in Arizona, South Dakota

(5), and elsewhere to undergo a higher failure rate than the dynel-back anion membranes, due apparently to mechanical or chemical-mechanical causes. The two new membranes are Nepton CR-61 resin on 4-ounce dynel for the cation and Nepton AR-111A resin on 4-ounce dynel for the anion.

Table I. Typical Physical Characteristics of Standard Nepton Ion Exchange Membranes

Type	Cation			Anion	
Designation	CR–61	CR–61	CR–61	AR–111A	AR–111A
Backing	9-oz. dynel	9-oz. glass	4-oz. dynel	9-oz. dynel	4-oz. dynel
Thickness, mils	30	30	23	30	23
Mullen burst strength, p.s.i.	275	225	140	275	140
Backing (dry basis), wt.%	50	50	50	50	50
Water content (resin only), %	45–50	45–50	45–50	40–45	40–45
Ion exchange capacity, meq./dry gram	2.8	2.8	2.8	2.0	2.0
Current efficiency (0.6N NaCl), %	90–95	90–95	90–95	90–95	90–95
Water transfer (0.6N NaCl), ml. water/meq. electrical	0.16	0.16	0.16	0.12	0.12

Table I lists the typical physical characteristics of the new and old membranes, including a Nepton CR-61 on 9-ounce dynel which was substituted for the 9-ounce glass in production a year or two earlier. Figure 2 shows the electrical resistance of the 4-ounce and 9-ounce membranes. From Table I, it can be seen that the reduction in thickness from 30 mils to 23 mils in both the cation and anion membranes led to reduction in Mullen burst strength to 140 p.s.i. The electrical through resistance (Figure 2) was decreased to approximately two thirds for the cation membranes and about one half for the anion membrane. The Nepton CR-61 9-ounce glass membrane had a much lower resistance than the 9-ounce dynel, because of a difference in the weave pattern in the cloth, so that there was actually little if any difference between the 4-ounce dynel cation and the 9-ounce glass cation in electrical through resistance. However, the superior resistance of the dynel backing to mechanical failures leads to its selection.

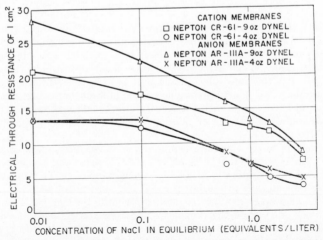

Figure 2. Electrical resistance of standard dynel-backed Nepton membranes in two thicknesses

Ion exchange membranes of very greatly reduced thickness have been prepared in a number of laboratories, including our own. As an extreme, Gregor (2) has reported on the electrical properties of membranes as thin as 10 microns produced by film-casting techniques. While some of these membranes had very low "through resistances" (ohms for a 1-sq. cm. section) as might have been expected from their thicknesses, no method has been proposed for utilizing such thin membranes in practical electric membrane equipment, as far as we are now aware. On the other hand, Lacey (6) has reported on membranes available from experimental production in this country which have thicknesses on the order of 6 or 8 mils. Attempts have been made to utilize these membranes in electric membrane stacks having low pressure drops (1), although commercially proved equipment has not yet been achieved using such membranes, in part because of their structural limitations. Lacey reports electrical through resistances of 22 ohms per sq. cm. for cation membranes and 27 to 38 ohms per sq. cm. for anion membranes of this type in 0.01N salt solution. If these through resistances are multiplied by a factor of 3 or 4, they can be compared on an equal thickness basis with the Nepton membranes on 4-ounce dynel. The 6- to 8-mil membranes extrapolated to 23 mils have through resistances of 66 to 88 ohms per sq. cm. for the cation membrane and from 80 to 150 ohms per sq. cm. for the anion membrane, compared with 14 ohms per sq. cm. for the Nepton 4-ounce membranes.

"Thin" membranes from 5 to 10 mils thick are currently being produced by several groups in this country and abroad on an experimental production basis and for sampling purposes. Considerable effort is being expended toward developing cells suitable for the use of such membranes (1). Their thinness generally leads to Mullen burst strengths considerably lower than the 140 p.s.i. reported for the reinforced Nepton membranes. However, the systems being proposed for their use would operate at relatively low pressures, perhaps 10 to 15 p.s.i. at the extreme. It might appear at first thought that if the operating pressure did not exceed the Mullen burst strength there would be no problem. However, the thinness of these membranes leads also to a considerable degree of flexibility. More precisely, there is a substantial deflection across an unsupported span when one of these membranes is exposed to even slight pressure variations of 1 pound or less. Because such variations are difficult to avoid in practical cell design and operation, thin membranes are subject to "bowing" in operation. Structures made of such membranes thus have varying dimensions under the conditions of operation of the equipment. Bowing leads to important local changes in velocity of flow, degree of turbulence, and consequent polarization point. Any precipitation which forms is injurious to the membranes and can block the flow path in the spacer.

While use of thin membranes, subject to bowing, has so far not been successful for use in brackish water demineralizers operating near polarization, such membranes offer more promise in treating solutions of high concentration such as sea water where polarization is less likely to be encountered.

Most natural waters contain substances which will precipitate at points where polarization occurs in electric membranes units. The most common such substances are calcium carbonate, magnesium hydroxide, and calcium sulfate. Natural waters vary widely in the amounts and proportions of these substances present and accordingly in the ease in which they precipitate salts under polarizing conditions. Accordingly, it is very difficult to predict the performance of spacer-membrane combinations without actual tests on the natural waters of interest.

Unfortunately, it is difficult in the laboratory or even under pilot plant conditions to obtain large supplies of natural waters. Hauling of water is expensive at best, and the handling, detention, and storage of water in tanks and associated equipment can introduce iron and other metals which are even more troublesome than some of the scaling constituents normally present. Most laboratory and testing work on electric membrane stacks in pilot plants is done with solutions of sodium chloride. Testing with pure solutions of sodium chloride yields only an approximate idea of the true performance of membrane systems. Sometimes attempts are made to synthesize natural waters in more detail, adding calcium and magnesium sulfate and even bicarbonate to the synthetic solutions. Unfortunately, the equilibria involving bicarbonate in natural waters are very difficult to maintain under laboratory or pilot plant conditions. Carbon dioxide can be absorbed from the atmosphere. Acid used at the electrode or for correction of the pH of the concentrate stream will slowly diffuse into the feed solution and markedly alter the bicarbonate equilibrium. Sometimes attempts are made to import a relatively large sample of natural water and then to re-use it by mixing the product and concentrate streams from the demineralizing unit. However, this procedure inevitably results in wide swings of pH and bicarbonate concentrations due to the factors noted above. Because of the practical difficulties detailed above, much laboratory and small scale testing of electric membrane equipment produces inaccurate and in fact misleading results. If pure sodium chloride is used, precipitation will not occur at "weak" points of the spacer-membrane combination, and systems which appear to be operating well in the laboratory can fail as soon as a natural water is encountered. If synthetic or recirculated natural waters are used, an additional complication is introduced, in that some precipitations and malfunctions may be noted due to extraneous metals such as iron and other metal oxides introduced from the tankage or water handling equipment.

The short history of electrodialysis to date provides several notable examples of field operation where substantial polarization-induced precipitation was encountered after apparently successful laboratory tests. For these reasons it is our firm conclusion that the only conclusive test of the mechanical and electromechanical adequacy of membrane-spacer combinations is operation on natural saline waters under field conditions over periods of several months and without recourse to "recirculation." By such field tests the suitability of Nepton CR-61 and Nepton AR-111A on 4-ounce dynel has now been demonstrated.

Two-Stage Single-Stack Continuous Unit

The Role of Current Density. Because current is carried through solutions by a stream of ions, the current-carrying capacity—i.e., conductivity of the solution—depends upon the number of ions present, or the normality. Thus the ratio of current density to normality (CD/N) is an important variable in membrane system design. This ratio tends to remain relatively constant over a wide range of current density as a measure of the degree to which the impressed current utilizes the current-carrying capacity of the solution. If CD/N becomes excessive, there will not be enough ions to carry the desired current. This phenomenon occurs first at membrane solution interfaces, where it is called film depletion or polarization (10). Polarization causes pH disturbances at the interface, loss of current efficiency, and high electrical resistance. If pH-sensitive substances are present in the solution, they may be precipitated by the pH disturbances, causing damage to the membrane or blockage of the cells. As previously indicated in natural waters, the most common substance to be precipitated by polarization is calcium carbonate.

Polarization can be minimized and allowable CD/N of a system maximized by creating rapid stirring or turbulence at the membrane solution interface (by high velocity flow or otherwise). Local spot polarization can be avoided by eliminating stagnant areas exposed to current. With a given spacer design, the allowable CD/N at which a system may be operated is also determined by the inlet pressure or velocity of flow. Some of the worst effects of polarization can be avoided by use of slightly acid pH environments. Polarization is not generally encountered in solutions of high concentration (greater than 0.1N) because the current density necessary to reach polarization would be uneconomical.

In dilute solutions, the avoidance of local or general polarization is the most crucial task of the cell designer. The so-called "tortuous path" spacer is utilized in Ionics electric membrane systems (8). A tortuous path spacer consists of one or more flow paths—for example, approximately 1 cm. in width—traversing the face of a membrane and folded on each other in order to allow a long length of path—for example, 10 to 15 feet—on an 18 × 20 inch or 18 × 40 inch membrane. The flow path is traversed by straps having approximately one half the thickness of the space between the membranes. These straps hold the spacer together and promote turbulence in the stream.

Late in 1958, Ionics began field tests of a new tortuous path spacer called the Mark II spacer. This spacer provided more turbulence, more evenly distributed turbulence, and an increase in area utilization, and was designed for operation at approximately double the pressure of the Mark I spacer—60 rather than 30 p.s.i. Table IV compares the Mark II with the Mark I stack. As a consequence of this change in the spacer design, it was possible to increase the maximum hydraulic flow rate of a 300-membrane 18 × 20 inch stack from 28,000 to 65,000 gallons per day. For a 3000-p.p.m. typical brackish water, the rated current requirement of the stack was increased from 18 to 50 amperes and the voltage from 175 to 500 volts in order to accomplish the much greater rate or demineralization. Also, the degree of demineralization associated with a single pass through this stack was increased from 40 to 48%.

As the flow through a Mark II stack is slowed, even greater demineralizations can result—up to a maximum of approximately 60%. To extend further the degree of demineralization possible on a single pass through a stack, a second version of the Mark II stack was made with fewer flow paths in parallel and a longer length of path. With this spacer it is possible to get a demineralization of greater than 70% on a single pass.

The advent of higher capacity spacer designs operating with relatively strong and thick membranes capable of withstanding the pressures and flows involved, made it possible to consider the design of units where demineralizations of 90% or better could be achieved on two passes through a single stack. Systems such as these would be applicable to situations where the total desired flow from an installation was considerably less than the full load flow through a single stack.

The Batch Unit. Previously, if high degrees of demineralization and low flows from a single stack installation were desired, a batch recirculating type of system was utilized (4). The standard batch unit utilized a single Mark I 300-membrane 18 × 20 inch stack. A schematic flow sheet of a recirculating batch unit is shown in Figure 3.

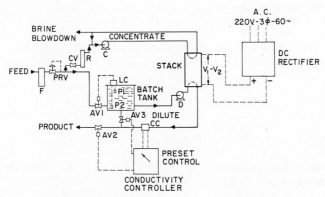

Figure 3. Schematic flow sheet of batch unit

In a batch unit, the water to be demineralized is fed into a batch tank under pressure until the batch tank is full. The filling of the tank is controlled by a level controller and an automatic valve, AV_1. The full batch tank of water to be demineralized is pumped through the membrane stack by a "dilute" pump, D, and recirculated back through the tank until the desired effluent conductivity of the water is achieved. The effluent conductivity is monitored by conductivity cell CC, controlling automatic valves AV_2 and AV_3. When the desired point has been reached, AV_3 closes, preventing return of the demineralized water to the batch tank, and AV_2 opens, allowing the demineralized water to flow to service.

The pumping out of the batch tank at the end of the cycle lowers the level in the batch tank which signals valve AV_1 to open again and a new batch of undemineralized water comes into the system. The cycle is repeated automatically for an indefinite period. The salts removed in the stack from the dilute stream are absorbed in a concentrated stream loop being pumped by concentrating pump C. Enough water is continuously added under control of valve CV and rotameter R to make up for the amount of water blown down as brine. The proportion of water which must be wasted as brine is determined by the chemical composition of the water to be treated. The blowdown is adjusted so that the least soluble salt component in the feed water will remain in solution.

During the progress of a batch cycle the voltage is maintained constant for the first part of the cycle and the current decreases as the water becomes demineralized. In order to avoid exceeding polarization limits of CD/N toward the end of the cycle, however, in many cases the voltage is stepped down automatically midway through the cycle to a lower voltage, V2, after which the amperage continues to fall gradually until the end of the cycle. As a consequence, one of the drawbacks of a batch system is that the rectifier is used at less than full load during practically all of the cycle.

In spite of the relative complexity of the batch cycle, fully automatic batch-recirculating units have given amazing service over many years. One unit installed in 1956 has now gone through 50 cycles a day, 365 days a year, for over 4 years to achieve a total number of cycles approaching 75,000.

The Two-Stage Continuous Unit. The new two-stage continuous unit has a much simpler flowsheet and method of operation than the recirculating batch unit. Figure 4 shows the schematic flow sheet of such a unit. If pressurized feed water is available and the blowdown is not recirculated, no pumps are essential to the operation of this unit. In addition, there are no automatic valves which operate on a regular basis. Automatic valves are furnished for automatic shutdown only. The rectifier utilized with the two-stage continuous units operates at constant voltage and amperage, unless there are changes in the composition or temperature of the water. Thus its full capacity is always utilized. The water to be demineralized is filtered and fed first through the bottom and then through the top of a single membrane stack having a pair of electrodes in the bottom half and a pair of electrodes in the top half. Equal or approximately equal numbers of membranes are spaced between the top and bottom pair of electrodes. The water emerging is the product. The salts removed in the stack are transferred to a blowdown stream which is separately fed through a rotameter, R, and then wasted. The addition of a single pump makes it possible to recirculate part of the waste water and reduce water wasted.

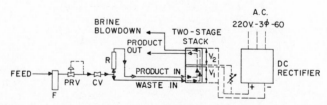

Figure 4. Schematic flow sheet of one-stack two-stage
continuous unit

The voltages in the top half of the stack are less than in the bottom half because of the lower normality of the water after it has been partly demineralized. The current in the top half is less than in the bottom, not only because of the lower voltage but also because the water has been partially demineralized in the bottom half. The flexibility achievable from a one-stack, two-stage continuous unit is not as great as from a recirculating batch unit, since demineralization is limited to a maximum of about 93% for the lowest flow case using the longest path currently available in this type of spacer. However, by the simple addition of a line to recycle part of the product to the feed, it is possible to utilize these continuous units to demineralize water of any desired salinity, including sea water.

Figure 5 compares the daily capacity of the 300-membrane 18 × 20 inch stacks utilizing different spacers and comparing the recirculating batch type unit with the two-stage continuous unit. The two-stage continuous unit is fitted with different spacers, depending on the expected range of feed water concentration. Spacer A is a 0.050-inch four-path spacer. Spacer B in a 0.040-inch four-path spacer. Spacer C is a 0.050-inch two-path spacer with longer path length than A or B. Spacer D is a 0.040-inch two-path spacer. As one progresses from spacer A to D, the allowable flow decreases and the degree of demineralization increases as shown on the graph. The new two-stage continuous units utilizing Mark II type spacers have from 250 to 167% as much capacity per unit of membrane area in the range of 2000 to 7500 p.p.m.

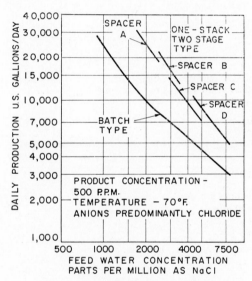

Figure 5. Daily capacity of 300-membrane 18 × 20
inch membrane demineralizers

In the fall of 1958, the first Mark II two-stage continuous unit was tested near Salt Lake City, Utah. Table II gives the analyses of two wells on which tests were run. Well 1 had total dissolved solids of 3300 p.p.m. as NaCl and well 2 had total dissolved solids of 1950 p.p.m. as NaCl. While the predominant anion in each of these waters was chloride, each had a significant bicarbonate concentration and from one third to almost one half of the cations were calcium and magnesium. A field test on a water of this composition over a period of several months would indicate whether or not polarization-induced precipitation of calcium carbonate would occur. It would thus show up any weak points in the spacer-membrane combination which might be overlooked in testing with sodium chloride, "synthetic" waters, or recirculated natural waters in the laboratory. Table III shows the performance characteristics of the one-stack, two-stage unit on the two brackish wells analyses of which are given in Table II.

Table II. Chemical Analysis of Two Brackish Wells near Salt Lake City, Utah

(Wells used for field tests of Ionics Model C-302 demineralizer)

	Well 1		Well 2	
	P.p.m.	E.p.m.[a]	P.p.m.	E.p.m.[a]
Sodium as Na	685	29.8	542	23.6
Calcium as Ca	266	13.3	102	5.1
Magnesium as Mg	139	11.6	54	4.5
Chloride as Cl	1940	54.7	1090	30.7
Sulfate as SO_4	33	0.7	38	0.8
Bicarbonate as HCO_3	67	1.1	110	1.8
Total dissolved solids	3130	56.5	1936	33.2
Total dissolved solids as NaCl	3310		1950	
pH		7.8		7.8

[a] Equivalents per million = p.p.m./equivalent weight.

Table III. Performance Characteristics of One-Stack, Two-Stage Electric Membrane Demineralizer on Two Brackish Wells

Designation. Ionics Model C–302
Membranes. 300 18 × 20 inch Nepton (CR–61 9-ounce glass and AR–111A 9-ounce dynel)

Performance	Well 1	Well 2
Feed water concn., total dissolved solids as p.p.m. NaCl	3,300	1,950
Product water concn., total dissolved solids as p.p.m. Na_l	515	283
Production per 24-hour day, gallons	12,250	12,250
Water wasted as brine, gallons per day	9,700[a]	9,700[a]
Pressure drop through two stages of membrane stack, p.s.i.g.	44	44
Feed water temp., ° F.	68	70
Current, amperes		
Stage 1	25.5	14.1
Stage 2	10.7	6.1
Voltage		
Stage 1	192	150
Stage 2	115	100
Over-all % demineralized	83	85
Demineralization, %		
Stage 1	60	59
Stage 2	62	63
Current efficiency, %	91.2	96.2
Energy consumption, kw.-hr./1000 gal. product		
D. c.	13.6	6.0
Total[b]	19.5	11.8

[a] Could be cut to about 3000 by addition of recirculating pump.
[b] Includes 3-kw. pumping power.

Production rate in each test was 12,250 gallons per day and the water wasted as brine was 9700 gallons per day. The flow rate achieved for the test on the 3300-p.p.m. well, No. 1, to yield a product water concentration of approximately 500 p.p.m. agrees closely with the generalized curve for spacer C (Figure 5). On well 2, the production rate was kept constant, so that the product water from a 1950-p.p.m. raw water was only 283 p.p.m. Accordingly, the data for this point cannot be read directly from Figure 5, which was constructed for a product water of 500 p.p.m.

The commercial availability of two-stage continuous units with high rates of demineralization per square foot of membrane substantially decreases the cost of demineralization for supplies in the neighborhood of a few thousand to a few tens of thousands of gallons per day. It is expected that the increased simplicity, economy, and reliability of this equipment will considerably broaden the use of electric membrane equipment in a number of fields and contribute to continued technical advancement in the field.

Development of Mark III Stack with Basic Hydraulic Capacity of 250,000 Gallons Per Day

While progress in the design of relatively small units advanced in 1959, much of the national and international interest in electric membrane demineralization and in other forms of saline water conversion derives from the expectation that relatively large scale municipal, industrial, and even agricultural water supplies will have to be converted from saline sources in the future. An important step forward toward large scale use of electric membrane demineralization was taken in 1959 with the design and factory testing of a very much larger stack than has previously been described. Table IV compares this Mark III stack with the Mark I and Mark II stacks which preceded it. The outstanding characteristic is its maximum hydraulic flow rate of 250,000 U. S. gallons per day or 175 gallons per minute, achieved at a pressure drop of 60 p.s.i. Unlike the Mark I and Mark II stacks which contain 300 membranes per stack, the new unit contains 550. The membranes for the new unit are 18 × 40 rather than 18 × 20 inches. Its total area of membrane surface is 2750 sq. feet and the area utilization is about 70%. Figure 6 shows an Ionics Mark III stack as it was prepared for shipment to its first field test at Oxnard, Calif. This test got under way in the late spring of 1960. A Mark III stack puts out approximately 1000 times its own weight of water every day and the average residence time of water within the unit is approximately 8 seconds.

Figure 6. Ionics Mark III membrane stack for electrodialytic membrane processing

Table IV. Design Characteristics of Standard Ionics Membrane Stacks

	Mark I	Mark II	Mark III
Max. hydraulic flow rate			
U. S. gal./24-hour day	28,800	65,000	250,000
U. S. gal./minute	20	45	175
Pressure drop at max. flow, p.s.i.	30	60	60
No. of membranes	300	300	550
Size of membranes, inches	18 × 20	18 × 20	18 × 40
Total area of membrane, sq. feet	750	750	2,750
% of total area available for transfer	50	65	70
Approx. weight, pounds	700	700	2,000
Approx. over-all height, inc. legs, feet	3$\frac{1}{2}$	3$\frac{1}{2}$	6
Demineralization per pass (70° F., Cl water, full flow), %	40	48	46
Current required for 3000-p.p.m. feed, amperes	18	50	100
Voltage required for 3000-p.p.m. feed (70° F., Cl water, full flow)	175	500	1,000
D. c. kw. per stack for 3000-p.p.m. feed	3.2[a]	25[a]	100[a]
D. c. kw.-hr./1000 gal. for 3000-p.p.m. feed	2.7[a]	9.3[a]	9.5[a]

[a] Power and current values for 3000-p.p.m. demineralization cover only 40, 48, and 46% demineralization (single stage) for Mark I, II, and III stacks, respectively.

The spacer for the Mark III unit is almost identical to that of the Mark II unit, with two identical lobes proceeding outward from central manifold holes. Each lobe is almost identical to a Mark II stack. The use of a Mark III unit makes possible demineralization of water supplies in the range of 250,000 to several million gallons per day at very much lower costs and in very much more compact installations than would have previously been possible. Table V lists estimated costs for production of 2,000,000 gallons per day of fresh water containing 500 p.p.m. total solids from brackish water containing 1000, 2000, and 4000 p.p.m. Total water costs, including operating costs, maintenance costs, and amortization, are 19.5 cents for the 1000-p.p.m. case,

Table V. Estimated Costs for Production of 2,000,000 Gallons per Day of Fresh Water (500 P.P.M. as NaCl) from Three Brackish Waters by Ionics Mark III Equipment

(Cents per 1000 gallons)

Basis
  Feed water temperature. 85° F.
  Anions. Predominantly chloride
  Electrical energy cost. 1.0 cent/kw.-hr.
  Membrane replacement rate. Average 1/5 per year
  Amortization basis. 25-year, 5% (7.1% per year)
  Maintenance costs other than membranes. 1.5% per year of capital
  Labor allowance. 2 hours per day plus 100 man-hours per stack-year at $4/hour including
    overhead

	Case 1	Case 2	Case 3
Feed water total dissolved solids, p.p.m.	1000	2000	4000
No. of stacks	8	16	24
Total capital costs	$450,000	$850,000	$1,300,000
Operating costs, cents			
Electrical energy	4.9	13.4	26.0
Chemicals	2.5	2.5	2.5
Prefiltration	3.0	3.0	3.0
Total	10.4	18.9	31.5
Maintenance costs, cents			
Membranes	3.0	6.0	9.0
Other	0.9	1.8	2.7
Labor	0.8	1.3	1.7
Total	4.7	9.1	13.4
Amortization, cents	4.4	8.3	12.6
Total water costs, cents/1000 gallons	19.5	36.3	57.5

36.6 cents for the 2000-p.p.m. case, and 57.5 cents for the 4000-p.p.m. case. The bases for the economic calculations are listed at the top of the table, so that they can be adjusted for other conditions. Among the most important cost assumptions are a membrane replacement rate averaging one fifth of the membranes present per year, amortization of principal on a 25-year basis with 5% interest, maintenance costs other than membranes at 1.5% per year of capital, and labor charges computed at $4 per hour including overhead.

The estimated capital costs for the complete installation are $450,000 for the 1000-p.p.m. case, $850,000 for the 2000-p.p.m. case, and $1,300,000 for the 4000-p.p.m. case.

It cannot be emphasized too strongly that these cost estimates are achievable in plants which could be contracted for at the present time and built in a year or less. Most of the major assumptions, including the membrane replacement rate, would be subject to guarantee by the manufacturer and the costs of the installation could be guaranteed by firm bids. Thus, early in 1960 we have already available a process in which the investment costs for a wide range of waters are from 22 to 65 cents per gallon per day and the total water conversion costs are from approximately 20 to 60 cents per thousand gallons. If power is available at less than one cent per kilowatt hour, substantial savings can be made even on these estimated figures.

Utilizing Mark III equipment it is also possible to build plants in the range of 10,000,000 to 20,000,000 gallons per day. Because of economies inherent in large scale production, these plants would have capital costs of one half to two thirds those cited for the case of 2,000,000 gallons per day. Total costs would be lowered in proportion, with some savings in membrane replacement costs as well.

Summary and Conclusions

A new commercially available cation membrane, Nepton CR-61 on 4-ounce dynel backing, is 23 mils thick and has an electrical through resistance in $0.01N$ NaCl of 14 ohms per sq. cm., about two thirds that of a similar membrane 30 mils thick on 9-ounce dynel backing. It has the same electrical resistance as a 9-ounce glass-backed CR-61 membrane, also 30 mils thick, but much better chemical stability to acids and alkalies and better mechanical stability to vibrations. The Mullen burst strength of the 4-ounce membranes is 140 p.s.i., about half that for the 9-ounce dynel, but still sufficient to be useful for field operation. Its stiffness and resistance to bowing, for which no standard measurements are yet available, are sufficient to allow its use in membrane stacks with tortuous path spacers operating at pressures of 60 p.s.i. and flow velocities of 60 cm. per second.

A new commercially available anion membrane, Nepton AR-111A on 4-ounce dynel backing, is 23 mils thick and has an electrical through resistance in $0.01N$ NaCl of 14 ohms per sq. cm., about one half that of a similar membrane 30 mils thick on 9-ounce dynel. Its Mullen burst strength of 140 p.s.i., stiffness, and resistance to bowing make it suitable for use in membrane stacks operating at pressures of 60 p.s.i. and flow velocities of 60 cm. per second.

The allowable current density—normality ratio for electric membrane operation has been approximately doubled by an improved tortuous path spacer with strap turbulence promoters and by operation at higher pressures up to 60 p.s.i. As a result, twice as much water can now be demineralized per square foot of membrane utilized and/or greater demineralization achieved per pass in electric membrane units. One practical result of this development is a new continuous-flow, two-stage single-stack demineralizer which will provide 93% demineralization at a capacity of 5000 gallons per day and 72% demineralization at a capacity of 30,000 gallons per day. These units produce from 67 to 150% more water per unit membrane area than previously used automatic batch-recirculating units and are far simpler in construction and operation.

The new Ionics Mark III membrane stack weighs about a ton, and contains 550

18 × 40 inch Nepton 4-ounce membranes for a total of 2750 sq. feet of membrane area. It has a hydraulic capacity of 175 gallons per minute or 250,000 gallons per day and will demineralize a predominantly chloride water at 70° F. by 46%.

Cost projections have been made for 2,000,000-gallon-per-day brackish water demineralization plants based on the Mark III stack. The plants, to produce water of 500 p.p.m. total dissolved solids, would require eight Mark III stacks for a plant to treat 1000 p.p.m. feed water, 16 stacks for 2000 p.p.m., and 24 for 4000 p.p.m. Total estimated capital costs are $450,000, $850,000, and $1,300,000, respectively. Total water costs (including 25-year × 5% amortization, $1/5$ per year membrane replacement at present market prices, 1 cent per kilowatt-hour electrical energy, and adequate labor, overhead, filtration, chemical, and maintenance costs) are 19.5 cents per thousand gallons for the 1000-p.p.m. water, 36.3 cents for the 2000-p.p.m. water, and 57.5 cents for the 4000-p.p.m. water. These cost figures are based on design principles which, except for the scale-up in size, have been developed and proved in field operation. Plants achieving such water costs could be installed late this year or early in 1961. Similar plants with capacities of 10,000,000 rather than 2,000,000 gallons per day can also be built immediately and would have costs about two thirds those cited above. Further cost reductions of a factor between 2 and 4 are envisaged in the next five years or less for electric membrane plants of tens or hundreds of millions of gallons per day, based on an even larger basic stack.

Literature Cited

(1) Boby, W. M. T., *Surveyor* (London), pp. 65–8 (January 1959).
(2) Gregor, H., "Interpolymer Ion-Selective Membranes," Proceedings of 1957 Symposium on Saline Water Conversion, Natl. Acad. Sci.–Natl. Research Council, Publ. 568, 250 (1958).
(3) Juda, W., McRae, W. A., U. S. Patent 2,636,851 (April 28, 1953).
(4) Katz, W. E., "Operation of Batch-Type and Continuous Electric Membrane Demineralizers on the Municipal Water Supply of Coalinga, California," Pacific Area National Meeting, Am. Soc. Testing Materials, October 1959 (Philadelphia proceedings in preparation).
(5) Kirkham, T. A., *et al.*, Saline Water Research and Development, Office of Saline Water, U. S. Dept. of Interior, Progr. Rept. 11 (December 1956).
(6) Lacey, R. E., "Development of the Osmionic Process and Factors Influencing Choice of Membranes," Proceedings of 1957 Symposium on Saline Water Conversion, Natl. Acad. Sci.–Natl. Research Council, Publ. 568, 229 (1958).
(7) Mason, E. A., Kirkham, T. A., *Chem. Eng. Progr., Symposium Series* 55, No. 24, 173 (1959).
(8) Rosenberg, N. W., U. S. Patent 2,708,658 (May 16, 1955).
(9) Rosenberg, N. W., George, J. H. B., Potter, W., *J. Electrochem. Soc.* 104, 111 (February 1957).
(10) Rosenberg, N. W., Tirrell, C. E., *Ind. Eng. Chem.* 49, 780 (1957).

RECEIVED for review August 15 1960. Accepted August 23. 1960.

DATE DUE

X17846	5 Jan'60	NOV 2 3 1984
53252	12 May'67	
58318	25 May'68	APR 2 6 1986
54794	26 Nov'68	
7882	11 Apr'70	DEC 2 3 1988
13454	17 Mar'73	
22863	4 Nov'75	MAY 0 7 1991
40184	21 Jun'77	JAN 0 3 1995
name	22 Dec'77	
name	12 Jan'78	JAN 1 9 1996
FEB 3 '82		SEP 0 5 1997
	FEB 0 5 '83	
	MAR 0 4 1983	OCT 0 2 2006
	FEB 1 7 1984	JAN 2 9 2009
	JUN 1 9 1984	
GAYLORD		PRINTED IN U.S.A.